# LEAD MI[...] IN TH[...] PEAK DISTRIC[...]

C000258786

**Above:** *James Hall's Engine Mine*

**Front cover:** *Magpie Mine*
**Back cover top:** *Cromford Moor Mine*
**Back cover below:** *Maury Sough*

# PEAK DISTRICT MINING MUSEUM, MATLOCK BATH.

Founded in 1978 by Peak District Mines Historical Society, the centrepiece of the museum, then and now, is the 30 feet (9 metres) high Wills Founder water pressure engine designed by Richard Trevithick, who also invented the locomotive, and cast at Coalbrookdale in 1819 - one of the oldest and finest engines in the world. Today, however there is very much more at this exciting and much commended museum, with artefacts of mining and miners dating back to the 3000 year old antler tool from Ecton copper mines. Here you can see the tools of lead, spar and copper miners and smelters, learn something of the thousand year old customs made when Derbyshire was still a "wild west" and see something of the miners' lives and the dangers and hardships which beset them. There is even a toy "spar cottage" made in the mid-19th century for a miner's children. The museum has been designed for all ages. It is "hands-on" as much as possible with pumps to wind and simulated tunnels and climbing shafts which delight all young and young at heart.

Over the road from the museum is Temple Mine, where, though there are a few 18th century sections, most of the workings are in a comfortably-sized fluorspar mine reworked in the 1920s and 1950s. Here you can see one of the world's oldest electric locomotives, built about 1934 and used underground in a local mine until a few years ago with the wagons and other tools of the period. Outside the mine is washing and dressing machinery, used to concentrate ores. You can try your hand and learn how to pan for minerals such as gold - though here it is usually only "fools gold" which is found!

Peak District Mining Museum is alongside the A6 road, with parking nearby and is open every day (except Christmas Day) from 11 am to 4 pm, longer at busy times. There is a shop with a large range of unusual gifts and general, local and specialised books. School and other parties are welcome, and there are also special low rates for families and joint visits to museum and mine. Telephone 01629-583834.

*A class tries out the reproduction rag-and-chain pump*

# LEAD MINING IN THE PEAK DISTRICT

Meerbrook Sough

EDITED BY
T. D. FORD &
J. H. RIEUWERTS

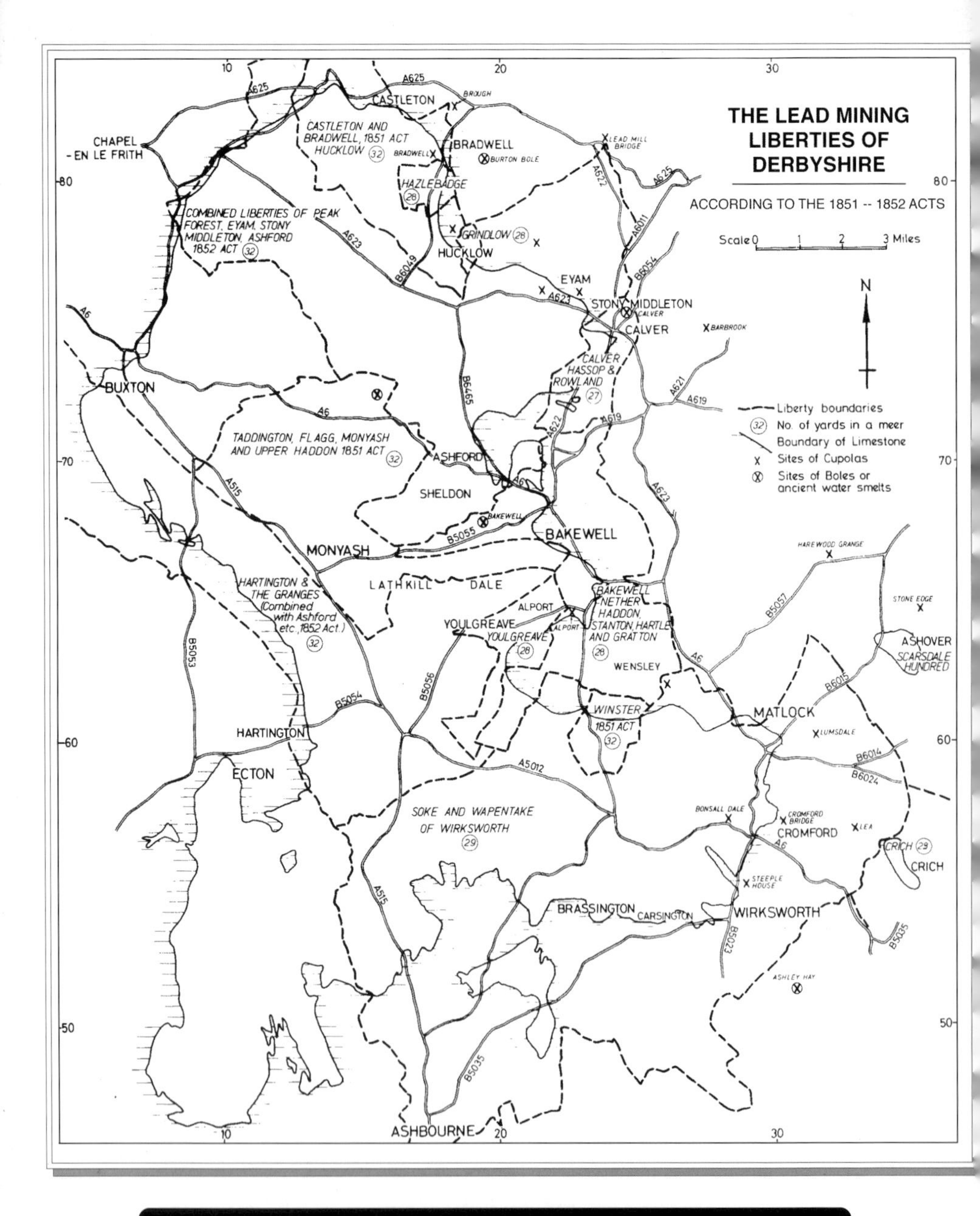


***Above: A map showing the various lead mining liberties or administrative areas of the Derbyshire lead mining district. In the 17th Century, this also extended into North Staffordshire***

***Opposite page: Drawing of the entrance to Odin MIne***

Barytes and fluorspar with disseminated chalcopyrite, Clayton Adit Level, Ecton

## LEAD AND OTHER ORES: GEOLOGICAL NOTES

### BY T. D. FORD

**The mineral veins of the Peak District are enclosed within the Carboniferous Limestone and associated basalt lavas, and these are described briefly first, setting the scene for more detail of the veins and their minerals.**

The limestones of the White Peak were formed as sediment on the floor of a tropical sea in the Carboniferous period of geological time, some 310-330 million years ago, when Britain lay close to the equator. The shallow sea was warm and clear and inhabited by a multitude of shellfish, corals, sea-lilies (crinoids) and various microscopic forms of life. When these died their remains accumulated as layer upon layer of shell debris which hardened with time to form limestone. These layers now outcrop along the dale sides as limestone strata. Around the fringes of the limestone sea was a ring of reefs composed of poorly bedded limestone largely built by the action of microscopic algae and other minute organisms, in places with abundant fossil shellfish, so that the White Peak can be compared roughly with a Pacific atoll of today. There is, however, a contrast between modern reefs and those of Carboniferous age in that corals are uncommon in the latter. The reefs are well developed at Castleton, in Dovedale, at Matlock and around the National Stone Centre at Wirksworth.

***A. Fluorspar B. Baryte on Calcite C. Calcite "dogteeth"***
***D. Blue John Fluorspar E. Galena crystals on Calcite F. Galena in Fluorspar***
***G. Baryte on dark Fluorspar H. Zinc Blende on Calcite***

Calcite crystals in Golconda Mine

The shallow seas of Carboniferous times were diversified by a scatter of small volcanoes pouring out basaltic lavas and ashes from time to time. These are now seen as dark bands interlayered with the limestones, for example in Cave Dale at Castleton, in Chee Dale, near Ashford-in-the Water and on Masson Hill at Matlock. The old lead miners had a variety of names for the basalts, such as "channel", and "cat-dirt", but they are commonly known today as "toadstones". This name may be derived from the German "todtstein" meaning dead or unproductive stone, as the lavas are usually poor in minerals; or it may refer to the toad-like colouring of green and brown, or it may be an expression of disgust when the miner met it in his shafts "t'owd .. stone, again"!

The study of the Peak District's limestones, toadstones, minerals and mines provided the stimulus for the early pioneers of the science of geology in the later 18th and early 19th centuries. Prominent among these were John Whitehurst, John Farey, White Watson and William Martin who became known both nationally and internationally by their published writings on Derbyshire's rocks, fossils and minerals.

The common lead ore of the Peak District is GALENA, lead sulphide, and it is found in association with a variety of other minerals in the various types of vein which cut the limestones. Notable amongst the other minerals are SPHALERITE (zinc sulphide), FLUORITE (calcium fluoride), BARYTE (barium sulphate) and CALCITE (calcium carbonate). To understand the nature of the mines and the reasons why certain mining practices were used, it is necessary to appreciate both the varied character of the mineral veins and the associations of minerals within them.

RAKES are the major veins, often running across country for several kilometres. They consist of minerals filling nearly vertical fissures, which may be up to 15 metres wide though more often about 2 or 3 m. A few have been mined to depths approaching 200 m but none has been totally bottomed. More often drainage problems have limited mining to shallow depths. A rake thus consists of a nearly vertical wall of minerals up to 15 m wide, 4 or 5 km long and usually around 200 m deep. Mining has been by means of shafts sunk at intervals with levels driven horizontally outwards along the vein. Lines of waste hillocks mark the courses of the rakes, whilst underground open stopes are left when the minerals have been removed.

SCRINS are smaller equivalents of rakes. They are fissures filled with minerals but not often more than 50 cm wide and usually course across country for less than 1 km. Mine workings do not normally go much deeper than 50 metres. Scrins sometimes branch out of rakes in semi-parallel groups or "swarms". They are mostly seen on the surface as lines of closely spaced waste hillocks and hollows where shafts have collapsed. A gradation in size between rakes and scrins means that there are intermediate veins with somewhat interchangeable names.

FLATS are mineral deposits lying more or less horizontal and thus parallel to the beds of enclosing limestone. They are often small and with irregular shape and commonly form offshoots of larger veins. Examples are to be found in the Masson Mines at Matlock, in Golconda Mine near Brassington and on Bonsall Moor. As flats rarely outcrop most were found by miners following a rake or scrin and finding these nearly horizontal deposits extending outwards from the fissure veins.

PIPES are irregularly shaped linings or fillings of cavities, generally parallel to the bedding of the limestones. Like flats they had little outcrop and were found by miners extending outwards from other veins. This has led to confusion of names at times, as Mandale Mine was in a rake with pipe-like branches and is referred to in old documents both as Mandale Rake and Mandale Pipe.

Both pipes and flats are often close to or even capped by thin volcanic ash layers within the limestone known as wayboards.

In addition to these four types of vein there are REPLACEMENT ORE-BODIES where the minerals have somewhat patchily replaced the limestone. In some cases the ore-bodies have collapsed yielding breccias partly replaced by a disorganized jumble of ores and limestone boulders. There are also GRAVEL ORES where loose lumps of mineral matter lie in surface hollows or in caverns, having become detached from the rock by weathering and solution. DOLOMITIZED LIMESTONE, locally known as dunstone, resulted from a process associated with the early phases of mineral deposition where parts of the limestone mass were converted to dolomite, the double carbonate of magnesium and calcium. Some later fissure veins and pipe veins were emplaced in the dolomite. Some mineral deposits lie in "pipes" developed along the contact of dolomite and limestone.

The mineral deposits were formed by hot fluids migrating within the Earth's crust. Such fluids were dilute solutions generally around 100-150°C slowly permeating the rock mass at depths of 2 or 3 km. The chemical radicals were derived from deeper rocks as the fluids passed through and they were precipitated to form the mineral suite by a combination of factors such as cooling, mixing with cooler waters percolating down from the surface, by reaction with sulphur compounds present in pore waters, and by reaction with the oxygen in such waters. Mineralization resulted from a slow series of pulses of fluid flow which reached a climax towards the end of the Carboniferous period around 270 million years ago. Subsequent erosion has stripped off the cover of younger Millstone Grit strata and revealed the limestones and mineral veins on the hills and dales of the Peak District.

The lead mineral sought by the miners was GALENA (PbS), easily recognizable by its silvery metallic lustre on a freshly broken surface. Few veins contained more than 10% of galena (which has 86% of lead metal as the maximum obtainable by smelting) and such an ore content was not consistent over any distance. An average galena content was 5% or less, and some veins with only 2% have been worked, though probably at a loss. Such poor veins were followed in the hope that they would "belly out" and yield more galena further on. Associated with galena, the veins along the eastern margin of the mineral field also contained SPHALERITE (ZnS). Generally recognized by its dark brown chocolate colour it was also called blende or blackjack. It was regarded as of little value until brass, an alloy of zinc and copper, became popular in Victorian times. Both galena and sphalerite may contain traces of other metals: galena sometimes contained silver though rarely enough to make it worth separation during the smelting process. Sphalerite sometimes contained trace amounts of mercury and/or cadmium, both rather toxic if released to the environment during processing.

In a few areas the lead and zinc sulphides have been oxidised to the carbonates, cerussite (lead carbonate) and smithsonite (zinc carbonate, commonly known as calamine). Cerussite has been worked for use in paint manufacture as it is the raw material for white lead. Several White Rakes, at Hucklow, Wardlow and Brassington, are alleged to have been named after their content of the lead carbonate ore. Smithsonite was used in brassmaking and for medical purposes. However other White Rakes relate to an abundance of calcite.

Production statistics are fairly complete in some areas but poor in others so that the full yield of ores cannot be assessed. Estimates vary but somewhere between 3 and 6 million tons of lead ore concentrates have been raised since mining began. Zinc ore production was much less, somewhere around $^1/_4$ or $^1/_2$ million tons of concentrates in total.

Whilst the lead and zinc minerals have long been regarded as the ores, they are found in veins with the gangue minerals fluorspar, barytes and calcite. Forming more than 90% of most veins these were regarded as waste until late in the 19th century. Wherever possible these gangue minerals were separated underground and stacked in the stopes as "deads"; otherwise they were discarded on the hillocks. Nowadays the gangue minerals are the important products and the metallic ores are recovered only as by-products. Many waste hillocks have been reworked in modern times to recover the gangue minerals.

FLUORSPAR (strictly fluorite if the mineral is pure) is calcium fluoride ($CaF_2$), the chief source of fluorine for chemical industry. It is used in the manufacture of

**Above: A solution cavity on Faucet Rake, Oxlow Mine**

**Below: Severe folding in Clayton Mine adit level, Ecton**

heat-resistant non-stick enamels (Teflon), for anaesthetics (fluorethane), for fluoridizing water-supplies and toothpaste, as a basis for artificial cryolite (sodium-aluminium fluoride) used in aluminium production, and in processing iron and steel slags.

Around 80 000 tons have been produced annually in the recent past, mainly from the two mines operated by Laporte Industries plc. on Longstone Edge and at Hucklow and from a scatter of opencast workings. Fluorspar is largely confined to veins in a strip little more than 2 km wide along the eastern margin of the ore field. Production has mainly come from mines at Castleton, Bradwell, Hucklow, Eyam, Youlgreave and Matlock. It is generally a translucent white to cream colour but may also occur in various shades of blue to purple. Freely grown crystals are cubic but break with an octahedral cleavage. Blue/purple and white banded fluorspar has long been mined in Treak Cliff near Castleton as "Blue John" used for a variety of ornamental purposes (see Castleton Itinerary).

BARYTE, barium sulphate ($BaSO_4$), often known in Derbyshire as "barytes", "cawk" or as "heavy spar", has yielded up to at about 40 000 tons per year in recent times. It is used in paint manufacture, for glossy paper, in some toothpastes, as barium meals for stomach X-rays, as a source of barium in chemical industry, and in large quantities for use in oil and gas well drilling in the North Sea etc. Baryte is an opaque cream colour, often without any obvious crystalline form. Clusters of sub-parallel tabular white glassy crystals are less common and are known as "cockscomb" baryte or as "boulder". Occasional large white or pink crystals can be found. It is distinguished by its weight, being nearly twice as heavy as fluorspar or limestone, though not as heavy as galena.

CALCITE, calcium carbonate ($CaCO_3$), is chemically the same as limestone and chalk. Its crystalline form (calc-spar) is sometimes in demand because of its opaque white character. Until recently two mines on Long Rake near Youlgreave produced calcite for use in terrazo flooring and panels, stucco pebble-dash wall-coverings, white lines in the middle of roads, grave ornamentation and for uses in chemical industry. Glass-clear calcite (Iceland spar) was once used in optical instruments but synthetic materials have replaced it. Calcite occurs in many forms; its crystals may be either pointed "dog-tooth" scalenohedra or blunt "nailhead" hexagonal prisms with flat rhombohedral terminations. Much more common is the opaque white to grey "comb-structured" interlocking prismatic form of calcite found in many of the rakes.

The above three gangue minerals, together with galena and sphalerite make up the bulk of the 2000 or so mineral veins in the Peak District, but nearly 100 other minerals are known in trace quantities. A full list may be found in "MINERALS OF THE PEAK DISTRICT by T.D.Ford, W.A.S. Sarjeant & M.E.Smith (1993).

Besides the above minerals several other materials have been mined in the Peak District. Perhaps the best known of these is the ASHFORD BLACK MARBLE, a very dark variety of fine-grained limestone which was mined at Ashford-in-the-Water during the 18th and 19th centuries. It takes a high polish and when inlaid with various coloured stones it was much sought after for tables, mantelpieces and smaller articles. Its history has been described by J.M.Tomlinson in DERBYSHIRE BLACK MARBLE (Special Publication no. 4 of the Peak District Mines Historical Society, 1996).

Two other varieties of limestone were also mined near Ashford-in-the-Water for use in ornamental work, particularly inlay. These were ROSE-WOOD MARBLE, a brownish laminated limestone which looks like the grain of rose wood when cut and polished. It was mined in Nettler Dale, north of Sheldon. The other was BIRDS EYE MARBLE, also quarried in Nettler Dale. It was a dark limestone with sparsely scattered bits of fossil crinoids. When cut and polished these showed up as white "Birds Eyes" in a black background.

Limestones rich in fossil crinoid remains were quarried at several sites around Monyash and used for various ornamental purposes as "figured" or "encrinital" marble.

DUKE'S RED MARBLE was a red iron-stained limestone found in a lead mine near Alport-by-Youlgreave. Entirely worked out on the orders of the Duke of Devonshire, it has been used for inlay work and small ornaments since the 1830s. A good example is a small pillar in Great Longstone church pulpit. The original site of the deposit is unknown.

Manganese "wad", a group of manganese oxides, has been worked from several lead mines around Elton and Winster for use as a pigment in paint. Less pure brownish manganese oxides have also been produced under the name "umber" for use as a pigment.

A brown variety of baryte found near the Arborlow stone circle was used in small quantities as an ornamental stone. Known as OAKSTONE it was used mainly for inlays in Ashford Black Marble.

Small amounts of earthy hematite, iron oxide, occur in calcite veins around Hartington and were worked both for iron ore and as a pigment.

A variety of silica sands and clays have been worked opencast in "pocket deposits" around Brassington and Friden for use in refractory brick manufacture.

Massive beds of CHERT, a silica replacement of limestone, have been mined around Bakewell for use as a grinding medium in the Potteries.

COPPER ORES were mined in an extensive group of mines around Ecton in Staffordshire. Though the first records of mining are in the 17th century, hammer stones and an antler pick indicate that prehistoric mining took place in the Bronze Age, more than 3000 years ago. Peak production was reached in the late 18th and early 19th centuries when mine workings went 300 m below the level of the River Manifold. Some 4000 tons of copper metal were obtained along with substantial quantities of lead and zinc ores. Occasional specimens of chalcopyrite, malachite and azurite may still be found on the waste heaps.

There are several major limestone quarries in the Peak District supplying stone for aggregate in concrete, in road-building and for cement manufacture. Some of these quarries have intersected mineral veins and old workings therein.

Finally, high purity LIMESTONE has been mined near Middleton-by-Wirksworth since 1959. Some 5000 tons per week are used in glass-making and in sugar-beet refining. The mine galleries extend under Middleton Moor for more than a mile and have intersected several old lead mines.

# INTRODUCTION: History

By J. H. Rieuwerts

*Above: Launder, or water channel, in Old Mill Close Mine*
*Opposite page: Climbing shaft utilising protruding limestone slabs as footholds/handholes, Greensward Mine near Monyash*

# 1. EARLY HISTORY:

## Prehistoric to Roman

**Present day historians cannot be sure of the origin of lead mining in the Peak District. Before the Roman occupation of this country, lead ore was obtained in the North Pennines, and so it seems likely, though not proven, that the veins in the Peak District would be exploited at the same period.**

Pieces of melted lead and burnt lead ore found in Early Bronze Age barrows in Derbyshire, a perforated lead bead from a barrow near Foolow and the more recent identification of a Late Bronze Age lead axe-head, found on MamTor, Castleton, serve to enhance the above speculation. At the Ecton copper mines just over the county border in Staffordshire, yet geologically within the Peak orefield, a Bronze Age antler and hammer stones found in shallow, outcrop workings near the hill-top prove that mineral exploitation was in progress well before the arrival of the Romans.

The Romans definitely worked lead ore in the Derbyshire ore-field and several 'pigs' or crude ingots of

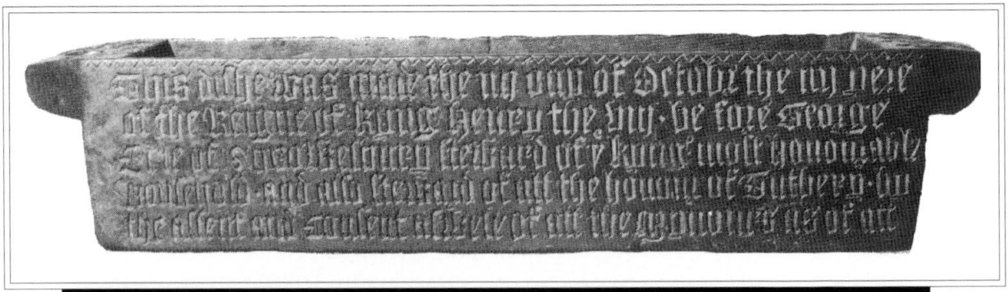

*The standard dish for measuring lead ore, kept in the Moot Hall at Wirksworth*

metallic lead have been unearthed from time to time. The first was found about a foot beneath the surface on Cromford Nether Moor in the year 1777. Since then others have been found at Matlock Bank, Tansley Moor and Bradwell; several others found outside the county, some as far away as Sussex, can be traced back to Derbyshire. Well over 30 pigs are now known to have been cast in metal obtained from the Peak Mines. Most of these have inscriptions on one or more faces and although drastically abbreviated, the owner and place of manufacture can usually be deduced.

The Derbyshire pigs are distinguished by the letters LVT or LVTVD, or in one case LVTVDARES, all of which are believed to refer to Lutudarum. This is popularly supposed to have been located on the site of Wirksworth, or Matlock or Carsington, but these suppositions are without direct evidence. Chesterfield, as a very ancient and well-established lead market, could be suggested or, more likely, the name may refer to the whole area of the mineral field.

A further difficult problem is presented by the letters EX ARG, and despite much speculation a wholly satisfactory translation and expansion is not available. Several translations seem possible, and include 'ex argento', meaning 'made from silver'; 'ex argenteriis', meaning 'from the silver mines'; or 'ex argentia officina', meaning 'from the silver refinery'. Two of the Roman pigs have pieces of galena embedded in them and it has been pointed out that galena could not have withstood the process of cupellation (the method of removing silver from lead) and remained unaltered. 'Ex arg' can also be taken to mean 'that from which silver has been removed', but analyses have shown that the silver content of the pigs is much the same as in galena. The Derbyshire ores are usually poor in silver content, and with the exception of the Ball Eye Mine near Bonsall (285 574) and certain mines near Nether Haddon they would not appear to be rich enough to be classed as silver-bearing lead ores. Dating the pigs is also difficult and only the one from Cromford Moor can be dated accurately to the period AD.117-138.

So far as the actual sites of the working are concerned, the commercial show caverns at Matlock Bath claim to contain 'Roman Galleries', and some written accounts quote descriptions of supposed Roman workings in Derbyshire mines. There are a number of mines containing very ancient workings. For example within the underground ramifications in 'Masson Cavern' and 'Rutland Cavern' at Matlock Bath, are workings of great antiquity, but unfortunately it is not possible to assign a positive date to them.

At Roystone Grange, near Ballidon, a small lead vein, worked as an opencast trench, has been bridged by a wall, probably of Roman age. Thus the lead working is either of Roman or even pre-Roman age.

The extraction of the lead ore by the Romans would probably be mainly confined to open workings along the outcrops of the major veins. Some veins are between 10 and 40 or even 50 yards (9 and 36 or even 46 m) wide at the surface and whilst not exclusively filled with lead ore, the workings could have been taken to a fair depth by opencast methods. Undoubtedly the Romans possessed the knowledge and technical skill required to undertake deep mining, but open-cast working would have been a far more economical proposition.

Roman artefacts have been found associated with lead mining operations at Elton, Crich and Longstone

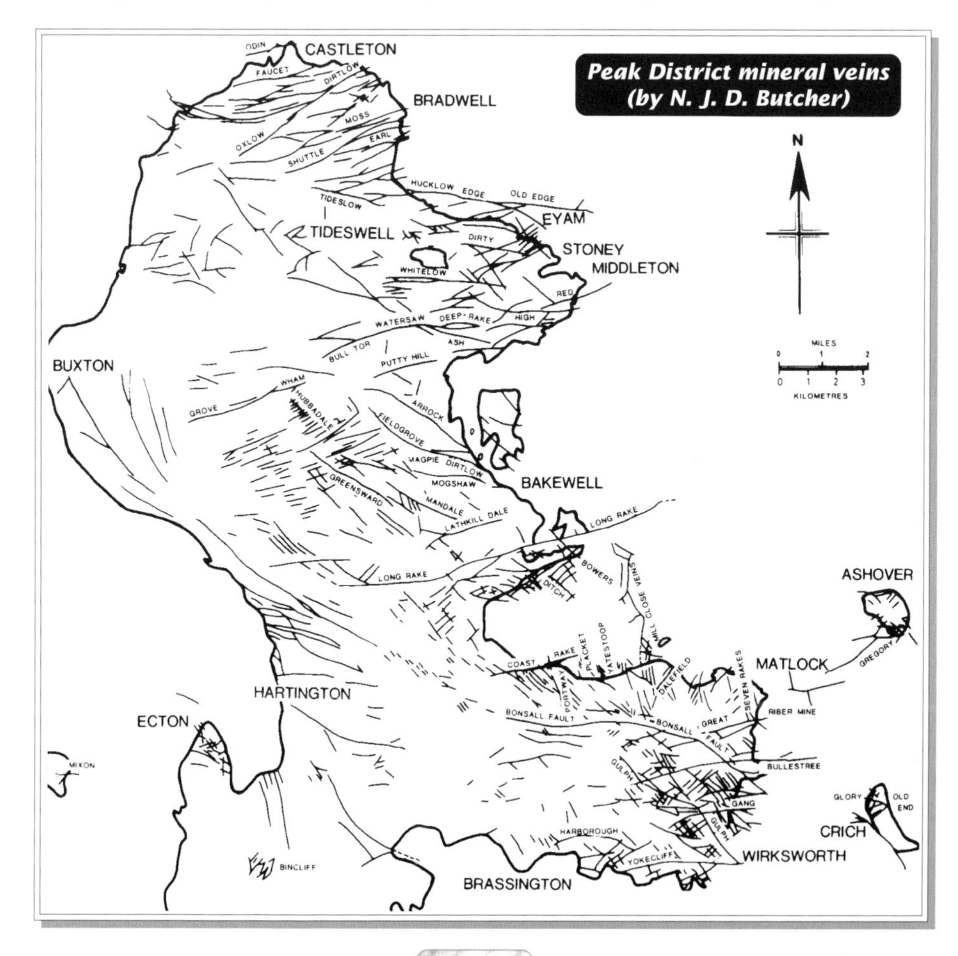


**Peak District mineral veins (by N. J. D. Butcher)**

*An underground dressing floor in James Hall's Engine Mine, Castleton*

Edge. Unfortunately no precise descriptions survive so it is not known if they were found at the surface or underground.

## The Anglo-Saxons and Domesday

After the withdrawal of the Roman forces, there was a lapse of some 600 years before the Norman Conquest. During the intervening period both the Saxons and the Danes filtered into the Peakland hills and mining continued but it is thought on a smaller scale than previously.

The mines at Wirksworth were owned by Repton Abbey and in 714 a leaden coffin was sent to Crowland Abbey, Lincolnshire, for the remains of St. Guthlac. In the 9th century the mines at Wirksworth were still attached to the Abbey of Repton, and were evidently of considerable importance because in 835 lead worth 300 shillings had to be paid as annual rent charge to Christ Church, Canterbury. The Danish army destroyed Repton Abbey in 874, and the Manor of Wirksworth along with the lead mines passed into the hands of the Danish King Ceolwulf. The mines at this date became the property of the Crown and the mineral duties in the Kingsfield/or Queensfield now belong to the Duchy of Lancaster. The Queensfield does not cover the entire mining field, and the owners of the different mining liberties will be discussed later.

Odin Mine (134 834) near Castleton traditionally derives its name from being worked at the time of the Danes, though its name was not recorded until about 1280 (17th – 19th century mining documents record the name as Oden, but Odin has been used since 1800).

The Domesday Survey, undertaken in 1086, recorded lead production at the time of Edward the Confessor (1042-1066). The combined manors of Hope, Ashford and Bakewell annually rendered 5 cartloads, each of 50 slabs of lead metal, each slab weighing about 40lbs (18 kg), as a levy or duty to the Crown. This levy, coupled with other rather tenuous evidence, suggests that a yearly output of about 1000 loads of lead ore (about 250 tons)was mined annually from within the three manors.

By 1086 seven *plumbariae* or 'lead works' were noted, three at Wirksworth, and one each at Matlock, Ashford, Bakewell and Crich. The five manors of Wirksworth, Matlock, Darley, Parwich and Ashbourne, not recorded during 1042-1066, rendered £40 of pure silver.

The mines within Hope manor received no mention, but because Domesday was a fiscal record, then maybe lack of record reflects work at the respective mines was by then under direct control of the Crown by 1086. During later centuries 'lead works' could mean a combined, communal ore washing and smelting site and such an explanation appears very likely within the context of the seven Domesday *plumbariae*.

The render of £40 of pure silver is far more interesting. Despite the low silver content of most Derbyshire lead ore, an annual production of about 3500 loads of ore containing 2oz/ton (57 grams/tonne) of galena, obtained specifically for de-silverisation, would have been required to supply the requisite quantity, a very considerable amount. Ball Eye Mine produced at least 20oz per ton, however. Maybe

**Date and initials in the roof of the Great Open in "Masson Mine", Matlock**

the render was paid in minted coin, not in silver metal.

A small stone carving in Wirksworth Church depicting a miner carrying his pick and a small basket, or wisket, is thought to be of Anglo-Saxon date.

### MIDDLE AGES – 1100 TO 1300

Lead was in demand for roofing and other building purposes and the numerous castles and religious houses constructed during the 11th, 12th and 13th centuries provided a steady outlet for Derbyshire lead. The metal was also exported; for example approximately 100 tons (101.6 tonnes) were sent to Clairvaux Abbey in France in the late 12th century.

Accounts indicate that the mining was widespread and well established throughout the ore field during this period and production reached a high level, though market demand produced wider fluctuations.

The Tideslow mines situated on Tideswell Moor were worked in 1195 and between 1216 and 1249: production statistics are available for the above mines, together with those at Wardlow Copp (now known as Cop Rake) at the extreme western end of Bradwell Moor. The Tideslow mines were richer, producing some 13000 loads in the period, or about 350-450 loads per annum. The workings at Wardlow Copp added a further 9000-9500 loads in the same period, averaging 200-300 loads each year. A mine at Rotherlowe, near Bradwell,' contributed nearly 600 loads in five years before being drowned out in 1247.

Remaining mines in the High Peak (i.e. Castleton, Bradwell and Hucklow) yielded 700-1000 loads each year between 1236 and 1249.

Distinctive 'v' shaped, opencast trenches, similar to gigantic plough furrows, yet remain at both Tideslow Rake and Cop Rake and though it cannot be proven, they may indicate the sites of the 13th century mining operations.

## 2. ORIGIN AND EARLY DEVELOPMENT OF MINING CUSTOMS

**At this point it may help if the broad outlines of the mining laws are considered.**

The orefield is divided into several administrative compartments, some of which belong to the Crown via the Duchy of Lancaster; others belong to private individuals. The Duchy owns the Queensfield or Kingsfield consisting of two principal areas, the High Peak and the Low Peak or Soke and Wapentake of Wirksworth. Each area consists of a collection of liberties corresponding, with few exceptions, to the parish boundaries. In the High Peak therefore Castleton Liberty is synonymous with the parish of Castleton.

Outside the Queens(Kings) field the lead mining royalties are owned by individuals such as the Duke of Devonshire and the Duke of

***Wind Bores or ventilation pipes in Royledge Mine, west of Ecton***

Rutland. Miners in these liberties did not have identical laws and customs with those in the Queensfield but they are broadly similar.

The lead mining royalties due to the Crown have been frequently leased to individuals since early times on payment of an annual rent. The Duke of Devonshire and Sir Richard Arkwright (of cotton fame) are amongst former lessees of the Kingsfield royalties.

The whole jurisdiction applicable to Derbyshire lead mining, with few exceptions too complicated to deal with here, is dealt with by the Barmote or Barmoot Court consisting of a Steward, a Barmaster and Jury of 12 (formally 24) miners or maintainers of mines.

Until two Acts of Parliament were passed in 1851 and 1852 these peculiar laws and customs were outside Common Law. The lead mining Acts are still in force and the Barmote Courts still meet annually. It should be noted the Acts do not cover all the private liberties.

Within the Queensfield any man could search for lead ore without hindrance from the landowner, only certain places being exempted from this peculiar custom. Church yards, gardens, orchards and highways could not be disturbed in the search for ore, although lead was worked from beneath such places on many occasions.

A vein, when first discovered, had to be "freed", that is, application had to be made to the Barmaster (a Crown official who deals with all lead mining queries and customs), to register the name of the new vein in his book; at the same time, one "freeing dish" of ore was paid to him by the miners. This dish represented the initial payment due to the owner of the mineral duties.

The volume of the Low Peak standard dish is 14 Winchester pints and the original dish presented to the miners by Henry VIII in 1513 is still preserved in the Moot Hall at Wirksworth. It holds about 65lbs (29.5 kg) of dressed lead ore.

The Barmaster, upon receipt of this freeing dish, allowed the finders of the new vein two "founder meers" of ground. The meer, which is a very ancient unit, is 32 yards (29 m) in length in the High Peak,

Mining methods illustrated in Agricola's "De Re Metallica", 1556

irrespective of the width or depth of the vein. The length of the meer varies in different parts of the mining area; some localities, for example the Low Peak and Ashford Southside Liberty have 29 yards (26.5 m) to the meer, whilst in Youlgreave Liberty it is only 28 yards (25.6 m).

The payment of the freeing dish to the Barmaster enabled the miners to work for a distance of two meers in their new vein, and as deep as their resources would allow, the width of the working being governed by the width of the vein itself. The third meer was called the Lord's meer and belonged exclusively to the owner of the mineral duties.

The Lord's meer could either be purchased outright by the miners, or they had the right to work through it, but in this latter case could not sell any of the ore they obtained in so doing. If they decided to purchase the Lord's meer outright then the Barmaster called members of the Barmote Court to descend the mine, view the vein, and place a valuation on it. The Barmote Court is still held and although today its function is somewhat traditional, in the mining days there was generally a great deal of work to be transacted and the jury men, who were miners or had connections with the industry, dealt with disputes of ownership, non-payment of debts, and other mining and mineral matters. After the miners had worked, or worked through the Lord's meer, they could free as many subsequent taker meers as they wished. These had to be kept at work or they could be "nicked" or counter-claimed by other miners wishing to work the vein. Providing that the vein was worked to the satisfaction of the Barmaster and the jurymen it could not be forfeited. Should the vein stand idle though the lack of adequate ventilation, or because it was drowned with water, then it could not be "nicked" or forfeited.

In addition to the "freeing dishes" paid by the miners to the owners of the mineral duties, other royalties were also payable. These included both "Lot" and "Cope" and also Tithe. Briefly, the Lot was taken as a certain fraction of the dressed ore. Normally this amount was one thirteenth, but at times this was altered by the Mineral Lords, sometimes on account of the low price of lead, which made mining less profitable than usual. The Cope was generally paid by the lead merchants and was, in places, 4d. per load, in others 6d. per load. The Cope was taken as payment in lieu of the Crown or his lessee having first right to the purchase the ore. Nine dishes were reckoned to equal one load, and the load varied in weight, depending upon the quality of the ore, so that about $3^3/_4$ loads would be equal to one ton.

At an Inquisition in 1288 the framework of these curious and ancient laws was set out. They may have been derived in the first place from the Saxons. After many additions and modifications, the Laws were finally passed as two Acts of Parliament, one in 1851 for the High Peak, and the other in 1852 for the Soke and Wapentake of Wirksworth, the combined liberties of Eyam and Stoney Middleton, Tideswell, Ashford and Hartington and the liberty of Crich.

More detailed accounts of the Laws will be found by consulting the bibliography, but possibly the most entertaining way to read them is to consult the "Rhymed Chronicle" of Edward Manlove, first published in 1653. Manlove was Steward of the Wirksworth Barmote Court, and he set down in verse the quaint customs with which he would obviously be very familiar.

# 3. MINING METHODS BEFORE 1600

## ORE EXTRACTION AND ROCK EXCAVATION

**The process of ore and rock extraction advanced but slowly. Gun powder blasting was not introduced into British mining until the 17th century, perhaps first in Central Wales in the late 1630's, in Derbyshire at Longe Sough, Cromford in 1662, at Bailliffe Croft Sough, Wirksworth in 1672, and at the Ecton copper mines, Staffordshire, perhaps about 1665-1670, but definitely by 1672.**

But long before that event working the vein outcrop by opencast methods was, as already noticed, probably utilised by the Romans, whilst the large trenches at Tideslow Rake and Cop Rake may date from the 13th century.

**A miner being lowered on the rope in a shaft within a coe**

Large vertical opencast workings such as those to be seen on High Tor, Matlock may be equally ancient, but the larger "quarry-like" opencast excavations along the north eastern portion of Dirtlow Rake, Castleton, formerly considered to pre-date 1600 are now thought to be a little later, probably the first half of the 17th century and are of a similar date to the narrower, but spectacular opencast work at Oden Mine, Castleton.

Because of imperfections in the technique of smelting ore in the bole furnace, only larger sized pieces of galena, preferably 1 to 2 inches (2.5 – 5 cm) in size, could be smelted economically in such a furnace. Thus, before the introduction of the ore-hearth furnace in about 1571 small sized ore was not preferentially mined. The small fragments of ore disseminated within the gangue mineral which constituted the major volume of most of the major rakes, such as Dirtlow Rake, was practically worthless and

**Stows illustrated by Agricola, 1556**

only the richer ribs of ore, generally near the vein walls, were mined. The resultant hand-picked, narrow stopes, often less than two feet in width and typically thirty to forty feet in depth, are the remains of working the richer ribs. Clearly they predate the large excavations seen at Dirtlow Rake and elsewhere.

An early form of shaft mining was by the bell pit method. Formerly it was considered that many such shafts existed in the orefield, strung out along the small veins and scrins like beads on a string. However, within recent years, extensive exploration of such areas on Bonsall Moor has demonstrated that many of the now grassed hollows were not shafts but merely "cast-holes" where the miners removed the sub-soil down to the vein head as a means of assessing the nature and ore content of the vein at that point. Most were abandoned without sinking deeper.

South west of Elton a series of shallow shafts have been sunk onto a flat of ore and here a few true bell pit workings have been found, in each case the base of the shaft having been under cut all round before danger of collapse dictated that it was abandoned and another shaft sunk only a few yards distant.

At the Whitelow mines, situated on the western edge of Bonsall Moor, ore was obtained from a series of shafts sunk on a boxwork of joints aligned at right angles to each other. At each joint intersection preferential solution of the limestone formed a small, four-pointed star-shaped cavity into which residually weathered silt and clay accompanied by pieces of lead ore, derived from higher veins long eroded away, all accumulated by gravity slumping. The shafts were sunk at each intersection and from each shaft foot the deposit of soft infill was worked for a few feet only along each joint before the limestone walls closed up. Shafts only a few feet apart are not interconnected. No other comparable deposit of this type is known in Derbyshire. The Whitelow mines were at work as early as 1541 –1542.

Underground exploitation, as opposed to work carried out either via shallow shafts or from stopes developed within rich ribs of ore, was in progress on the Heights of Abraham, Matlock Bath, before 1470. Here the Nestalls mines, (now known as the Masson and the Rutland tourist show caverns) were worked through an intricate series of pipe-type deposits, in reality an interconnected warren of mineralised vughs, known to the old miners as jouph holes or lough holes. The ore was extracted by the use of long, extremely fine pointed chisels and small picks. The workmanship has left behind a curious, and so far as presently known, unique pattern of thousands of extremely fine peck marks in the rock surface and in some of the workings a characteristic, undulating floor surface, not seen in any other Derbyshire lead mine. Some of the resultant openings are very small and in these specific places the employment of children cannot be excluded, although admittedly very long handled chisels may have been adequate for the purpose of ore extraction. Locally fire setting was used to break down harder rock.

There are possibilities of yet earlier underground exploitation at Rotherlowe Mine near Bradwell about 1242-1247, and Mandale Mine, Over Haddon, before 1287.

Elsewhere excavation was accomplished by a variety of methods and tools. Those used most often were the poll-pick or stone pick, having one end pointed and the other squared. The square end was struck with a heavy hammer, the pointed end being used in the fashion of a chisel. The very small foudenhead pick was used only for ore extraction, whilst the slightly larger pillow pick and larger sticking pick were used mainly for extraction of ore and gangue minerals. Large and small hammers, chisels, gads and a variety of wedges were adequate for most purposes.

Fire-setting was frequently employed: a fire built against the rock face resulted in its being fractured and even shattered by the heat generated. The usage of fire-setting necessitated the introduction of laws into the Barmote Court to prevent fires being lit before 4pm, so preventing suffocation of men in adjacent workings. Fire-set workings can be examined in Coalpit Rake Mine (Devonshire Cavern), Nestus Pipe and Owlet Hole Mine, Matlock Bath. The process was obsolete in Derbyshire by about 1720-1730.

## HAULAGE

After the ore and adherent spar and rock fragments had been broken out of the enclosing rock mass, it was conveyed to the shaft, or adit entrance where one existed, either in baskets (called "wiskets"), or dragged over the uneven floor in a corfe/corve or sledge. At the shaft the material was wound to the surface by a small windlass, or stowes. The stowes was wound by one or sometimes two men.

## ORE DRESSING AND SMELTING

Before the last quarter of the 16th century, the cleaning and dressing of lead ore ready for smelting was a comparatively simple operation.

Much of the pure "bing ore" obtained from rich ribs and veins required little attention, save for breaking and sieving to a manageable size; washing was not necessary. Some poorer quality ore called "boose" or "bouse" was taken for cleaning in water and several locations are recorded where there were communal ore washing sites. They existed for example at Shothouse Spring near Grange Mill; near Wirksworth; north west of Tideswell and no doubt along the courses of many streams and rivers. The resultant material was known as "wash ore".

During the sixteenth century there was an increase in the volume of ore washed at individual mining sites and in 1557 the Low Peak mining customs stated that:

*"everie man that hath a Washing trough of his own – ought to have a space of seven feet about the said Washing trough".*

All this ore was smelted in a bole furnace; typically each charge consisted mainly of bing ore, but a small proportion of wash ore could be added. The boles were usually sited on the tops of westwardly facing hills or scarp edges, thus taking advantage of the prevailing winds. The furnace consisted of a three sided stone structure into which were placed alternate layers of wood and lead ore.

Bole furnaces are first recorded in Derbyshire in the 12th century. Medieval boles were small, about three feet in diameter and clustered close together. Post Medieval boles were much larger, up to twenty feet in diameter, but usually at each site there were only two or three hearths. They were not very efficient and in the 12th to 14th centuries the quantity of lead metal obtained from the ore was only about 20% – 25%; by the time of their demise in the early 17th century efficiency had increased to 50% or even greater.

**Washing ore in a wooden buddle, as illustrated by Agricola, 1556**

Over one hundred bole sites are known, some within the mining area itself, but most were sited on the gritstone hills to the east of the ore-field, or on the western fringes of Sheffield and Chesterfield.

Bole furnace slag was rich in lead and re-smelting, a viable economic operation, was carried out in a charcoal-fired furnace known as a blackwork oven. A high temperature was required for the operation, hence the use as charcoal as a fuel. The bellows which provided the air blast were operated by manpower.

William Humphrey of the Mineral and Battery Works, in conjunction with men versed in methods employed in European mining technology, is usually credited with the introduction into Derbyshire of the vat and sieve for ore dressing about 1572 and the slightly earlier introduction, c 1570-1571 of the ore-hearth smelting furnace, but both claims were vigorously contested. Nevertheless, these innovations revolutionised ore dressing and smelting processes.

Humphrey's first furnaces were similar to a charcoal-fired blast furnace used by one Burchard Cranich at Duffield in 1553-1554 and were a failure. The ore-hearth furnace, the bellows worked by men's feet and hence known as a "footblast", was brought to Derbyshire from the Mendip Hills, but Humphrey modified it by using water power to blow the bellows.

Great quantities of fine sized "bouse" ore, discarded by previous generations of miners, because it could not be smelted satisfactorily in the bole furnace, suddenly became of great economic importance. Dry sieving of bouse had been carried out using a wooden sieve with slots about $^{1}/_{2}$ inch (1.2 cm) diameter, but about 1572 a fine meshed wire sieve, probably originating from Germany, and used both with and without a water-filled vat, had been tried without success.

The sieve was not used for sizing purposes but was forced rapidly up and down in the water, and effected a gravity separation of the much heavier galena from the dirt and other minerals. Though Humphrey claimed responsibility for the process, some Derbyshire miners stated that, like the ore-hearth, they had brought the process to Derbyshire from the Mendip Hills along with miners, ore dressers and smelters.

Whatever its origin, large numbers of poor mining families appeared and were able to extract sufficient lead ore, previously discarded onto the hillocks, to maintain themselves. The operations were carried out at Longstone Edge Rake, on the old rakes at Wardlow, at Northcliffe near Calver and elsewhere.

The ore-hearth furnace was similar in construction to the blacksmith's hearth. The first water driven furnace was built by Humphrey on the River Sheaf, south of Sheffield, about 1572. Nearly ninety examples are known, the last being obsolete before 1800. Of the earlier variety, or "footblast" sixteen such furnaces are recorded from Derbyshire. Just as lead-rich slags arising from bole smelting operations were re-smelted in the blackwork oven, so too lead-bearing slag derived from ore hearth smelting was dealt with in another charcoal-fired furnace, known as a slag hearth. Unlike the blackwork oven, here the bellows were worked by a water wheel; the hearth was introduced about 1572, contemporary with the ore hearth furnace. The process of buddling, that is washing fine particles of lead ore intimately mixed and covered with clay and other dirt, in a stream of water contained within a slightly sloping wooden or stone trough, must have been introduced into Derbyshire in either the late 16th century or early 17th century.

# 4. MINING METHODS 1600-1700

## ORE EXTRACTION AND ROCK EXCAVATION

**Towards the end of the 17th century the Derbyshire miners adopted an excavation technique used in antiquity by the Greeks and also in mining regions of the Near and Middle East and employed in European mines at least since the 15th century, if not earlier. Agricola in 1556 depicted the method, a miner digging a tunnel by means of striking the squared end of a pick with a hammer. Whereas only ore and zones of weakness were originally exploited in this way, by cutting a series of parallel grooves in the rock face and subsequently trimming the sides of the level the expertise was acquired so that it became possible to construct long cross-cut levels in hard, relatively unjointed rock. Progress was painfully slow, averaging about 1½ inches (3.8 cm) per shift in 1670, reaching only 2½ to 3 inches (6.4 to 7.6 cm) per shift almost half a century later.**

These levels have become known to modern mine explorers as "coffin levels" due to their often distinctive cross-sectional shape.

Excellent examples of coffin levels can be seen throughout mines in the Matlock, Wensley, Winster and Elton mining fields and also in the Ball Eye Mine near Bonsall and in the Crimbo and Whalf mines at Monyash.

It has already been noticed that rock excavation using gunpowder blasting was introduced into British mining operations in the mid 17th century. Notwithstanding these events, the older techniques of rock breakage using hammer, poll-pick, gad and wedge were still in widespread use and continued to be so until the last quarter of the 18th century. Gradually, however, gunpowder became used on an ever larger scale; extensively so at the Dovegang mines, Cromford, in the 1670s and in the Earl of Rutland's mines at Nether Haddon at the same period; by 1700, mine reckoning books record its use all over the orefield.

The technology of gunpowder blasting varied and, as might be expected, became more refined with time and experience. After the shot hole had been bored about 12 inches to 15 inches (30 to 51 cm) in depth about 2oz. to 4oz (57 to 113 g) of powder was placed in the hole. Iron wedges were sometimes used to secure the charge, but hammering these wedges into place caused sparks and resulted in premature firing causing serious injury or death to the miners. The earliest recorded injuries due to gunpowder blasting accidents occurred in the Nether Haddon mines in 1676.

A safer procedure involved the use of wooden rather than iron wedges, or perhaps more frequently by stemming the charge with clay or stone dust. The technique was used at Longe Sough, Cromford, in 1662-1663 probably twenty five years before its so-called invention in Germany. Despite the newer technologies, fears for miners' safety and expense, a pound of powder cost the equivalent of a man's daily wage, ensured that older breakage techniques still continued, side by side with the new.

The process of ore extraction was known as stoping. Hitherto in Derbyshire this had been a rather haphazard process due to the fact that most mining operations were of limited lateral and vertical extent within each individually owned, small scale mine and only rich bunches of ore were randomly exploited.

After the onset of the 17th century there was continuity in this older type of operation, but gradually stoping became more organised. The new innovations of ore-hearth smelting and the sieve and vat dictated that poorer quality ores could be exploited. The stoping pattern which evolved consisted of cutting out the vein in a series of downward steps, much like a staircase, each step about four to six feet in height, a miner working at each one; waste

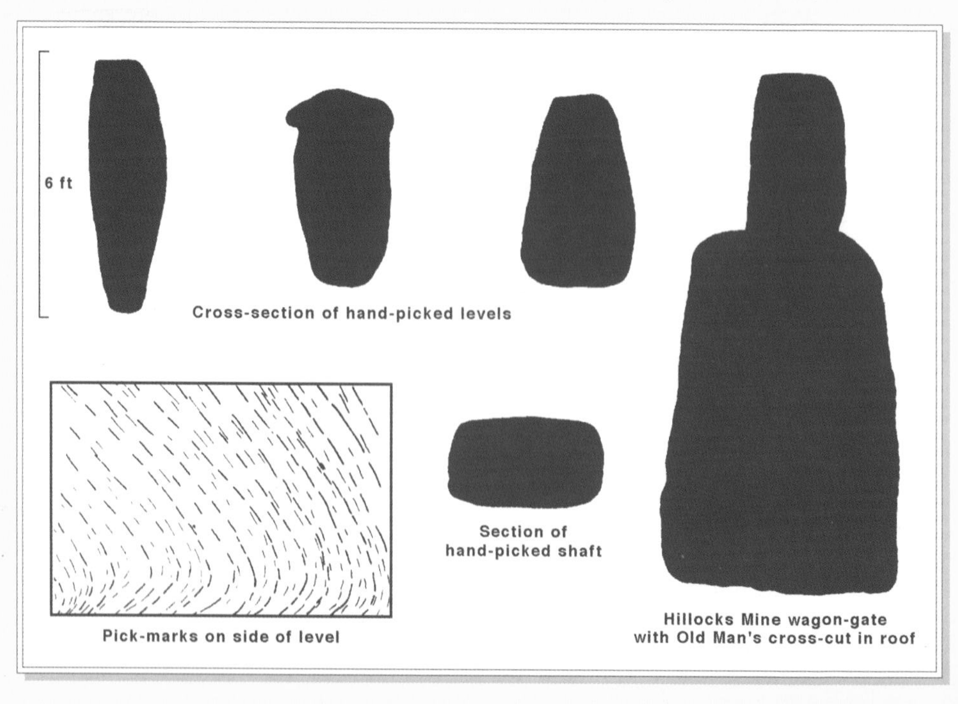

rock was thrown down underfoot. Beautiful examples can be seen for instance in Coal-pit Rake, Matlock Bath, the vein walls, or as the miner termed them 'woughs' or 'skirts', adorned with sweeping pick or chisel marks.

The 17th century lead mining industry was one of great expansion and prosperity. A petition handed to Parliament in 1641-42, listed by name some 20 000 people who were miners, ore dressers, carriers or others directly involved with the industry. The large number of cases involving lengthy litigation between opposing miners handled in the Duchy of Lancaster Court and in Chancery is testimony enough to the richness of many mines, the documents substantiate the large sums of money invested by entrepreneurs. For example about £4000 was expended in a sough at Elton between 1655 and 1665, whilst at Portaway Yate Grove, near Winster, before 1694 the partners had expended £2000 in mining, soughing and installing engines (presumably horse-powered rag and chain pumps).

Amongst the principal mines at work might be cited Oden Mine, Castleton; Tideslow Rake; Old Edge Groves, Hucklow; the Great Rake or Wheels Rake, Haddon; Millclose Groves, Wensley; Winster Pitts and Portaway Groves, Winster; Cowclose, Leadnams and Waste Groves near Elton; Nestus Groves, Side Groves, both at Matlock, Ball Lee (or (Ball Eye) Mine, Bonsall; the Cromford Moor – Dovegang complex and the Ratchwood and Raventor Mines, Wirksworth. These, and many more scarcely less important, were the backbone of a great industry. Some idea of the scale of these operations may be formed from the following typical examples.

Output from the Milne Close Groves, Wensley, was considerable throughout the 17th century. The construction of six soughs to drain the workings is an indication of the potential and although records are fragmentary, 9800 loads of ore, exclusive of Lot ore, sold from the mine in a four year period in the 1680's, give a hint of the richness of the deposit. This output level was probably maintained from at least 1665 until 1693 because payments for Lot and Cope to the Duchy of Lancaster were about £300/annum throughout that period, suggesting an annual output from the mine of about 2500 loads.

The Hucklow Edge Vein was pursued eastwardly from Great Hucklow, ever deeper beneath the shale cover. The Old Edge Grove and New Edge Grove produced 8500 loads from 1683 until 1701 and the wealth of these two mines attracted lengthy lawsuits in the Barmote Court, but more particularly in the Duchy Court around 1695-1710.

## EARLY DRAINAGE TECHNOLOGY

Two other problems concern the early techniques of lead ore extraction, namely ventilation and drainage. Both were considerable obstacles to the sinking of deep workings. By the seventeenth century the workings along the lead veins were generally approaching the water table. This is usually determined by the contour of the nearest valley floor, but there may be local irregularities due to impervious layers of igneous rock or other geo-

***Transfer of mining title at Greaves Croft, Moss Rake, Bradwell, in 1906***

logical complications. Above the water table, the mines were tolerably dry, but below this level the miners were quite often in serious difficulties with large volumes of water. Anyone who has explored old lead mines in the limestone in Derbyshire will appreciate that considerable seepage takes place through the upper workings, and although these may be as much as 300 ft (91m) or more above the local water table, they can be uncomfortably damp. One of the earliest dewatering methods employed was that of winding water in leather buckets by means of a windlass. Wherever possible water was run off into natural cavities underground, or if a small tunnel conveniently led to a nearby valley this might be utilised. Because of the cavernous nature of the limestone, natural cavities or "self-opens" as the old miners called them, were regularly encountered. Later, many drainage levels were driven from these caves and underground river courses, thus saving the miners the trouble of driving a level all the way from the nearest valley side.

Although documentary evidence is strangely lacking before the 17th century, hand-operated rag and chain pumps must have been in use; so too force pumps and sweep pumps. A rag and chain pump consisted of a wooden barrel, internal diameter about 3-4 inches (7.6 – 10 cm), and about 20 ft (6m) in length. An endless chain wound by a hand windlass descended outside the barrel into a water-filled sump and ascended inside the barrel. Attached to the endless chain were either leather discs or blobs of leather. Thus water was lifted from the sump through the barrel and was discharged into either a drainage level or into the sump of a higher shaft. Sometimes a series of rag and chain pumps lifted water from a depth of 150 ft (45 m); each pump about 20-25 ft (6-7.6 m) in length required 24 men to operate it day and night. Only 10-15 gallons (45-68 litres) of water per minute was raised by each pump so clearly they were very inefficient. The work was physically exhausting for the pumpers.

"Engines" or "Ingins" used for dewatering purposes are recorded at many Derbyshire lead mines before 1700. The earliest was at work in 1581 and was sited at Ashbury Crofts Mine, Matlock; it used horses for motive power, but the pumping arrangements are not known. Unfortunately, its precise location is yet unproven, though it was within Matlock Liberty. It was installed at the expense of Sir Francis Willoughby of Wollaton Hall, Nottingham.

A horse-powered rag and chain pump working in a shaft 240 ft (73 m) in depth was unsuccessful in unwatering the Dovegang Mine in 1615. At least eight "Engines" worked at this mine, two of which were Tread Wheels, installed in 1651 and 1657; they are the only known examples of this type of applied power in the orefield.

The depth of the Dovegang shafts (there was an adjacent winding shaft of the same depth) in 1615 was exceptional for the period and other early engines, such as the one at Waste Grove, Winster, and another at Tearsall Mine, Wensley, pumped from shallower shafts about 140ft to 170ft (42 to 52 m) in depth. Water wheels were also used, perhaps first at Ladygate Rake, Matlock in 1655 and at about the same time at Paddock Torr Rake, also at Matlock. Water wheels were also used on a large scale at mines in the Harthill, Haddon and Youlgreave area. At least forty "engines" operated on Derbyshire lead mines before 1700.

In addition to the above engines, sites where drainage problems were acute were termed "Water works". Documentary evidence does not always clarify the situation at such mines. Some of them, such as Ashbury Crofts, Barley Flatt and Raventor mines were the sites of pumping engines as described above, but at others, for example Ball Lee (=Ball Eye), Hallacres near Middleton by Wirksworth and Gurdall at Wensley all described as 'Water works' in 1597-1599, there are no explanations of the difficulties, or their alleviation.

## SOUGHS OR LEVELS IN THE 17TH CENTURY

By the beginning of the 17th century many of the larger lead veins in the Peak District had been worked down to, or were rapidly approaching, the water table. The driving of soughs from a lower contour in an adjacent valley, or from a deeper valley. which could be 2 or 3 miles (3.2 or 4.8 km) distant from the mines, enabled the water table to be lowered still further. These soughs were to become very much the symbol of the Derbyshire lead miner's skill, perseverance and endurance. Today some of these soughs, although driven between 250 and 350 years ago, are still in good condition.

Mining historians have accepted an oft-quoted statement dating from the 17th century that the first sough in Derbyshire was that begun in 1632 by Sir Cornelius Vermuyden and driven from Cromford Hill into the Gang or Dovegang mines. More recent research in the archive at Chatsworth House and in the Public Record Office indicates that in fact Vermuyden's level is pre-dated by at least one and possibly three earlier soughs. The first, known as Wet or Weet Sough dates from 1627 and is situated at Winster. Only recently re-opened; it is but 100 ft (30 m) in length, driven entirely in shale.

During the protracted and many faceted arguments relating to the Dovegang mines, it was claimed that before Vermuyden began his sough, one John Bartholomew had nearly completed a sough to the same mines, but had been prevented from doing so by Vermuyden and his partner Sir Robert Heath. No other documentary evidence has come to light relating to Bartholomew's Sough but the proximity of the deep Dean Hollow valley a short distance to the north of the mines would make its construction an attractive proposition.

A short sough level driven from an underground swallow hole towards the Tearsall mines may date from about 1627-1630. A sough at these mines was certainly in existence by 1633.

Before the end of the 17th century over seventy soughs had been driven, or were in the process of construction. Some were short and relatively unimportant levels, serving perhaps only one mine, but at least nine can be considered to be major levels, several thousand feet in length. Vermuyden's Sough; Longe Sough or Cromford Sough begun in 1657-58; Bates Sough, Cromford, begun in 1657; Stanton Sough, a mile in length by 1700 and Tideslow Sough, begun in 1654 and nearly half a mile in length by the winter of 1685, are probably the best examples. The latter sough therefore advanced at about two to three inches (5-7.6 cm) each day for a time span of just over thirty years!

Other large soughs under construction at this time were the Hannage Sough, commenced about 1693 at Willowbath Mill and driven to the mines north of Wirksworth; the Cockwell Sough at Ashover; the Winster Sough started in 1687 draining the Portaway Pipe and the sough started in 1659 or just before, to take water from the old and rich Oden Vein, near Castleton.

## VENTILATION

Mining could not proceed very far from the mine entrance or the foot of the shaft before bad air became a problem. Shallow, interconnected workings could be ventilated adequately by a natural air flow, but as shafts and levels penetrated ever deeper into the hills more radical solutions became essential.

Before the onset of the 17th century there is an isolated reference to a mine being worked through the shale, at Shaley Grove, Matlock Bath in 1576, whilst the large scale workings at Milne Close (or Mill Close) Groves, Wensley were worked through the shale cover by 1617, and at Oden Mine before 1638. Working levels were pursued ever deeper and exploratory cross-cuts became longer; some of the mid 17th century sough levels were driven through shale for considerable distances. There are records of miners being killed or "damped" by noxious gases in Derbyshire lead mines in the late 16th century and early 17th century.

The old method of rock breakage by firing or "fire-setting" created volumes of smoke and noxious fumes. The Barmote Court had long legislated that firing could be carried out only after 4pm and all fires extinguished before 8am, but clearly smoke and fumes lingered in the workings. The advent of gunpowder blasting created its own problems, although fire-setting became obsolete in Derbyshire about 1720-1730.

Efficient methods of bringing fresh air into the workings were needed. The easiest way was the promotion of a natural air flow by provision of closely spaced air shafts, a noticeable feature along the line of many old soughs. Good examples can be seen at Mr. Thornhill's Sough, an early sough driven through shale to Bowers Rake near Stanton; Foolow Edge Sough on Eyam Edge, and at the "Peakshill" Sough on the western extremity of Oden Vein.

Fresh air could be directed into a funnel, or "horsehead" at the shaft top, then conveyed to the working places through closely sealed, interlocked sections of wooden ducting known as "fangs". Wind shafts and fangs were noted at the Wirksworth mines in 1629. Bellows were in operation at the Dovegang mines in 1676 and again air was forced through fangs. A fan was noted at Moorfurlong Mine in 1692-94 and although no documentary evidence has yet been found the use of both bellows and fans must have preceded these dates by many years.

## ORE DRESSING AND SMELTING

Bole hearth smelting became obsolete within the first decade of the 17th century, the ore-hearth reigned supreme until the introduction of the cupola furnace in the 1730's.

Ore dressing techniques improved too. The crude ore drawn from the mine was classified as either bing, being lumps of almost pure galena, or lesser quality bouse. The bing might have required some crushing to a managable size, but bouse was subjected to a series of crushing, sieving and washing operations. Crushing was accomplished by a square, flat headed iron hammer called a bucker, the ore being beaten down on a stone slab called a knockstone. The resultant grades of ore were variously known as peasy ore, knock-bark ore and a fine-grained powder ore called smitham.

Smitham was then subjected to buddling; yet finer particles of galena remained, known as belland but until the next century it was discarded. Cattle, horses and poultry eating grass contaminated by belland were poisoned and were said to have been "bellanded".

## GEOLOGICAL CONCEPTS RELATED TO MINING – A BRIEF OVERVIEW

The miners, by long acquaintance and observation, acquired a degree of knowledge relating to local geology. For example perhaps as early as the late 16th century and certainly by the second decade of the 17th century they realised that the ore-bearing limestone continued beneath the

A horse-gin on Long Rake, near Youlgreave

shale cover. They began to exploit these concealed deposits at Milne Close (Mill Close) Groves, Wensley by 1617 and at Oden Groves, Castleton, before 1638. Shaley Grove, Matlock, was at work in 1576, but maybe only as a trial shaft.

Workings beneath igneous horizons such as lava beds and clay wayboards developed at much the same time, maybe first as Tearsall mines, Wensley, about 1633. It is not clear whether the miners differentiated between the usual limestones and the igneous rocks at this date, but references to Robinsons Stone at the same mines might refer to a very localised name for the Matlock Lower Lava. Blackstone, a miners' name for lava, was recorded at Blackstones Grove, Winster in the 1661 and this mine was situated within, or very close to the outcrop of the Matlock Lower Lava. A little over a decade later in 1675, the Fletchers Rake on Middleton Moor, near Wirksworth, had reached the 'Great Clay', yet another reference to the Matlock Lower Lava.

Due to technological difficulties in excavation through solid limestone, some levels constructed before 1700 tended to be driven along veins, joints or similar zones of weakness. Driving along, or very close to the sub-surface interface between the shale and underlying limestone provided easier digging in the shale, whilst the miners were able to observe any mineralisation in the limestone. The technique was probably developed in the Cromford-Wirksworth district during the 1650's, perhaps first at Old Rantor Sough, or maybe at either Bates Sough or Longe (Cromford) Sough.

During the construction of the Longe (or Cromford) Sough, an unforeseen bed of very hard limestone was encountered, interbedded within the shale. This event took place in the early 1660's and eventually it defeated the miners who had to deflect the course of their sough. The level was turned to the south west but soon entered the main limestone. However, a thin vein or leading was soon found and very probably the hope of pursuing this leading into a richer deposit led directly to the introduction of gunpowder blasting there in 1662.

## 5. MINING METHODS FROM 1700 TO 1800

**The opening of the 18th century proved to be the dawn of a particularly active period, and during the next 190 years saw the industry rise to a peak of technological advance, and of ore production. It witnessed also the beginning of the decline which was to terminate in the mid 20th century, with the ultimate closing of virtually all of the mines as purely lead producers, and the parallel growth from about 1900 of the fluorspar industry. The 18th century saw the introduction of the steam engine as a motive power for pumping in the Peak lead mines, the driving of major soughs, and an increase in commitment to capitalised mining in the district.**

Often substantial sums on money and capital had been invested in the 17th century as wealthy London merchants and local lead merchants and smelters became partners in mines and soughs. They provided a certain proportion of the finance for the day to day working of the mines, difficult for the working miner/shareholder to contribute on his own. However the installation of steam powered pumping engines enabled mining to be carried on to great depths on a scale not seen previously, often beneath the shale cover, and which required a huge injection of capital.

Mining throughout the orefield expanded and from Castleton in the north to Wirksworth in the south large capitalised mines emerged. Some areas, notably Bonsall and localities on the western fringes of the orefield such as Tissington, Parwich, Hartington and Buxton, continued, with few exceptions, to be worked on a much more modest scale, typically by small groups of working miners.

### Ore extraction and rock excavation

Fire-setting became obsolete about 1725 – 1730, but otherwise breakage techniques varied little from the previous century. The use of gunpowder continued to increase, but driving levels through solid rock using hammer, pick, gads and wedges also continued and indeed levels were still constructed in this way in the 1760's and 1770's. Sometimes a combination of gunpowder blasting, followed by traditional wall trimming by sweeping pick or chisel work was carried out; a good example can be seen in a drainage adit known as Hallicarr Wood Sough, situated in the Via Gellia. The rate of progress in the forefield of a handpicked level was about 1-1½ inches (2.5-3.8 cm) per shift in the mid 17th century to 2-2½ inches (5-6.3 cm) per shift by about 1700. The depth of shafts increased dramatically. Whereas a depth of 300 ft (91 m) was exceptional in the 17th century, by 1732 the Stoke Old Engine had been sunk 700 ft (210 m) in two stages and by 1749 the nearby Ladywash Shaft was 624 ft (190 m) in depth and may have been the deepest single shaft in Great Britain at that time. Before 1800 the Whimsey Shaft at Gregory Mine, Ashover had reached a depth in excess of 900 ft (274 m).

## DRAINAGE

Some of the larger soughs begun in the 17th century, such as Longe Sough (or Cromford Sough); Hannage Sough, Wirksworth; Portaway Yate or Winster Sough; Stanton Sough and Cockwell Sough, Ashover, were continued towards their objective. Great drainage levels were begun all over the orefield and although, as previously noted, over seventy soughs can be attributed to the 17th century, the principal era of sough making in the Derbyshire orefield was undoubtedly the 18th century and the first quarter of the 19th century. Parallel with these developments, many smaller soughs were driven, often serving only one mine or vein. Hand pumping by means of rag and chain pumps continued, either as the only means economically available at the smaller mines, or for lifting water up a series of shallow sumps to a sough level or to the engine shaft foot.

A major leap forward toward mine drainage was achieved by the introduction of the Newcomen Fire Engine. The first Derbyshire engine was installed at Yatestoop Mine, Winster, in 1719 and during the following one hundred years more than thirty such engines, or its modifications by James Watt, Francis Thompson, John Curr and others, were installed at Derbyshire lead mines.

The use of water wheels became important as prime movers for pumping purposes. Two such wheels, both installed underground, operated at Mill Close Mine, Wensley in 1746-1747 and in the latter year a wheel of 40 feet diameter, capable of raising 1000 gallons/minute (4546 litres) was installed at Stoney Lee Mine, Stanton. Several water wheels serving mines at Matlock and Matlock Bath operated along the River Derwent and two wheels, one above the other, operated at the Coalpithole Mine, Peak Forest in the 1780s; these last were seen and noted by the great civil engineer, John Rennie.

About 1765-1770 it is possible, though not proven, that an hydraulic engine invented by William Westgarth, the noted mining engineer based in the Northern Pennine orefield, may have been installed at Lathkilldale Mine by the London Lead Company. The engine, if it existed, is of great historical importance, being one of the earliest of its kind in the country and pre-dating the well-known water pressure engines designed by Richard Trevithick by 35 to 40 years.

The men who undertook to drive the long soughs were generally capitalists with large sums of ready money to invest. Sometimes they were partners in mines and sometimes they were lead smelters or merchants. The Alsop family had shares in numerous lead mining ventures including Hill Carr Sough. The Bagshawe, Nightingale, Barker, Wilkinson, Nodder and Clay families all had extensive shares in Derbyshire lead mines and there were many more. The gentry too invested heavily and the Duke of Devonshire and the Duke of Rutland were shareholders in several soughing and mining adventures. The minor gentry were keen participants in mining schemes and typical were the Twigg's of Holme Hall, the Thornhill family of Stanton Hall, Lord Scarsdale of Kedleston and the Gells of Hopton Hall. Before a sough was made, the usual procedure was to draw up a legal agreement between the soughmasters or "undertakers" and the proprietors of the mines to be "unwatered". Usually marks were made in the mines at the standing water level, and the soughmasters received a certain proportion of the ore, generally $^1/_4$ to $^1/_6$th, obtained below these marks when drained by the sough, and a smaller proportion of any ore mined below the actual level of the sough itself. The arrangements for the installation of pumping machinery to enable the miners to work below sough level varied, as did the procedure for the maintenance of shafts and levels and even the sough itself.

Some soughs were not driven in this way, but were made by the owners of a mine by themselves and were driven along the "sole", or bottom level of their own veins. Good examples of this can be seen at Smallpenny Sough (181 657) in the upper reaches of Lathkill Dale, Wardlow Sough (175 747) in Cressbrook Dale, and a sough draining the western end of the Rath Rake (later known as Coast Rake) into Gratton Dale (209 609). A great deal of activity was focussed on the mines lying south of the River Lathkill, near Alport. Several soughs had been driven to this rich complex of veins during the latter years of the 17th century and the early years of the 18th century. The Stanton Sough (245 643) was driven through the shale approximately parallel to, and south of the river Lathkill, in order to relieve the Bowers Rake; while Rainstor Sough (237 652) was driven to veins on the north side of the same river. Alport Sough (227 648), begun in 1706, and the Blythe and Grime Soughs (231 643) were other shallow levels, which enabled considerable quantities of lead to be raised.

However in 1766, a large, low level sough called Hill Carr Sough, or sometimes Stanton Moor Sough, was begun from the side of the River Derwent (259 634) to give deeper drainage to the Alport mines. The making of this long sough proved to be an immense undertaking. Explosive methane gas issued from the shales and several men were killed during the 1770's by ignition of the gas by candle flames. The limestone rock was of such extreme hardness that drills suitable for boring the shot holes were difficult to obtain. The black blasting powder had to be sealed in containers prevent moisture getting to it, and much trouble was experienced providing adequate ventilation for the sough forefield. Not until 1787 was the Guy Vein reached. The sough had several branches and boats were used to bring out the waste rock.

## UNDERGROUND TRANSPORT AND HAULAGE TO SURFACE

Primitive methods lingered on in many mines. Ore was removed in baskets or "wiskets", whilst dead rock was stored underground wherever possible. Carting waste rock was a non-profitable operation. Occasionally old documents make reference to a carrying gate, that is a purpose-made level used for transport, a task performed by boys carrying wiskets.

Larger quantities were taken from the mine in sledges or corves. The corves were usually fitted with iron runners and often a primitive plankway was laid on the floor of the level to facilitate movement of the heavy sledges.

From these primitive plankways cartgates developed in which small, plain-wheeled, wooden wagons or carts were pulled or pushed by boys along the plankways. Cartgates were associated with larger mines where greater volumes of material were removed and when finance was available to fund such innovations. The first recorded cartgate in Derbyshire was in Oden Mine, Castleton in 1730, but a later, much more substantial cartgate, a mile in length was driven at this mine in the second half of the 18th century. A part of it, finely walled and arched with dressed stone masonry is still accessible.

Wooden rails developed in the mid 18th century, though by then they had been in use in European mines for at least three centuries. The wagons were similar to those employed in the cartgates, but they had flanged wheels. These purpose-made haulage levels were called wagon gates or wagon roads. Very substantial wooden rails and larger wagons were employed in some mines, for example in the 1770's at Stoke Sough, Eyam, and White Coe Mine, Hassop; known as Newcastle Roads, they were far more common in the mining fields of the North of England.

A unusual form of transport was utilised at the Speedwell Mine, Castleton. Here the underground movement of waste rock and lead ore was accomplished by boats in a system of canals or partially flooded levels. This was not a new idea having been used some years previously at the Duke of Bridgwater's collieries at Worsley near Manchester. Boats had also been used to remove waste rock during the digging of the Hill Carr Sough since the late 1760's. An interesting fact is that John Gilbert, the engineer with James Brindley at Worsley, was a shareholder at both Hill Carr Sough and at Speedwell Mine. One reference specifically states that the Speedwell Level was driven "under the direction of Mr Gilbert". The principal shareholder appears to have been Ralph Oakden of Waterhouses, Staffordshire; old mining records refer to the mine as "Oakden Level". Work on the main level was commenced in the summer of 1771 and was not continued until 1782. A series of natural stream caverns was intersected by the level and lead ore was obtained from several veins and pipes accessible via the level and these natural caverns. Mining continued intermittently until 1813-14, but the venture was a costly failure.

The raising of the ore to the surface was either up a number of small, shallow shafts wound by hand winches known as stowes or stoces, or by horse gin at the usually deeper and wider engine shafts. This latter type of haulage had been introduced into the Derbyshire lead mines in the first half of the 17th century at Dovegang Mine, Cromford and at Tearsall Mine, Wensley. Apparently there was then a long gap before other horse-gins were erected, probably late in the 17th century, but more especially in the early years of the following century.

Horse gins became common in the period after about 1710-1715. The winding drum was horizontal mounted on a central vertical axle, all contained within a massive timber frame. It was operated by the horse walking in a circle, the winding ropes passing over pulleys and so into the shaft. The ore and rock was wound in large buckets known as kibbles. Usually one horse could wind from a depth of around 240 ft (73 m), but up to six horses were used to wind from shafts of 600 ft (183 m) or more as, for example, at the Eyam Edge mines. A typical surface feature of lead mining ground is the still conspicuous "gin circle".

## VENTILATION

Because the mines were worked to ever deeper levels and exploited further into the hills than ever before, ventilation became a much more serious problem than hitherto. Although fire-setting became obsolete well before 1750, nevertheless increased volumes of smoke and fumes

**A corve found in Tearsall Mine**

from gunpowder blasting restored the status quo.

Promotion of a current of fresh air was achieved by installation of a basket of burning coals suspended in an upcast shaft or by a fire or small furnace contained within a small building known as a Fire-House or in a short brick or stone chimney called a Cupola. Fire houses date from the 1730's and 1740's, but the first reference to a Cupola dates from 1766. Air circulation underground was made possible by fresh air being taken down an open shaft carefully "coursed" through passages, or stopes, linked by connecting gates or thurls, the rising air extracted from the upcast shaft by virtue of the hot fumes of the fire.

***A surveyor's tripod found in Snake Mine, Hopton Wood. The can probably held lamp oil***

At Cromford Sough, driven in shale deep beneath Cromford Moor, two closely parallel passages were connected at regular intervals by thurls. As the sough was driven forwards the redundant thurls were closed to prevent a short circuit in the air circulation. At Rogden Coe Shaft it is highly likely that a fire-basket was suspended in the shaft in order to cause an upward draft.

Fans of unknown size or operation were in use at Foolow Edge Sough in 1713, the level being cut for a considerable distance through shale. At Orchard Mine, Winster, there was a Fan-House in existence by 1724. Its precise construction is not stated but if it was a small building containing a revolving blade fan, either forcing air into the workings, or sucking it out, then it is the earliest known British example. Very large fans were operational in Hill Carr Sough by 1776, operated and kept in constant revolution by boys.

Water blasts were introduced into the Derbyshire orefield by 1766, though only six examples are known. The fresh air, trapped in a pipe by the action of falling water, was taken down the mine shaft and fed with the water into a closed box. The air compressed by this procedure found exit along a horizontal pipe leading from the box to the workings to be ventilated.

## THE PRINCIPAL MINES

Although rewards could often be considerable, the financial outlay in operating a large scale mine was very high and only groups of partners, consisting largely of wealthy businessmen, lead merchants, the landed gentry and nobility such as the Duke of Devonshire, could sustain such expenditure.

The following examples serve to illustrate the situation. The Yatestoop Mine, Winster, produced no less than 40 000 loads of ore between the years 1708 and 1739, yet expenditure from 1710 to 1713 amounted to £10,500, whilst from 1728 to 1733 a staggering £18,900 was spent in operating the mine. Running costs in operating three Newcomen Fire Engines and the necessary employment of large scale hand pumping contributed significantly to these high charges.

Similarly at Portaway Mine, Winster, charges of £18,700 during the period 1724 to 1733 ensured a loss of £5,400, despite raising 6900 loads of ore.

The early years of the 18th century were characterised by the discovery of extensions to several old and well tried veins. The Hucklow Edge Vein had been worked during the 17th century west of the village of Great Hucklow. The mines were initially worked in the upper limestones above the highest lava (toadstone) and they became successively deeper as the vein approached the village of Great Hucklow. Not until the 1760's was an attempt made to sink through this bed of toadstone and work the vein in the limestone beneath. The vein was also very "shackey" or cavernous and in the latter half of the 17th century drainage levels had been driven and their water turned underground into these "shacks" or "self opens" as the old miners termed them. At Great Hucklow, the vein disappears beneath the overlying Edale Shales, and this covering becomes progressively thicker as the vein ranges eastwards under Eyam Edge, until at the Ladywash Mine, north of Eyam village, a total thickness of 796 feet of shales and gritstone had to be sunk through before the underlying limestone was reached.

About 1711, it was realised that this large vein was continuing in an eastwardly direction, running approximately parallel with the scarp face of Eyam Edge. Almost simultaneously several mines, amongst them Little Pasture, Haycliffe, and Middleton Engine, began cutting shale-gates northwardly to locate the extension of the main vein, which they presumed would range across the northern end of their ground. These shale-gates not only acted as trial levels, but later, when signs of the vein had been seen in the shale, and shafts had been sunk down to the actual vein itself, they acted as drainage levels and were titled soughs on mining plans. They were not true soughs, but pumpways, not being deep enough to intersect the vein, but at the same time saved 200 or 300 ft (61 or 91 m) of laborious hand pumping all the way to the surface. The main engine shafts of the Eyam Edge mines were generally between 400 and 1000 ft (122 and 305 m) deep.

The vein was extremely rich and ore worth many thousands of pounds was raised annually from its mines. For example at Ladywash Mine between 1721 and 1739 over 19400 loads of ore were raised giving the fortunate proprietors an overall profit of nearly £8,500. The results at other mines along Eyam Edge were hardly less spectacular; Little Pasture Mine gave profits of close to £7,000 between 1721 and 1724. Middleton Engine, Moorwood Engine and Haycliff Mine raised 23300 loads of ore from 1736 until 1739; at Miners Engine 10700 loads were mined from 1733 until 1736.

Disputes regarding ownership of parts of the vein between neighbouring mines were fairly common, and one such dispute between the partners of the Little Pasture mine and the Miners Engine (205 775) lasted for over 50 years without being successfully resolved. The trouble started in the 1730's and developed because of the discovery of a branch vein, to which each mine claimed title. Adding to the confusion was the fact that it was not altogether clear at the time which of the two veins was the continuation of the Hucklow Edge Vein. Due largely to the complex mineral laws, extended litigation followed, which passed from the hands of the Barmaster and the Barmote Court into the Court of Chancery. The argument was still not settled in 1792, although the Barmote Court had meanwhile decided that the more northerly of the two veins was the Hucklow Edge Vein, ranging through the Broadlow (211 777) and Ladywash mines (220 777) whilst the other vein ranged nearly south east towards Shaw Engine Mine (222 771) and became known as the Old Edge vein.

The well known Oden Vein, Castleton was exploited within the limestone outcrop at the northwestern end of Treak Cliff, but passed quickly beneath the overlying shale. The vein had been worked beneath the shale cover by 1638. Water was already a problem and was raised from the workings in bags. Before 1658 an abortive attempt had been made to drive a sough into the waterlogged workings, but the first, partially successful attempt, was begun about 1658-1659. This old level had its entrance northeast of Knowlegates Farm and was driven through the toe of the Mam Tor landslip and Edale Shales to the working beneath Oden Gorge. During the first half of the 18th century the vein was worked progressively further west under the south eastern flank of Mam Tor. Natural caverns were intersected, and in times of flood great volumes of water flowed into the mine via these caverns. Their position, deep beneath the shale of Mam Tor, is geologically interesting. The mine nevertheless proved to be very rich and large profits were recorded in the mine reckoning books.

Watergrove Mine (188 758) near Foolow, was another mine to be worked in the first half of the century; before 1750 no less than three soughs had been started in an attempt to alleviate the water problem. Two of them did not ultimately extend for any distance and did not help in the eventual draining of the mine. The high costs of running the heavily watered mine resulted in a loss of £5,000 between about 1720 and 1734, this despite high production. The main drainage level, Watergrove Sough (212 757) did not reach the mine until 1770, and two Newcomen pumping engines had been erected by 1800. The first of them was in use by 1748 and by the end of the century, another had been put to work. The latter engine had a 40 inch (102 cm) diameter cylinder, a 7ft (2 m) stroke and pumps of 16 inch (41 cm) diameter. It was put up for sale with other mining plant when the mine was abandoned in 1853.

The area also had several other early soughs, which, besides that driven to Watergrove Mine, included the Stoke Sough (240 766) begun about 1720-1724 from the side of the River Derwent, north of Stoke Hall. This was one of the major soughs in Derbyshire, being intended to drain the Eyam Edge mines at a much deeper level than the earlier shale gate soughs, previously discussed, and which only served individual mines. Men were killed by both noxious gases and by explosions of firedamp during the making of Stoke Sough, and rock-oil was found in nodules in the shale. The miners used this oil in the first place for greasing their boots, but found that it shrivelled the leather so afterwards the oil was used to provide illumination for the mining operations.

Explosions of a spectacular kind occurred in the Haycliffe Mine (214 773), situated on the lower slopes of Eyam Edge north west of the village. The vein in this mine was "slickensided", i.e. its walls had been fluted and polished by the movement of rocks in opposition to each other during earth movements. Occasionally the stresses produced during the movements remained unrelieved and when struck with a miner's pick the adjacent minerals exploded with great violence.

In Haycliff Mine such surfaces were coated with a film of galena and were polished like a mirror. One writer, in describing an explosion in 1738, recorded that over 30 tons of rock was blown down by the blast. On other occasions men were injured, but often creakings were heard beforehand and gave miners a chance to run clear. Theories offering possible explanations for this curious phenomenon include ignition of firedamp by a spark from a pick striking the rock; a sudden release of stress within the vein-stuff caused by the removal of the adjacent rock; and chemical reactions taking place, particularly when the vein minerals are freshly exposed. The explosions have also occurred in the Oden Mine, Castleton, in the Gang Mine on Cromford Moor; in Cockersfield Vein, near Great Hucklow and in the Clayton Adit at the Ecton copper mines.

The Magclough Sough (237 775) was begun in 1724 and finished in 1736, being driven in opposition to Stoke Sough, to provide deep level drainage for the Eyam Edge mines.

The richest period of work at the Portaway Mine was from 1744 until 1760 when no less than 31 900 loads of ore were raised at a value of £63, 700. This ore was obtained from the down-dip workings north of Buckdale Lane, the waterlogged workings being drained in part at least by a Newcomen Fire Engine installed at a cost of £2000 (including ancillary work) in 1745.

The Cowclose and Leadnams Mines, near Elton,became very rich about 1741. For example, in the following 10 years lead ore to the value of £23,000 was mined, and a Newcomen pumping engine was erected on the Cowclose Mine in 1755, probably on Coast Rake.

The London Lead Company was active principally in the Northern Pennines, but became involved in Derbyshire in 1720, initially at a series of small mines lying on the hillside south and south east of Winster village and extending into the Wensley Liberty.

The company bought the Mill Close Mine in 1743 and here they carried out a great deal of work. The complex of pipes at the old 'Milne Close Groves' had produced huge quantities of ore throughout the 17th century and clearly the Lead Company felt they had bought a mine of enormous potential. They began by continuing an old sough westwardly towards their holdings on Gurdall, Wattering Close and other veins near to Winster. But their most important work involved developing the great pipe complex beneath the shale cover north of Cowley brook. To this end in 1746 and 1747 they erected two underground water wheels and a Newcomen engine for pumping water, utilising the old sough as a pumpway.

The London Lead Company were also active in Lathkill Dale between 1761 and 1777. Despite locating a large ore-body along Lathkilldale Vein, it seems highly likely the venture was a loss making operation due to heavy pumping costs and driving a long sough level along the sole of that vein. There is an exciting possibility that a very early hydraulic engine, invented by William Westgarth, a mining engineer from the Northern Pennines, might have been installed at Lathkill Dale Mine about 1765-1771. Unfortunately, many of the Lead Company records have been destroyed and no complete financial accounts for their Derbyshire operations have survived.

The second half of the 18th century was distinguished by large ore strikes and some mines returning immense profits, although the smaller mines exploited by the working shareholders continued to be very much in evidence. The Hubberdale Mine near Flagg, was the scene of a remarkable discovery of a rich pipe in 1767, from which 14 600 loads of lead ore were extracted, at a profit of over £1 per load between that year and 1769. This sudden ore bonanza was a typical feature of pipe workings, the ore, often in large, pure lumps being found embedded in clay in a wide "cavern". Then just as suddenly it was lost and thinned to a "stringer" of calcite or other gangue minerals, of a $^1/_4$ inch (0.6 cm) or less. The miners still followed these leadings, hoping to find another similar "Belly" or widening of a pipe. For example, earlier in the century, a large pipe was worked at the Ball-Eye Mine in Via Gellia, where it is said £50 000 worth of lead was extracted in a period of three years.

Breachside Sough near Hassop, Oden Mine at Castleton, Placket Mine at Winster, Waterhole Mine near Rowland and some of the mines on the Hucklow Edge Vein were all highly productive. Blythe Sough near Alport produced nearly £33 000 worth of ore between 1790 and 1800, and similarly Shining Sough, another venture associated with the draining of the Alport mines which had been started in 1756, ten years previously to the Hill Carr Sough, raised £42 000 worth of ore.

Mines situated beneath and adjacent to a trough of shale known as the 'Gulf', lying north of the town of Wirksworth, including Ratchwood Mine and mines along Northcliffe Vein, were very productive in the 18th century, initially due to the drainage offered by Hannage Sough. Later in the century large returns of ore were obtained from the Rantor Mine and again from the Ratchwood Mine, both benefitting from yet deeper drainage given by the driving of a long branch level out of Cromford Sough, southwards from Gang Vein. Another extension of the sough, westwards along the Gang Vein complex, produced similar results at Samuel Mine and Slack Rake Mine on Middleton Moor.

## ORE DRESSING AND SMELTING

The dressing of lead ore continued in much the same fashion as that employed during the previous century. The introduction of improved smelting techniques about 1737 allowed very fine ore known as belland, hitherto discarded, to be used and therefore buddling operations became somewhat more refined with the process being repeated as appropriate in order to extract the very fine ore dust.

Despite a threat to the women ore dressers at Portaway Mine, Winster to erect mechanised stamping machines, it is extremely unlikely that any such were installed.

The major advance in the 18th century was the introduction, about 1737 of the cupola furnace, or low arched reverberatory furnace. The innovation appears to have been made in Derbyshire simultaneously but independently by the Bagshawe's and the London Lead Company.

The furnace was fired by coal, but the ore charge was separated from the fuel by a bridge inside the furnace, the flames being drawn into the ore compartment by draught provided by a combination of long flues and a high chimney. The cupola had superceded the ore hearth by the 1780s Most of them closed down in the late 19th century, but two continued in operation until 1918 and 1936 respectively. About forty cupola sites are known.

## GEOLOGICAL UNDERSTANDING IN THE 18TH CENTURY

The ever expanding Derbyshire lead mining industry presented hitherto unavailable opportunities for new insight into geological problems.

Well before the onset of the 18th century the continuation of the ore-bearing limestone beneath the shale cover was well understood, so too the occurrence of the various beds of igneous rock, known to the miners as toadstone, blackstone, clay, channel and other less well-known terms.

Before 1700 there must have been a general recognition of a downward sequence of shale, limestone and an upper lava, but only during the mid 18th century was it realised that a more regularised sequence was present.

The pioneer Derbyshire geologist John Whitehurst (1713-1789) prepared various geological sections through parts of the orefield. These depicted a regular, recognizable sequence of rocks extending downwards from the shale cover, beneath which lay four thick limestone units, each separated from the next unit beneath it by a bed of toadstone; to all of these beds was assigned an accurately measured thickness.

This early recognition of stratigraphy may have been derived originally from work done by Thomas Westgarth, an agent of the London Lead Company, who frequently visited that Company's Derbyshire holdings. Westgarth had prepared similar, detailed sections for parts of the Northern Pennine orefield. He must have become well known to George Tissington of Winster, mine owner and agent and keen observer of local geology. When Whitehurst published his book in 1778 he was at pains to acknowledge his debt of gratitude to Tissington.

For example a section of Basrobin Sough, Wensley, drawn in 1767 by George Tissington, shows a sequence of First Limestone, blackstone, Second Limestone, underlain by a bed of clay.

Although the lavas interbedded within the limestones had been recognised in the 17th century, and mining operations carried out beneath them, it is only from the first decade of the 18th century that there is positive evidence that the miners specifically sought ore deposits beneath the lavas, for example in mines on the south side of the Via Gellia, near Cromford.

Specific efforts to sink deep shafts through these beds can be proved only from the mid 18th century, on Bonsall Moor; near Winster; on Middleton Moor; Tideswell Moor and elsewhere.

Towards the end of the century there arose a great debate whether all rocks were sedimentary in origin, as postulated by Werner in Saxony, or whether some were igneous, as proposed by the Scottish geologist James Hutton. Each school had its devoted followers and mines at Castleton, Bradwell, Tideswell Moor and Bonsall Moor were examined by Whitehurst, Faujas St Fond, Ferber, Mawe and others seeking to prove or disprove the igneous origin of the lavas. The working miners were obviously involved in these examinations and Elias Pedley, a Castleton miner, personally escorted St Fond to his mine so that he could examine the strata there. It was not until well into the 19th century that the volcanic origin of toadstones was fully accepted.

## 6. THE FINAL CENTURY; MINING METHODS FROM 1800 TO 1900

**The opening of the 19th century witnessed further developments in the scale of mining operations, some ventures soundly based on previous experience and knowledge, others, though well financed, based on the most slender indications of profitable ore deposits.**

Rather than relying on acquiring meers along an individual vein, these larger ventures obtained title to a compact area of ground, known in Derbyshire as a 'Consolidated Title'. The workings could be developed to depths exceeding 700 ft (213 m); much plundering of the 'old man's'

*Lord's Cupola, Middleton Dale, drawn by F. L. Chantrey c 1820*

stopes would be in evidence and the removal of riders and stalches – pillars left by former miners as being too poor to repay stoping. The mine might be expected to include mechanised winding, pumping and ancillary equipment; outlying shafts would be furnished with a horse-gin. Drainage could be implemented by a deep level sough, driven from a valley maybe 2 miles (3.2 km) distant. Underground, haulage gates laid with iron rails carried vein-stuff to the shafts to await removal to the surface.

There were also many medium scale ventures carried on by old mining families, for example the mines operated by the Royse, Hall, Eeeds, Barber, Middleton and Hill families at many mines in the Castleton, Peak Forest and Bradwell district. Steam-powered mechanisation would not be expected at these mines and often a horse-gin was shared between two adjacent mines. As at the larger mines, haulage gates were common and occasionally these mines too reached significant depths, for example 700 ft (213 m) at Hazard Mine worked by the Hall family of Castleton and 660 ft (210 m) at Windle and Rush Mine (commonly known as Slitherstones), near Eldon Hill, owned by the Royses.

Further south, the Ashton's of Winster, the Simpson, Henstock and Poundall families at Bonsall, all of whom worked mines on Winster Moor and Bonsall Moor; the Pearsons at Cromford and Matlock and the Doxey and College families at Middleton and Wirksworth were hardly less important.

Within most liberties, very small operations still continued, worked typically by a couple or three men on a part time basis.

## ORE EXTRACTION AND ROCK EXCAVATION

Regularised stoping became normal at the larger mines, whilst improved dressing and smelting technology allowed the removal of very poor quality ore from previously unworked portions of old veins. The arrival in Derbyshire of the well-known mining engineer John Taylor dictated that, for example, at the Alport mines the entire mineral contents of a vein were removed. The crude ore was then subjected to a most thorough and rigorous dressing cycle.

Overhand stoping in Derbyshire lead mines is sometimes incorrectly attributed to Taylor. By the time of his arrival in the orefield about 1839, it had already been employed for many years, but it was usually of a very random nature; Taylor's methodical ideas ensured that it was adopted as normal practice not only at his own mines but at many other large and medium scale mines.

The vein was worked forwards by a series of stoops, much like the underside of a staircase; unwanted rock (or deads) was stacked in the resultant void, supported on either wooden or stone platforms called bunnings. The vein-stuff was thrown down into a haulage level at the base of the stope. A series of stoops, one above the other, might be worked concurrently within one vein at the larger mines.

Boring shot holes had changed little in the previous century, steel-tipped cast iron borers being used, but in 1837 cast steel borers were introduced, perhaps first at Black

Woodern cart, used for haulage, Longstone Edge

in 1816 from Tricket Bridge (150 833) in Castleton. One of the chief proprietors of the mine in these last years was Robert How Ashton, of Losehill Hall, who was a well known lead-mine owner and who also owned lead smelting works at Brough and Marsh Farm situated between Castleton and Hope.

The Peak Forest Mining Company commenced operations in 1858 to re-work the Coalpithole Mine. This venture was also financed largely by Sheffield businessmen, but closed in the 1880's. The Company spent a great deal of money sinking new shafts and erecting pumping and winding machinery. The pumping shaft (098 813) over 66 fathoms deep, was at the side of the road at Perryfoot; and another very deep shaft, 110 fathoms in depth, was sunk through a considerable thickness of shale at the western extremity of the vein. The mine was one of the few to have a steam winding engine, this one made by Bray & Co., Leeds, in 1853 originally for Brightside Mine, Hassop. It was a horizontal engine used for pumping as well as winding. In 1870 it was purchased by the Peak Forest Mining Co. for £188.

## Ore dressing and smelting

Ore dressing processes altered considerably within the century, though no doubt at the smaller mines the bucking hammer and knockstone still prevailed. About 1817, a horse powered ore crusher was introduced, probably initially at Cross Grove, Moss Rake, Bradwell. The crude ore, or bouse from the mine was fed onto a circular, paved stone, or sometimes a segmental iron track. The ore was broken by means of a

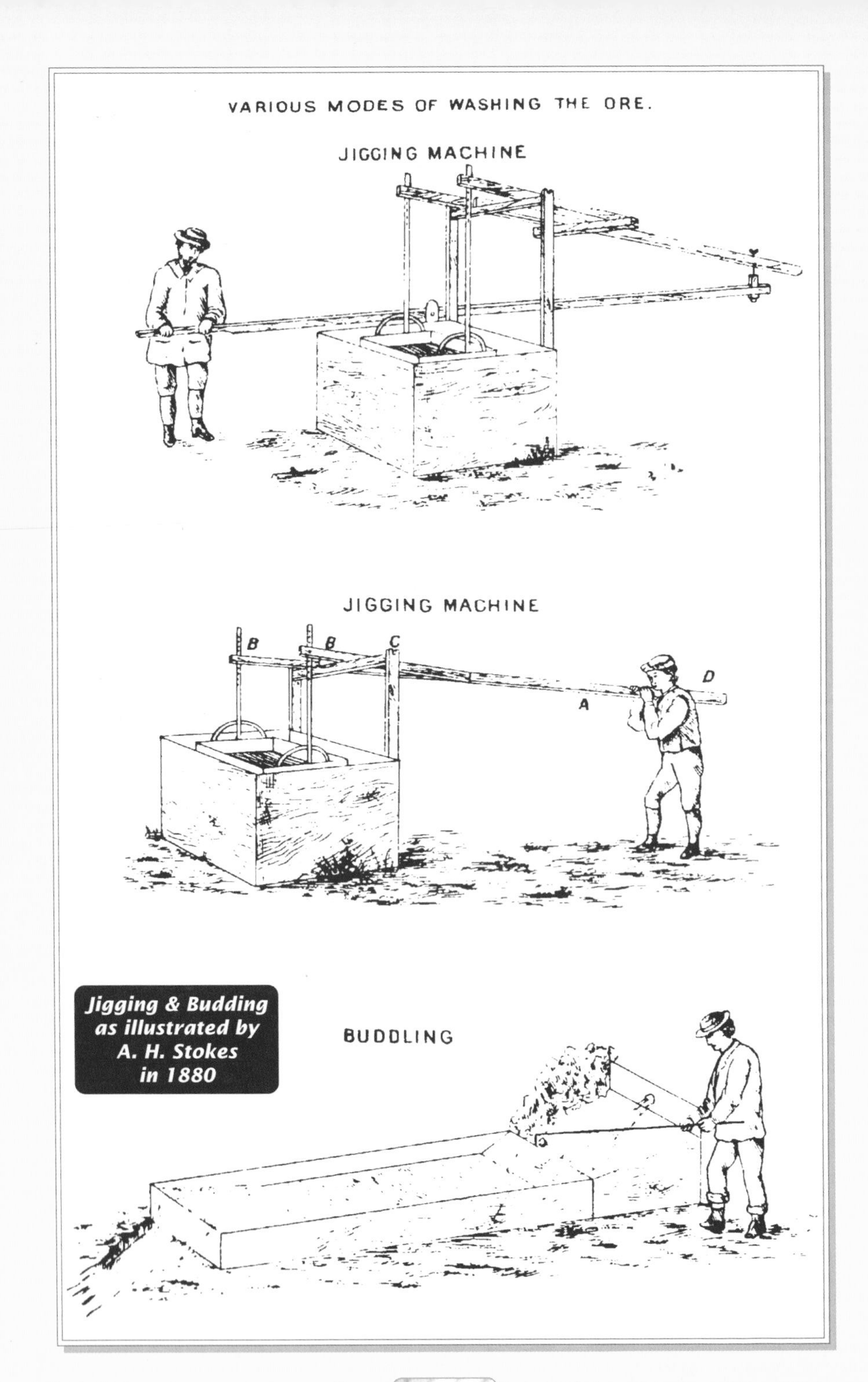
VARIOUS MODES OF WASHING THE ORE.
JIGGING MACHINE
JIGGING MACHINE
B
B
C
D
A
BUDDLING
Jigging & Budding as illustrated by A. H. Stokes in 1880

*Above: Pipe workings in "Masson Mine", Matlock Bath*

*Below: The bottom of a stope with deads stacked on the right, Maury Sough, Millers Dale*

large crushing wheel, about 5 ft (1.5 m) in diameter, made from gritstone, or sometimes from limestone, being dragged around the track by a horse, harnessed to a wooden axle, centrally pivoted. The remains of several of these old crushing circles still remain.

The hotcher, or jigging machine, or 'washing machine' is said to have been invented in Derbyshire in the early part of the century, but the earliest reference so far located dates from 1825. The crude ore was placed on a large sieve which was suspended from a pole within a wooden box nearly full of water. The sieve was repeatedly immersed and withdrawn from the water in the box, by the operator jerking the pole rapidly. This action enabled a gravity separation of the ore from the other minerals and waste rock fragments to be achieved.

There were extensive buddling operations all over the orefield but mainly around Wensley, Winster, Elton, Bonsall Moor and elsewhere, and the land owners sought legal advice to redress what they saw as spoilation of considerable acreage of grazing land.

Today, the conspicuous, flat-topped buddle dams or sludge dams are still a noticeable feature in the fields on the south side of Wensley Dale, opposite to the village; at the Winster Pitts mines and particularly west of Elton village where the old mining ground adjacent to Gratton Dale is pock-marked, furrowed and disturbed by the intensive 19th century buddling operations.

Iron crushing rollers were introduced about 1836 and steam power applied to the operation by 1842. Ore breakers on the Blake or Blake-Marsden principle date from the 1850s – 1860s, but little is known about their distribution at Derbyshire lead mines.

Mechanised dressing floors, operated by steam and/or water power were introduced about 1868.

The Spanish Slag Hearth was brought to the orefield in 1849 and allowed not only re-smelting of lead rich slags, but also smelting of low quality linnet ores, also known as brown ore and green ore. These ores were obtained principally from the Winster, Elton, Wirksworth and Brassington districts. Green ore had been commercially extracted from the Winster mines in the first decade of the 19th century, if not earlier.

Smelters were set up by E.M. Wass to deal with the large amounts of ore raised from Mill Close Mine, firstly at Lea and later at the mine itself, but even they could not cope with the mine output and some ore was sold for processing elsewhere. The Mill Close smelter survives as H.J. Enthoven's scrap lead recovery works today.

## 7. THE DECLINING YEARS: 1850 TO THE PRESENT DAY

**After 1860 there was a rapid decline in the numbers of men employed in lead mining in the county. In 1861, 2,333 men were engaged in the industry, this number falling to 871 in 1881 and to a mere 285 in 1901.**

Capital mines opened in the 19th century, equipped with pumping engines of varying types, worked side by side with small mines operated in the most primitive ways. A.H. Stokes, the Inspector of Mines for the area, writing in 1880, stated that he believed some mines were then utilising methods little better than the Saxon mode of mining. This is an exaggeration but it vividly illustrates the poverty under which some mines worked. An old Monyash miner, Mr. Charles H. Millington, who died in 1968, aged 90, vividly remembered hand-drilling shot holes by the light of tallow candles in mines near Monyash. These mines, though not deep, were entered by means of climbing shafts, the minerals being wound up by hand stowes.

One exception to this general run-down stands out, and that is the case of the Mill Close Mine, Darley Dale. This old mine, after standing idle was re-opened in 1859 by E.M. Wass, who also owned the Lea Lead Works. The old pipe vein complex, exploited so profitably since the early 17th century was worked northwards beneath an ever increasing thick mass of shale. At the time of his death in 1886, the mine had produced over 36000 tons of lead ore. Afterwards the production figures remained high, and from the date that Wass began production in 1861, until 1939 when the mine was finally closed some 430,000 tons of lead concentrate was obtained. Ultimately three pumping engines were employed, rising over 7 million gallons (32 million litres) of water per day. In 1938 some 5550 galls/min were pumped from the workings, the deepest having reached over 1000 ft (3048 meters) beneath the River Derwent. At the same time, in excess of 800 tons (813 tonnes) of crude lead ore were raised daily to be dressed and smelted, and zinc ore was obtained in fairly large quantities. The mine finally closed just before the Second World War due to the failure to locate new ore-bearing ground, the low price of lead on the market and the immense pumping costs. These factors, coupled with the prospect of having to sink a new shaft, somewhere in the vicinity of Rowsley or Stanton and possibly 1000 ft (305 m) deep, for haulage and ventilation purposes, made the continuance of this great mine an impossibility.

During this century there have been several speculative attempts to re-open old mines, and some have produced some ore for limited periods, but have not been able to sustain a high level of production for a long enough period. Acting on the advice of an old Middleton miner, the Blobber Mine (281 533) near Wirksworth located good ore in the early 1920's but this soon ran out. Ventures at Raithe Mine, Elton in the 1920s, and later at Portway Mine, Winster and Riber Mine, Matlock all failed to find workable ore shoots.

Today, fluorspar, the mineral discarded by the old miners as worthless, is a far more valuable commodity than lead. Large mines at Hucklow and Longstone Edge have produced considerable quantities of this mineral which, along with the output from surface dumps and smaller mines, made the Peak District one of the world's leading producers. Some thousands of tons of lead-ore form a valuable by-product so that it may be said that lead-mining is still an active industry.

# 1 CASTLETON

*Tourist boats at the Halfway House, Speedwell Mine*

By T. D. Ford

Maps: 1:25000 SK 18; 1:10000 SK 18 SW & SE

Walking distance about 4 miles (6 km)

Lying at the northern extremity of the limestone area, Castleton has numerous mineral veins outcropping and has had a long history of mining for both lead ore and Blue John fluorspar. Lead has been worked at least since Roman times and Blue John since the mid 18th century. Small quantities of blende and calamine have been raised as well. Since the 1950s there has been much open-pit working for industrial fluorspar, baryte and calcite, particularly on Dirtlow Rake.

Two separate walks are advised to cover all the important features still visible though it is possible to modify the walks and combine them if necessary. A more detailed guide to the geology, geomorphology, caves and mines has been prepared by the writer and it was published by the Geologists Association in 1996 (see reading list at the back).

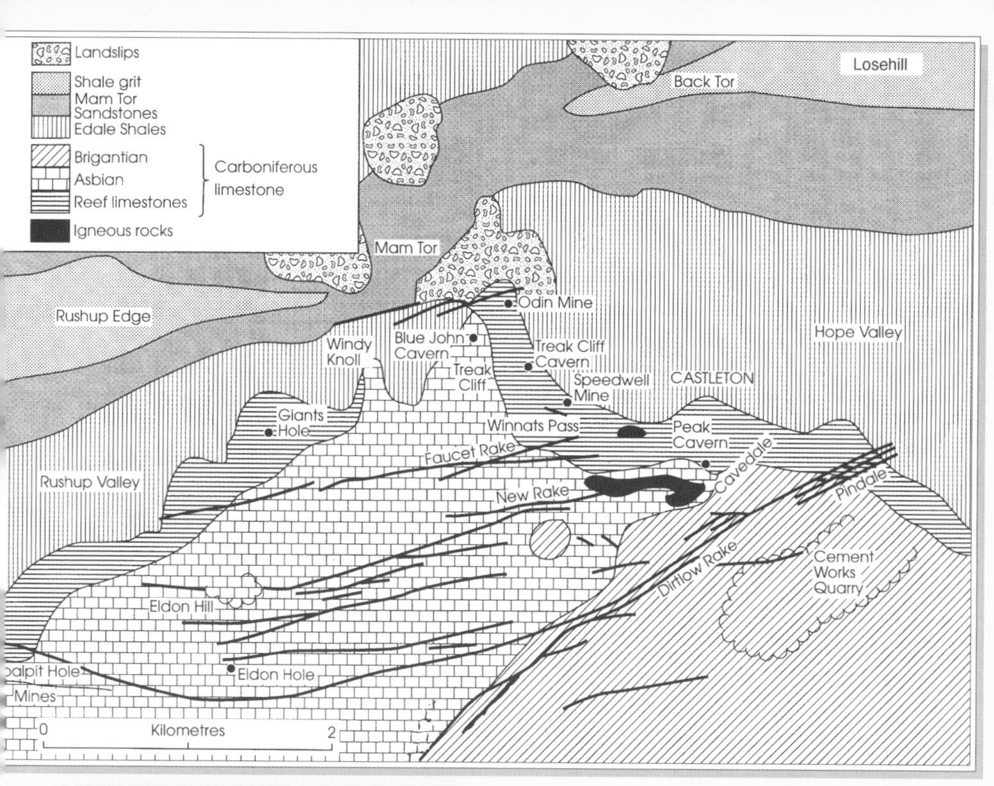


**Above: Geological sketch map of the Castleton area Below: Sunken boat formerly used for transport in Speedwell Mine**

## THE VEINS AND MINES SOUTH AND WEST OF CASTLETON

From Castleton village car park follow the Peak Cavern stream towards Peak Cavern, which lies in the Gorge beneath Peveril Castle. Behind the last house on the left (east) bank (Rose Cottage) Russet Well (148 827) is an important spring draining the Speedwell stream caves and associated veins and mines lying west of the Gorge, demonstrating that drainage passes beneath the Gorge before rising to the surface. Under flood conditions water backs up underground and overflows via Peak Cavern. Continuing towards Peak Cavern the tail (outfall) of Peakshole Sough lies in the last garden left of the path, partly hidden by bushes. Peakshole Sough was driven westwards between about 1770 and 1783 beneath the adjacent hill, Cowlow. The cliffs on both sides of the Gorge just beyond the sough show traces of workings in a scrin vein.

PEAK CAVERN (149 826) is open to the public and should be visited as a fine example of what the lead miners called a "self-open" – a natural cavern, though there is little evidence of mining activities within. The tourist route extends about half a mile (1 km) and explorers have been another 2 miles (3km) beyond, mainly beneath the upper parts of Cavedale. A scrin with about 50 cm width of calcite occurs in Roger Rain's House where surface water leaking in from Cavedale is responsible for the "rain".

Leaving Peak Cavern Gorge turn left up Goosehill and take the road which peters out into a path along the foot of Cowlow. This lies above Peakshole Sough and Tankersley Vein: all there is to see on the surface is Wall Shaft Mine, with the shaft directly under the wall on the right. On bearing to the right just before an iron wicket gate the rising ground on the left marks an outcrop of volcanic agglomerate, the so-called Speedwell Vent (143 825) which may be the site of a small submarine volcano. West of the Vent a steep gulley is Cowlow Nick (142 824) separating Cowlow from Long Cliff. Several scrins may be seen crossing Cowlow Nick and continuing high up across the face of Long Cliff. Immediately after the iron wicket gate and about 100 yards (100 m) uphill from the path a prominent mound has the remains of a miners' coe on the top. Beyond it Long Cliff Rake is marked by a line of shaft hillocks trending obliquely up the hillside. Branching from Long Cliff Rake is Slack Hole Scrin going steeply up and over the hilltop. At the junction is Long Cliff Mine which entered a natural cavern. The Speedwell Mine's first tunnel cut through Long Cliff Rake at the Halfway House deep beneath this point.

Walk on to the foot of the Winnats Pass, where a visit may be paid to the SPEEDWELL MINE (139 827), operated as a tourist cavern using boats along the miners' tunnel. From the foot of a shaft 72 ft (21 m) deep by the garage a few yards north of the road a canal tunnel was driven southwards under Long Cliff between 1771 and 1781. After some 500 yards (450 m) the level encountered a large cavern in Faucet Rake, now known as the Bottomless Pit. The bottom of this cavern is a lake some 50 ft (15 m) below the canal and it swallowed many thousands of tons of waste rock from the miners' second tunnel. Water overflowing from the canals cascades into the Bottomless Pit to re-appear at Russet Well. Beyond the tourist route the second tunnel intersected a long series of natural caverns with a stream flowing eastwards close to the line of New Rake; both this and several branch scrins were mined from the stream caves. The miners built a dam to maintain the water level in their tunnels so that they could use boats to haul ore and waste rock. In doing this they were probably inspired by the success of the canal tunnels engineered by James Brindley and John Gilbert in the Duke of Bridgwater's coal mines at Worsley near Manchester. Visitors can easily appreciate the task the Speedwell miners faced in driving through solid limestone for over a mile using hand-held drills and gunpowder for blasting. Progress was about $4^1/_2$ ft (1.5 m) per week.

Leaving the Speedwell Mine return along the path just traversed and near the Speedwell Vent take the path sloping obliquely uphill towards Peveril Castle to reach the top of Cowlow. Crossing the level ground gives views into Cavedale, but by the group of trees and a low cliff called Roger, turn right (west) along the grassy path towards the ruined Hurdlow Barn (141 821). This path follows the line of waste hillocks and shaft hollows of lead mine workings on NEW RAKE and the closely parallel Horse Pit Rake to the south. Some 600 ft (190 m) beneath the barn is roughly where the Speedwell canal tunnel met the stream caves. Somewhere near here is the lost Hourdlo Stile Mine, recorded in old documents. Continuing westwards over the high stile the low grassed-over waste hillocks of New and Horse Pit Rakes lie in a long narrow field. At the top end of this enclosure over the wall is a small walled off area with the shaft of JAMES HALL'S ENGINE MINE (135 820) among the waste hillocks. Cavers exploring at the bottom of this 150 ft (45 m) deep shaft have rediscovered a long lost late 18th century route through old mine workings into high caverns and down to the Speedwell stream caves nearly 600 ft (190 m) below. The nearby stile is almost directly above Cliff Cavern, a vast chamber at the southwestern end of the Speedwell cave system.

Continue westwards following New Rake, noting the deep hollows which probably lie above collapsed caverns, and climb the high stile on to the Rowter track. Turning right leads to the B6061 road where turning right again leads back to Castleton via the Winnats Pass.

However, to extend the excursion turn left after the stile and follow the Rowter track southwards through a gate. Away to the right the fields on LINICAR are crossed by a network of scrins. The track turns left round to the HAZARD MINE

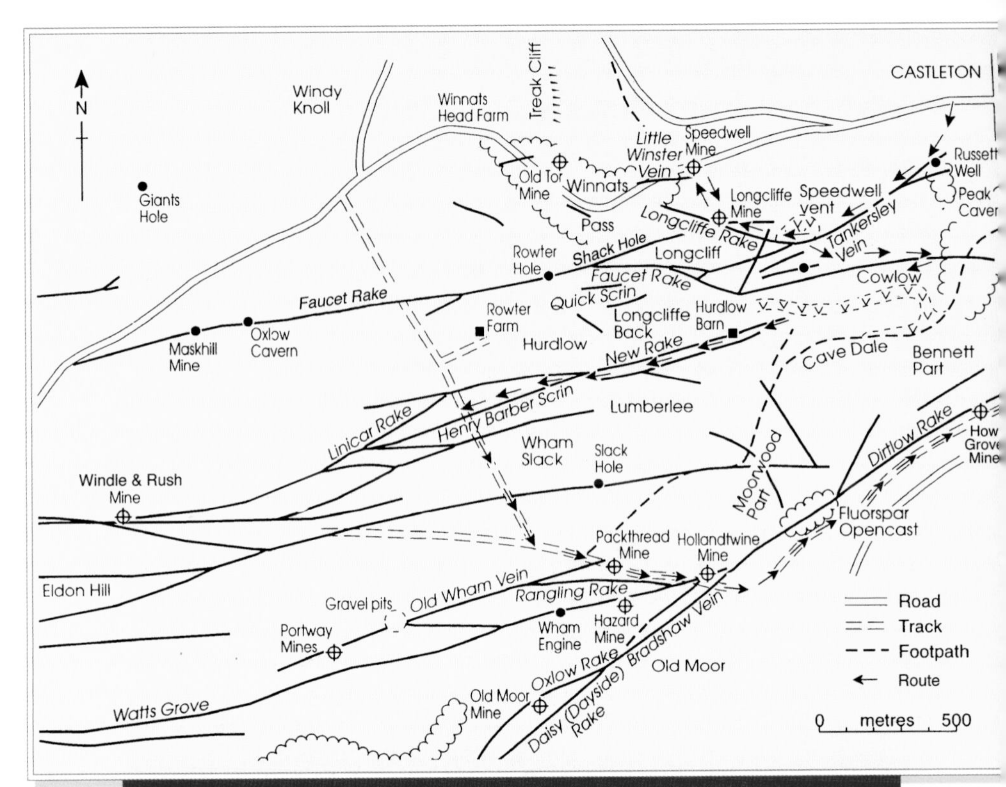


**Above: Mineral veins South-West of Castleton**
**Opposite page: The veins around Dirtlow and Pindale, Castleton**

(136 812), close to the top of the Cavedale path. Recently opencast for fluorspar the land has now been restored but an embayment in the far wall encloses the gin circle and shaft (grilled for safety). Hazard Mine reached a depth of 700 ft (210 m) in 1838.

Directly west of Hazard Mine a series of veins has been worked intermittently in recent years for both fluorspar and baryte: these include Wham and Rangling Rakes, and, branching southwest, the OLD MOOR MINES on Oxlow Rake which can be inspected along a path leading to Peak Forest. About 500 m west along WHAM RAKE are modern open-pit works for fluorspar and baryte at PORTWAY MINES (128 812), now partly filled in. These were once marked on Ordnance Survey maps as "Gravel Pits", not gravel in the usual sense, but with the ore in loose lumps, partly mixed with loessic clays. Blocks of quartz rock, replacing limestone, may also be found here. Some of the blocks have crystals of goethite in joints and some have "worm holes" – the moulds of fossil corals.

Wham, Rangling and Oxlow Rakes are branches splitting westwards from DIRTLOW RAKE which has seen much openpit working for fluorspar and baryte in recent years. Close to Hazard Mine a grassy hillock under the wall covers Packthread Mine. Through the next gate to the east a large waste heap marks the site of HOLLANDTWINE MINE (140 813), once nearly 600 ft (190 m) deep with drainage going via a natural "swallow" to re-appear in Peak Cavern.

Following the DIRTLOW RAKE road eastwards the large fluorspar open-pit (143 814) is soon reached. The northern and southern faces show brecciated and partly replaced limestones as well as folded beds in the far wall. Worked for the last 20 years it is due to be back-filled in the next few years to satisfy planning conditions. About 300 yards (290 m) beyond its huge waste heap a narrow chasm on Dirtlow Rake (147 817) marks an open working for baryte (beware loose walls). Plenty of mineral specimens are to be found here, including white, cream or pink baryte, white calcite and scattered galena. Just beyond it is a grassy bank with the remains of a lead miners' coe marking HOW GROVE MINE (148 818). An unusual lay-out of a dished crushing wheel track and two circular buddles lie close by and fine-grained waste from crushing and washing is visible in a roadside bank. Over the wall to the south is the new diversion road bypassing the cement works quarry. In the fields beside the new road are numerous blocks of quartz rock, the residue from the solutional weathering of the enclosing limestone.

Where the Dirtlow track joins the tarmac road (153 820), the ground to the left (north) has been landscaped but within it are preserved sections of old open workings in Dirtlow Rake, with many pick marks in the walls of the trench. Nearby are some grilled shafts. Much of Dirtlow Rake has only calcite with the galena lining the

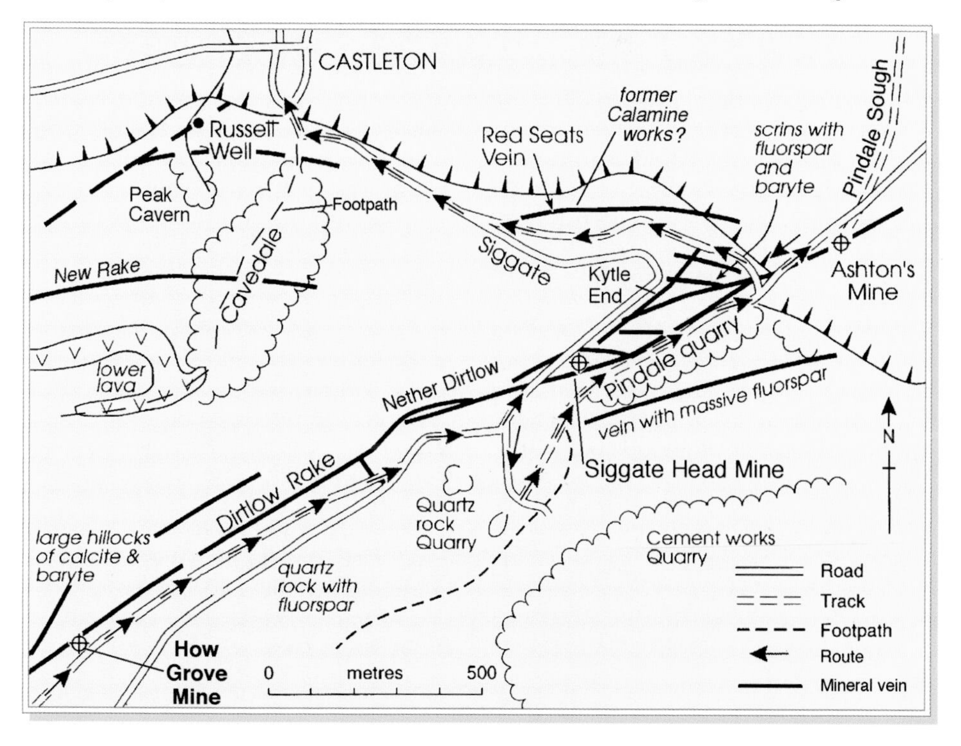

walls, but one short section of the south wall is in quartz rock with blue fluorspar in joints.

Some 300 m downhill the road splits. Continue to the left towards Castleton for 200 m and on the right, on the lip of Pindale, are the remains of SIGGATE HEAD MINE (156 822) comprising a concrete cap on the shaft, a crushing circle mostly hidden in the grass and an overgrown water storage pond. The shaft was 240 ft deep (70 m) and was sunk to work Dirtlow Rake below the Pindale Tuff layer. Dirtlow Rake splits here into Kytle End Vein and Pindale Scrins, which can be traced along the northern flank of Pindale.

Return to the last road fork and bear right towards the quarry along the line of trees: a little way along this a steep track turns left down PINDALE (155 819). Descend this track past the disused Pindale quarry on the right. A small vein with both blue and amber-coloured fluorspar occurs on the upper bench but there is no public right of access. Opposite the main quarry, the north side of Pindale is crossed by several veins, branches off Dirtlow Rake. Most have been worked out and are seen today as open trenches (danger!). Much spoil litters the hillside some having been removed as road-making fill. The largest vein (PINDALE SCRIN or Lawyers Vein) is mostly calcite but others contain varying amounts of cream-coloured "cawk" baryte and blue or amber-coloured fluorspar.

The cottage at the foot of Pindale is all that remains of a lead mining settlement known as BLACK RABBIT. Close by is the site of Pindale End Mine. Continuing down the lane, just beyond the farm on the right is ASHTON'S ENGINE HOUSE (163 826) marking the site of a mine sunk through the shales to reach the mineral vein in the limestone. Unexpectedly the shaft penetrated toadstone (locally called "Channel" or "Cat Dirt") and the vein was very poor, but PINDALE SOUGH was driven to it from the riverside about $^1/_4$mile (500 m) to the north and the engine pumped from beneath sough level. The sough was then continued southwest following the Pindale scrins but surviving mining records do not tell us how far it went. An agreement to drive the sough dates from 1743 and by 1800 the mine had evidently reached a rich part of the vein and the mine was producing more lead ore than Odin Mine. This bonanza did not last long and production fell off after 1802. Whilst viewing Ashton's Engine House, it is worth contrasting the small scale nature of lead mining with its lack of capital with the vast enterprise of the Blue Circle Cement works nearby with its huge limestone quarry and shale pits.

Turn back up the road and opposite the farm take the right-hand road along the hillside to Castleton. The road is just above RED SEATS VEIN marked by shallow trenches and low waste hillocks. This vein was noted for its content of the zinc ore sphalerite and particularly its oxidation product calamine. The latter is an inconspicuous light cream-coloured material known to the miners as "bone ore", or "dry bone" from its porous texture. It was once used for the manufacture of brass and for medicinal purposes.

Continue along the road back into Castleton to conclude the excursion.

## ODIN MINE AND THE BLUE JOHN VEINS OF TREAK CLIFF

Walking distance about 2½ miles (4 km).

**From Castleton village car park take the lane at the lower right (northeast) corner to reach Hollowford Lane. Turn left towards Losehill and cross Tricket Bridge over Peakshole Water. Some 20 yards (20 m) further on a trickle of water emerges from a low slabbed arch in the wall on the left (150 832). This is the tail of ODIN or TRICKETT BRIDGE SOUGH, a drainage level proposed in 1772 but not driven until 1816 and it only reached the vein at Odin Mine in 1822. The sough was continued westwards along the sole (lowest working level) of Odin Mine for a further mile (1.6 km) to reach Forest Shaft beneath Mam Nick car park in 1850. Adjacent to the sough tail the well-named Dirty Lane follows the course of the sough and waste heaps at intervals mark the sites of shafts. However, it is easier to return to the main car park and take the main road (A625) westwards for about 200 yards (190 m). Look for a footpath between the houses on the right opposite Peak Cavern car park entrance and walk along The Flats beside Odin Sitch. Shale can be seen here and there in the stream bank, in places covered with fine-grained waste calcite washed down from the processing floors at Odin Mine.**

After about 600 yards (1 km) the path crosses the lane to Dunscar Farm (143 833). Do not turn off on the path to Hollins Cross but keep straight ahead following the stream. On the right a tree-covered mound by the farm is a waste heap from Odin Sough. Keep straight on passing immediately left of Knowlegates Farm and climb on to the rough ground of the toe of the Mam Tor landslip. The earlier and higher Knowlegates Sough (1711-1713) was driven from by the farm but nothing can be seen of its tail. However, on the left a few metres after the stile is the first of a line of shaft hollows on this sough. Continue up the path, passing two other shaft hollows, to reach the fenced off KNOWLE-GATES SHAFT (135 835). Originally some 240 ft (75 m) deep it is flooded a short way down and has probably collapsed below water level.

From Knowlegates Shaft to the road the path crosses what is left of ODIN MINE'S vast waste heaps, much material having been removed for pre-war road-building. Ores from the mine were crushed, washed and sorted here, often with women labourers. The remains of a crushing circle erected in 1823 at a cost of £38-10-6 (£38.55) are still in place. An innovation here was to use an iron-tyred gritstone wheel on an iron track. The wheel was pulled

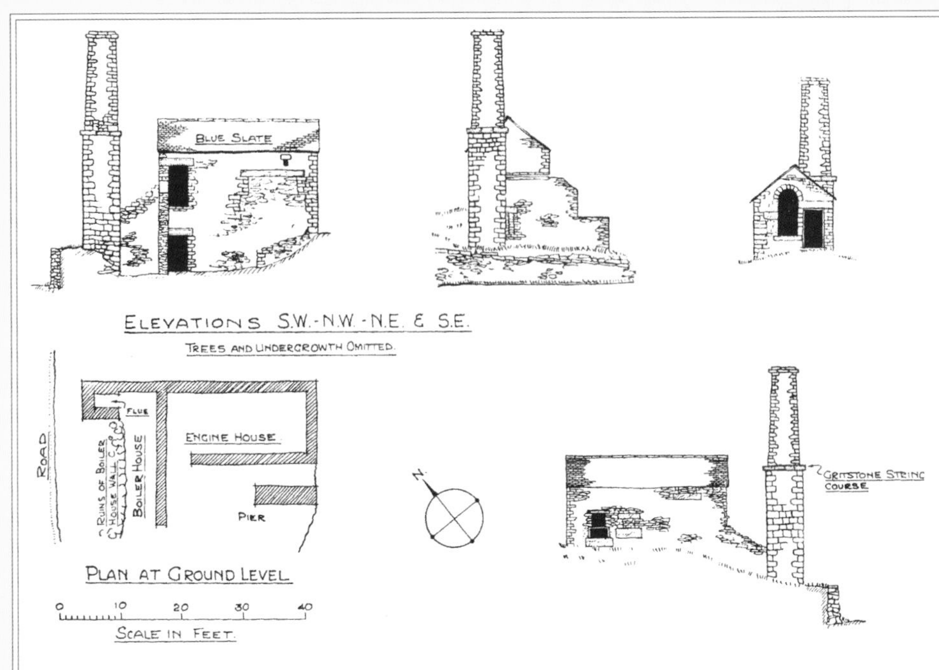


**Pumping Engine House, Pindale or Ashton's Mine, Nr. Hope**

***Circular buddle on How Grove Mine***

**Above; Left: A broken crushing wheel at the How Grove Mine, Dirtlow Rake**
**Right: The crushing circle and wheel at Odin Mine**

round the track by a horse whilst crude ore was fed in and then shovelled off after crushing. The remains of the wooden axle are still present but the centre pivot block is missing. Nearby two knockstones were found in the stream bed: these were used for hand-crushing using a flat hammer known as a bucker.

Odin Mine, Mam Tor, Windy Knoll and Treak Cliff are National Trust land and visitors should respect paths, stiles and gates.

A few metres from the crusher a step down in the path marks the margin of the moving ground of the Mam Tor landslip. Ahead the sloping embankment conceals an adit under the road which went in to the Cartgate of Odin Mine beneath the flat grassy area across the road. Climb to the vehicle turning circle to view Odin Mine and Gorge.

Odin Mine is reputed to have been worked in Saxon if not Roman times but the earliest documentary evidence is in 1280. Before 1669 the workings had become extensive enough for there to be a dispute about rights and ownership. It was worked almost continuously through the 18th and in to the mid 19th century, closing about 1869. Annual production varied but reached a maximum of 800 tons per annum with peak periods in the 1720s, 1770s and around 1800.

From the road one can look into the open gash of ODIN GORGE where the vein has been worked out at the northern extremity of the limestone outcrop. Climb the stile and cross the flat area (grassed over tailings from a 1940s spar washer) into the Gorge and one can see pick marks and holes where wooden stemples were once installed. There are traces of the mineral fill with galena, blue fluorspar and creamy baryte on the walls, which are grooved with nearly horizontal slickensides owing to fault movements.

A small branch vein at the entrance to the narrow part of the Gorge has deposits of the soft white clay mineral allophane inside. At the far end of the Gorge a climb up fallen blocks (or a descent using ropes from the gorge side) gives access to the mine via an adit with a shale roof. The workings are very dirty owing to fallen shale, and dangerous owing to loose blocks. Only experts should attempt exploration. It is possible to go in some 500 ft (150 m) to a descent requiring ropes for 50 ft (15 m) into a level going back under the Gorge. This has a fine stone-arched roof over what was once part of the Cartgate. Unstable holes in the floor have been descended almost to the deep sough level but the inner parts of the mine are inaccessible. Workings once extended a mile (1.6 km) under the south flank of Mam Tor as far as the West Shaft close to where the Edale road branches off the Chapel-en-le-Frith road.

A climb up above the north (Mam Tor) side of the Gorge leads back to ODIN SITCH, here flowing in an artificial leat. Of probable 17th century date it was excavated to divert the stream away from Odin Gully which cuts the limestone south of the Gorge. Without such a diversion the stream was liable to flow into the mine workings.

Continue uphill to reach the road opposite the Blue John Cavern and turn right downhill to the fence at the margin of the Mam Tor landslip (132 835). From here the damage to the road is obvious. According to 18th century plans of Odin Mine Tinkers Shaft lay beneath the road near this fence but no evidence of it can be found on the surface. It is tempting to speculate whether the workings of Odin Mine had anything to do with the landslip but no evidence to support this idea has been found. Indeed much of the slip took place in prehistoric times long before there was any mining at all.

Turn back up the road westwards past the Blue John Cavern. Odin Mine's workings pass beneath your feet. The mine plans show a dog-leg in both vein and Cartgate and it is possible to follow its course across the fields south of Mam Tor. Two shale hillocks in the field on the right mark the sites of shafts which apparently never reached the limestone or the mineral vein. Further west ENGINE SHAFT (127 833) is close to the footpath up the fields to Mam Nick. It once had extensive waste heaps around it though only a veneer of waste remains today. The large hillocks were removed for recovery of fluorspar about 1908 and there are traces of a tramway down to the road. Engine Shaft is still open (but covered for safety) but has collapsed about 150 ft (45 m) down. Still further west CASTLETON and FOREST SHAFTS (124 833) were close together either side of the Mining Liberty boundary where a fence lies alongside the Mam Nick car park. Both shafts collapsed many years ago but a grassy hillock marks Castleton Shaft: Forest Shaft is beneath the car park! Both would have been some 500 ft (150 m) deep to the Cartgate. West Shaft lay in the wood west of the car park (123 832). Beyond West Shaft the miners found that the shale/limestone surface dipped steeply below sough level and they lost the vein. Some $^{1}/_{4}$ mile (500 m) further west a line of hillocks (117 830) near Peakshill Farm marks a sough driven c. 1726-1729: little is known about it but it may have been an abortive attempt to reach Odin Rake west of the known limits of mine workings.

Some 200 m east of the Mam Nick car park, climb the stile on the right (south) of the A 625 road and straight ahead is WINDY KNOLL (136 830) with a boulder bed both lying on the limestone in the cave roof and visible in fissures in the quarry face. Bitumens ooze from the rock, particularly within the boulder bed: collectively known as elaterite the bitumens include some thirty different hydrocarbons (natural oils) believed to have been distilled from organic traces in both limestone and shale by the hot mineralizing solutions responsible for forming the nearby mineral veins (samples may only be collected for bona fide research). Equivalent hydrocarbons in the rocks of Treak Cliff are thought to have been responsible for the colour of Blue John fluorspar as they tend to absorb trace quantities of uranium from surrounding rocks; the radiation from such traces over time causes distortions in the crystals' molecular lattices; these in turn are thought to affect the transmission of light and hence yield the blue colour. The cave in the quarry yielded the bones of many Ice Age mammals during excavations in the 1870s.

From Windy Knoll take the footpath eastwards, across the road and the fields beyond towards Winnats Head Farm but bear left near the farm towards the BLUE JOHN CAVERN. The rough ground on top of Treak Cliff marks the site of opencast workings for fluorspar during World War II, as a result of which many tons of Blue John went into blast furnaces to flux the slag.

The BLUE JOHN CAVERN (132 832) is open to visitors. It is a fine system of natural caverns with a small stream in the bottom. The caverns intersected several pipe veins of Blue John fluorspar which have been mined since their discovery about 1700 though there are earlier records of mining "on Treak Cliff Knab" which cannot be located today. Blue John Cavern was opened to the public in 1843 after a stone staircase was built down a narrow "pothole" fissure near the entrance.

From the Blue John Cavern take the path eastwards down the face of Treak Cliff to Treak Cliff Cavern (136 832). Odin Mine's hillocks may be seen far below the path. A circular crater near the foot of the hill slope marks another sort of mine – a Nazi aerial land-mine dropped in May 1941!

TREAK CLIFF CAVERN (136 832) is entered via a mid 18th century adit through a patch of shale into the boulder bed lying on the steeply-dipping reef limestone. Voids between the boulders were mineralized with a fill or lining of Blue John fluorspar. The void system was later exploited by underground drainage to form caverns within the boulder bed. The Blue John deposits here constitute one type of pipe vein and the tourist route through the cave follows this upwards parallel to the hill slope. The patches of Blue John show varying patterns of colour-banding and are known as fourteen different "veins". The first part of Treak Cliff Cavern was the principal source of this rare mineral for ornamental purposes. Mining for industrial fluorspar just after World

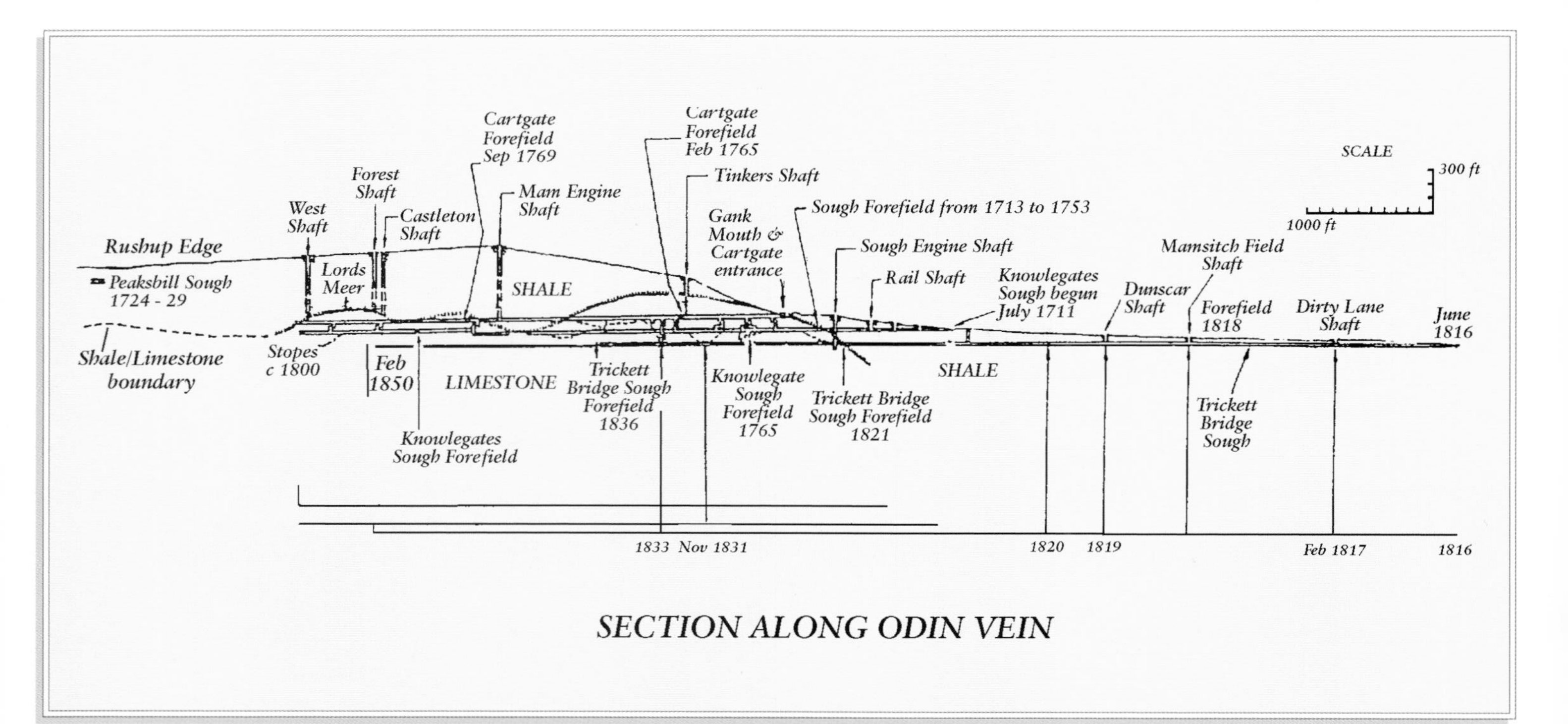

SECTION ALONG ODIN VEIN

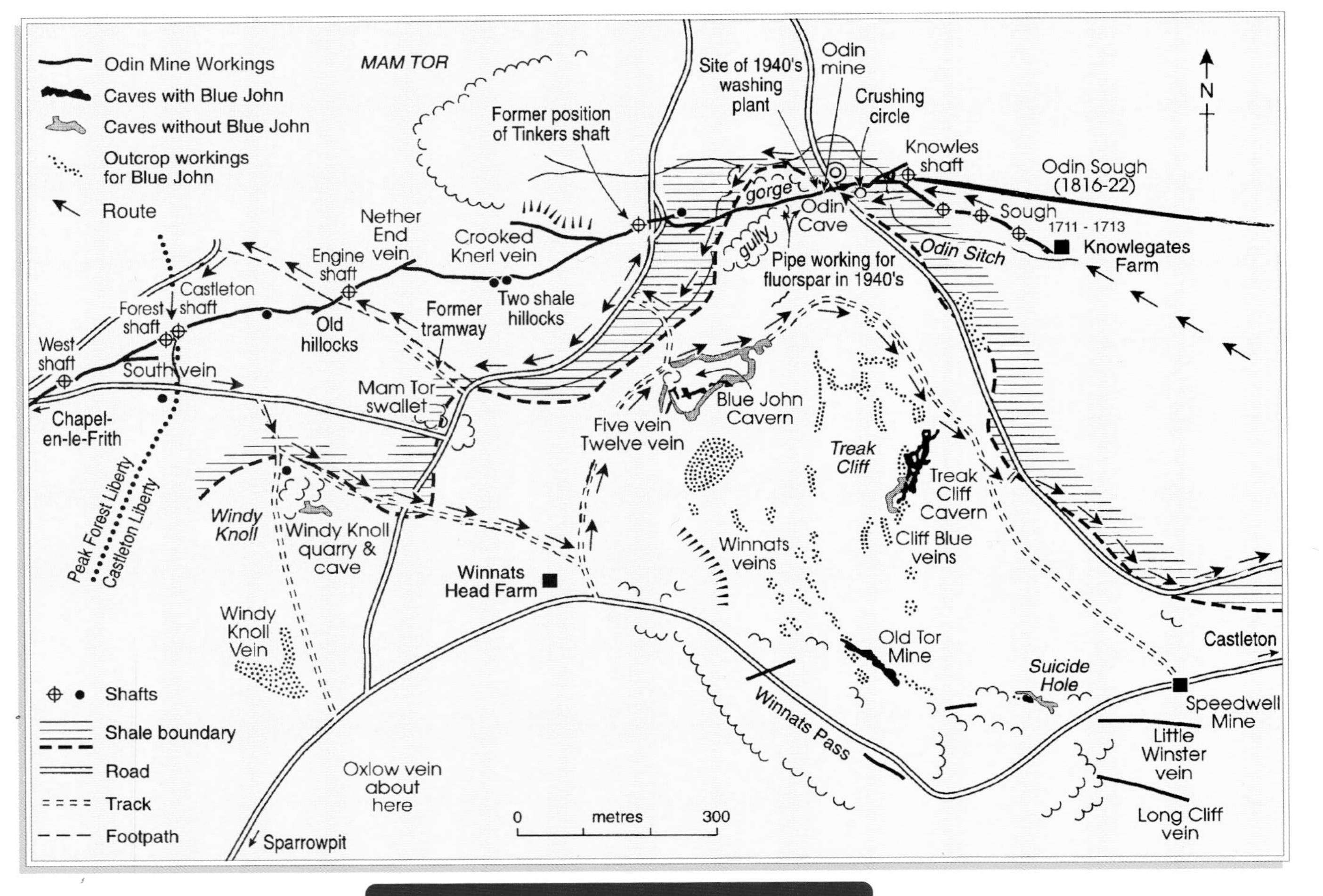


Excursion map; Odin Mine and Treak Cliff

War I revealed the inner series of caverns in 1926. This series has a magnificent display of stalactites and stalagmites and both series of caverns were opened to the public in 1935. The outer series is still worked for ornamental Blue John. Annual production today is about $^1/_2$ ton.

There were other workings for Blue John in the disturbed ground high on the face of Treak Cliff and in the Old Tor Mine high in the Winnats Pass (now grilled for safety).

There is an oft-repeated story that Blue John was used by the Romans but no evidence to support the story has ever been found and blue fluorspar was first recorded by Thomas Webster in 1671. The ornamental use of Blue John dates from around 1750. In 1765 Henry Watson, marble mason of Ashford-in-the-Water, had 16 pairs of stows (i.e. 16 shafts with windlasses) on Treak Cliff for extracting Blue John but their exact location is not known. Blue John rapidly gained popularity when Matthew Boulton used it as a foil for the gilt-work of his ormulu vases and other ornaments. In 1768 Boulton tried to obtain a monopoly of the Blue John mines but succeeded only in buying 14 tons for £5-15s-6d per ton. In his day production was around 20 tons per annum. About the same time Robert Adam, the architect of stately homes, designed fireplaces with inlaid Blue John panels in white marble. The work was mostly done by Brown & Son's marble works in Derby. A good example of a fireplace with Blue

***"A Health to all Miners and Maintainers of Mines". T. D. Ford celebrates the bicentenary of the miners' toast of October 20th 1781***

The excavated rake in Odin Mine

John is in Kedleston Hall near Derby.

During the 19th century many fine vases were made, particularly in Matlock and Buxton. Good examples are to be seen in Chatsworth House and in the geological section of the Natural History Museum in South Kensington, London.

The 20th century saw many tons of Blue John wasted through use as ordinary fluorspar in iron-smelting furnaces. Later the use of Blue John turned more to small ornaments such as finger bowls and to jewellry.

Both Blue John and Treak Cliff Caverns should be visited to gain a full appreciation of the nature of the deposits and their surroundings.

Further details of the story of Blue John may be found in DERBYSHIRE BLUE JOHN by T.D.Ford, available from Ashbourne Editions, 12 Compton, Ashbourne, Derbyshire.

After visiting Treak Cliff Cavern it is an easy walk back down the main road to Castleton, with good views into the Winnats Pass and of the lead veins crossing Cowlow Nick and Long Cliff.

# 2 PEAK FOREST

By C. Heathcote

**Maps: 1:25000 sheets SK 17 & 18, & 1:10000 sheets SK 18 SW and SK 17 NW.**

**Walking distance 3 to 4 miles**

**The first section of this itinerary is the same for all three routes, but later it diverges to give Routes A, B and C as indicated below. The routes are designed to give a view of many examples of relics of early mining activities before many are swept away by fluorspar workings.**

From the centre of Peak Forest village take Church Lane northeast to Old Dam (1150 7970). At the T-junction turn left towards Perryfoot and after about 300 yards (270m) turn right up Eldon Lane. After Sweetknoll Farm on the left the road becomes a grass track and beyond a gate and stile the track forks but bear right along the field wall to an area of disturbed ground crossing from west to east. This is WATTS GROVE or WHITE RAKE (119 806). To the left a walled area surrounds the former belland yard (where a wall prevented cattle getting to lead rich wastes) (locality 1: 1178 8067). Adjacent are small exposures of the vein, mostly walled up, capped shafts and buddling dams at SMILER MINE.

From here are good views over the Peak Forest area, whilst to the northwest is a distant view of ELDON HOLE, Derbyshire's largest natural pothole (locality 2: 1159 8092). The continuation of White Rake can be seen descending westwards into Perry Dale where it splits into Gautries and Coalpithole Rakes, each marked by a line of trees.

Follow White Rake eastwards passing on the left a lime kiln (locality 3: 1202 8072). Such "pudding pie" kilns are widespread evidence of a vanished industry which provided lime fertilizer for fields. Ahead. over a stile, a much disturbed area is the site of WATTS GROVE MINE with its sleeper-capped shaft overlooking Conies Dale (locality 4: 1221 8077). A run-in shaft lies ahead, adjacent to the circular track of a gin circle with sheltering wall (locality 5: 1230 8085). Nearby are the remains of a circular water-storage pond and coes.

The path soon leads to the site of JOWLE GROVE MINE (also called Jewel Grove) (locality 6: 1239 8088). A capped shaft, coes, crushing circle and a fragment of a stone wheel can be found.

The well-defined path then trends northeast across the rather barren Eldon Moor to a stile in the far corner of the field. Over the stile is a rough track trending east-west. To the left it leads towards the large ELDON HILL QUARRY, and to the right (north) of the next gate over the wall disturbed ground marks SLITHERSTONES RAKE, more correctly known as Windle and Rush Vein (locality 7: 1230 8145). Several shafts, coes, a gin circle and three belland yards mark Two Rakes Head Mine, Barbers Mine and Windle and Rush Mine.

Retrace your route along the rough track to a field gate and stile which mark the boundaries of the Peak Forest and Castleton Mining Liberties. Following the rough track eastwards, the large field on the left is crossed by several veins, the principal one being LINICAR RAKE. Again, this area contains numerous shaft hollows, coes, belland yards, water-storage ponds and buddle dams. Closer, and crossed by the rough track is SLACK HOLE RAKE (locality 9: 1279 8144).

Cross another stile and continue eastwards to another gate and stile marking the crossing point of paths and rough roads from Castleton via Cavedale and Dirtlow Rake. From here there is a choice of three routes back to Peak Forest:

Route A: Climb the stile to the right (south) on to Old Moor. A well-defined path follows the right-hand wall. Soon it crosses a line of waste hillocks marking WRANGLING RAKE. Across the wall to the right are several sleeper-capped shafts including WHAM ENGINE MINE (locality 10: 1331 8101). Alongside the path ahead lies OXLOW RAKE, with the Old Moor Mines (locality 11: 1341 8085). Nearby are covered shafts, traces of

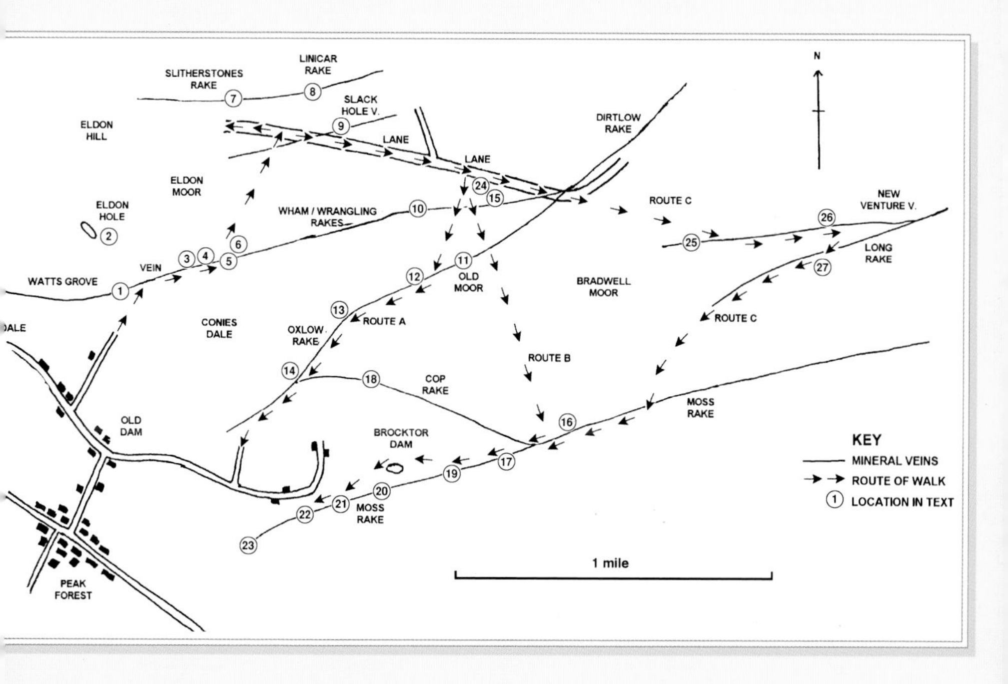

a crushing circle and a large belland yard. The path merges into a rough lane along Oxlow Rake and the stile over a wall marks the return from Castleton Liberty into Peak Forest Liberty. Large hillocks ahead mark OXLOW HEAD ENGINE MINE (locality 12: 1311 8061), worked by the Royse family of Castleton in the late 18th century.

Continue along the lane to where it heads gently downhill. On the right at the gate is CLEAR THE WAY MINE (locality 13: 1281 8031). On the steep hillside to the left, shaft hollows and hillocks mark the course of COP RAKE. Some of the mines on this vein are thought to be amongst the earliest worked in the Peak District, dating from the early 13th century. Half way down the slope is the quaintly named STARVEHOUSE MINE.

Passing downhill through another gate, about 30 m ahead on the right is a horseshoe-shaped enclosure built into the side of a hillock (locality 14: 1255 8000). This is an ore hopper or bouseteem, used for initial washing of ore from the nearby mines: it is one of the last known such structures in the Derbyshire ore-field. The lane continues along Oxlow Rake until another gate is reached, where a capped shaft marks its western limit. Go through the gate and turn left and then right along the lane to reach Old Dam.

Route B: Leaving the crossing of the paths at the start of Route A, climb the same stile on to Old Moor but then go left along the barbed wire fence surrounding the recently worked HAZARD MINE (locality 15: 1365 8121), which was worked to a depth of nearly 700 ft (210 m) in the 1830s. Hazard Mine's shaft, covered by a grill, and its gin circle lie in an enclosure beyond the area recently restored from fluorspar opencast mining. The path rises uphill to Oxlow Rake, with surface relics largely undisturbed since mining days. Away to the right are the relics of the Old Moor Mines (noted above – locality 11) and Oxlow Head Engine Mine (noted above – locality 12).

Continuing uphill to a gate and stile the route enters Bradwell Liberty. The path continues to a recently worked opencast on MOSS RAKE. To the left is a large boulder on a mound, capping the shaft of MOSS RAKE HEAD MINE (locality 16: 1412 7995). Much of the adjacent area has previously been opencast and restored. Route C joins at this point.

The wooden stile over the wall on the right (west) leads into an enclosure with the western continuation of Moss Rake with large opencuts alongside the path. Such opencuts marked most of the rakes before opencasting obliterated the features. Going slightly downhill a square feature marks a buddle dam with a coe nearby, adjacent to CLAYTON'S ENGINE MINE (locality 17: 1373 7972). The path continues towards a clump of trees. Through a stile the rough ground of Moss Rake continues. Away to the right Cop Rake is currently being opencast (locality 18: 1310 8008). Crossing the track to the barn, there are the ruins of another coe and several capped shafts (locality 19: 1350 7963). Cross the field to another stile and pass to the right of BROCKTOR DAM, where water was stored for the miners' use in washing their ore.

Beyond the dam, a complex of small veins marks ROYAL OAK MINE and the western continuation of Moss Rake, and there is a large crushing wheel of gritstone set up on edge (locality 20: 1292 7935). Continue towards Peak Forest into an area of many small sleeper-capped shafts which may have been sunk to test the ground for the continuation of the vein (locality 21: 1271 7938).

Cross the stile on to the lane to Brocktor Cottage. The lane marks a return to Peak Forest Liberty. Turn left and go up the grass track known as Boggart Hole Lane. At the brow a small walled enclosure on the right with a well-preserved though partly buried crushing circle and stone, marks BOGGART HOLE MINE (locality 22: 1251 7928).

Retrace your route to the lane and turn downhill passing Portobello Cottage. On the far side of the dry valley on the left the disturbed ground of Moss Rake ends abruptly in the valley bottom on reaching the dolerite of the PEAK FOREST SILL (locality 23: 1230 7927).

Continue downhill joining the end of Route A back into Old Dam and Peak Forest.

Route C: From the crossing of the paths continue eastwards along the rough road heading for the high waste heaps on Dirtlow Rake. The right-hand wall soon rises over the grassy hillock of PACKTHREAD MINE (locality 24: 1362 8130). Behind is the partly restored site of an opencast at HAZARD MINE. The gin circle is in a partly walled enclosure at the far side with the adjacent shaft protected by a grill. Continue along the rough road past the site of HOLLANDTWINE MINE marked by modern waste heaps on the left. The lane bends to the right and then left. Ahead is the large openpit where fluorspar has been obtained by opencast methods, with a huge waste heap beyond. Before this on the right is a stile to a path along the Half Mile Wall. Soon a line of shafts (Care – some are open!) old hillocks, coes, a buddle dam and belland yard can be seen to the right (locality 25: 1475 8091).

Follow the path to the third gate in the Half Mile Wall with the new road alongside. Across the road is a walled enclosure with the surface remains of NEW VENTURE MINE (locality 26: 1540 8105). Features of this site (on private land) include walled-up vein exposures, shafts, two natural potholes, a water-storage pond, buddle dam, and a bingstead, preserved by the Peak District Mines Historical Society (Care! There are several deep stopes beneath).

After viewing New Venture Mine, go diagonally across the field passing over LONG RAKE, with its lidded founder shaft (locality 27: 1530 8073). The stopes extend into natural caverns which have been explored to a depth of 500 ft (150 m). Close by a fence surrounds the impressive natural pothole of BATHAM POT. Now only about 40 ft (10 m) deep it was once described as being like Eldon Hole, so presumably much deeper than at present. The miners may have used it as a convenient dumping ground.

The path leads across the fields to an obvious opencast working on Moss Rake. Follow the track to the right (west) alongside Moss Rake until Route B is joined. Continue on the latter as noted above, back to Old Dam and Peak Forest.

# 3 THE HUCKLOW – EYAM – STONEY MIDDLETON AREA

*A view over Watergrove Mine. The chimney has now gone*

## By T. D. Ford

**Maps: 1:25000 SK 17 and SK 27: 1:10000 SK 17 NE and SE, SK 27 SW and NW**

The other itineraries in this book are concerned with the ancient history of the lead-mining industry and the Eyam – Stoney Middleton area is an essential part of this, but history is still being made here by modern fluorspar miners. Many of the old relics have vanished in recent years but new monuments of industry have appeared in their place. Only a brief guide to these is given as things change so rapidly. The fluorspar mines were operated by Laporte Industries plc from the 1950s to 1999, producing some 80,000 tons of fluorspar per annum, with around 20,000 tons of baryte and 2000-3000 tons of galena as by-products. Some of the waste rock goes for concrete aggregate. In recent years the bulk of the fluorspar has come from the SALLET HOLE MINES beneath Longstone Edge and from the MILL-DAM MINE at Great Hucklow. The last-named entered the Hucklow Edge vein by a decline into a westward extension of the former workings from Glebe Mine in Eyam village and Ladywash Mine at the east end of Hucklow Edge. Much ore was also brought in from Dirtlow Rake at Castleton and a scatter of other open-pits operated by various contractors. Competition from cheap fluorspar imports from China resulted in the suspension of Laporte's operations in 1999.

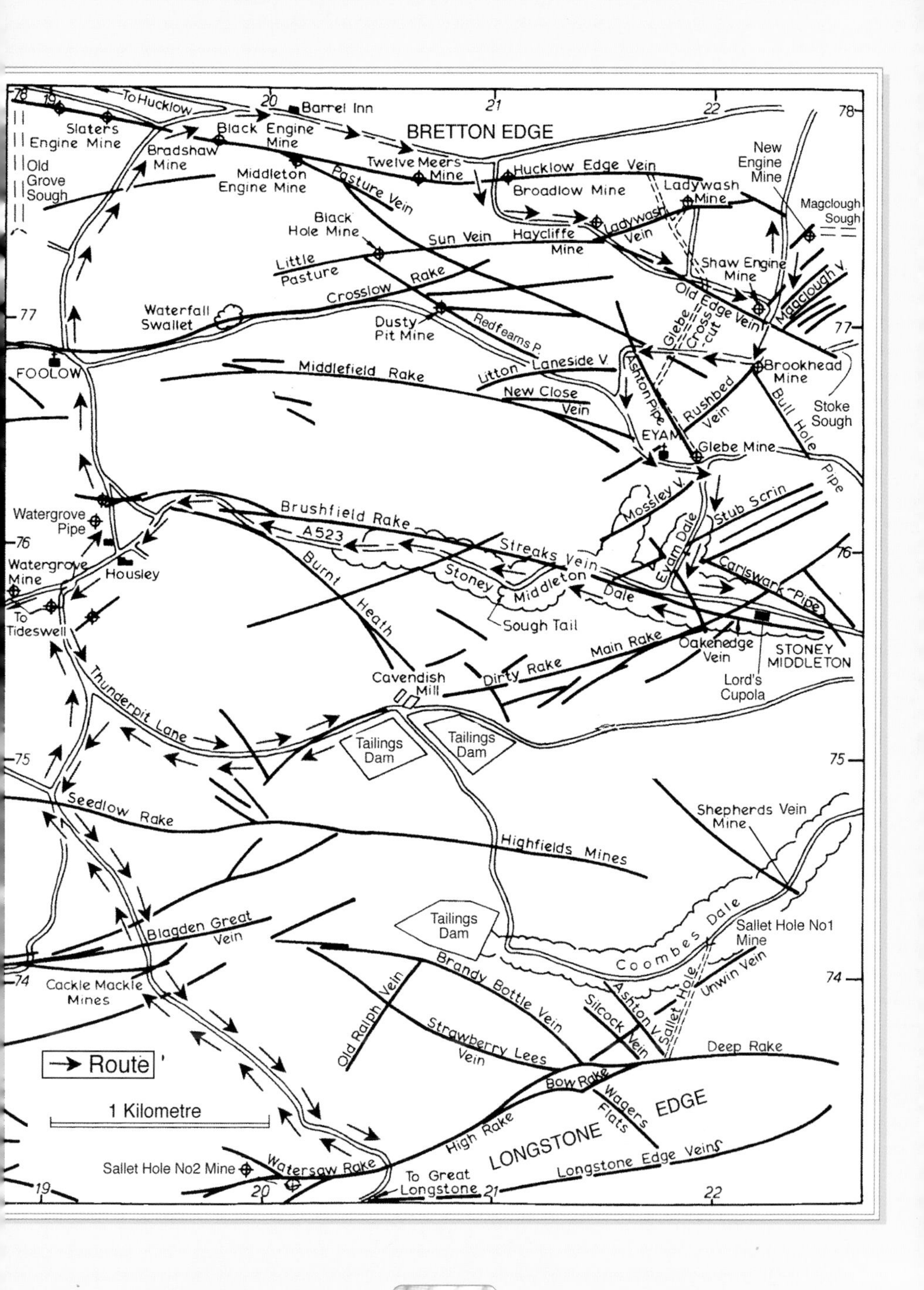

To Hucklow
Barrel Inn
BRETTON EDGE
Slaters Engine Mine
Old Grove Sough
Bradshaw Mine
Black Engine Mine
Middleton Engine Mine
Twelve Meers Mine
Hucklow Edge Vein
Broadlow Mine
Ladywash Mine
New Engine Mine
Magclough Sough
Pasture Vein
Black Hole Mine
Sun Vein
Haycliffe Mine
Ladywash Vein
Little Pasture
Crosslow Rake
Shaw Engine Mine
Magclough V.
Waterfall Swallet
Dusty Pit Mine
Redfearns P
Old Edge Vein
Glebe Cross-cut
FOOLOW
Middlefield Rake
Litton
Laneside V.
Ashton Pipe
Brookhead Mine
New Close Vein
Rushbed Vein
Bull Hole Pipe
Stoke Sough
EYAM
Glebe Mine
Watergrove Pipe
Mossley V.
Stub Scrin
Brushfield Rake
A523
Streaks Vein
Eyam Dale
Watergrove Mine
Housley
Burnt Heath
Stoney Middleton Dale
Carlswark Pipe
To Tideswell
Sough Tail
Oakenedge Vein
STONEY MIDDLETON
Main Rake
Thunderpit Lane
Cavendish Mill
Dirty Rake
Lord's Cupola
Tailings Dam
Tailings Dam
Seedlow Rake
Highfields Mines
Shepherds Vein Mine
Blagden Great Vein
Tailings Dam
Coombes Dale
Sallet Hole No1 Mine
Cackle Mackle Mines
Brandy Bottle Vein
Old Ralph Vein
Silcock Vein
Ashton V.
Sallet Hole
Unwin Vein
Strawberry Lees Vein
Deep Rake
Route
Bow Rake
Wagers Flats
EDGE
1 Kilometre
High Rake
LONGSTONE
Sallet Hole No2 Mine
Watersaw Rake
To Great Longstone
Longstone Edge Veins
19
20
21
22
78
77
76
75
74

The fluorspar ore from these mines and open-pits was processed at Cavendish Mill high on the south side of Stoney Middleton Dale (205 752) (the mill is not open to the public but a right of way footpath passes between the buildings).

At CAVENDISH MILL the ore was crushed and waste limestone and chert removed by density separation. The ore minerals were then ground to a fine powder and mixed with water to make a slurry from which the minerals were separated by the froth flotation process. The slurry was fed into rows of tanks with chemical reagents added which have the effect of selectively allowing one or other of the minerals to adhere to bubbles. Air was blown up through the tanks and the bubbles form froth on the slurry surface. The froth with the adherent minerals was skimmed off and dried before bagging for despatch to the customers. By this process the intimate mixture of minerals received from the mines was separated to yield fluorspar, baryte and galena each at around 98% purity. Together these constituted about 50% of the mill feed and the rest was unwanted limestone, calcite and chert, much of it in slurry form. The slurry was disposed of in tailings dams south of the works on nearby Middleton Moor and in Blakedon Hollow at the head of Coombs Dale.

## ITINERARY

The itinerary is planned to be taken by car. A convenient place to start is in Eyam village, where immediately east of the school a mound marks the site of GLEBE MINE (219 764). The shaft here was sunk to a depth of about 200 ft (60 m) in the 18th century to work ASHTON'S PIPE for lead ore. Work ceased in the mid 19th century and, after a long period of idleness, the shaft was refitted in the late 1930s and fluorspar was raised to be processed at a mill on site, since demolished. A cross-cut was driven from Glebe Mine through the limestone northwards towards another 18th century lead mine, LADYWASH MINE (219 775). This was close to the Old Edge and Hucklow Edge rakes, both rich in fluorspar. The shaft of Ladywash Mine was lined with concrete and refitted in the 1940s. A steel headframe was erected over this 800 ft (240 m) deep shaft and the mine worked up to around 1980. About 1 mile (1.6 km) of each rake was extracted from beneath the shale cover leaving large open stopes, though the shale was liable to collapse into these. Other veins branching out were also worked. Declines were driven down below the level of the cross-cut and the veins were worked more than 100 ft (30 m) lower. Drainage was turned into the 18th century STOKE SOUGH which still discharges near Grindleford (240 766).

From Eyam turn south down Eyam Dale and left at the bottom towards Stoney Middleton. After about 300 metres the group of buildings on the right, now partly a lorry garage and partly a furniture workshop, are all that remains of LORD'S CUPOLA (224 757), the lead smelter illustrated by the Sheffield artist Chantrey in an engraving of 1817. In use from 1740 to 1885, its main period of smelting activity was around 1800.

Turn round and drive west along the Tideswell road (A 623) for about 1.5 miles (2 km) up to the hamlet of HOUSLEY on the limestone plateau. To the west are the agent's and engineer's houses of WATERGROVE MINE (188 757 to 192 758). The remains of the smithy and reservoir can also be seen, as well as shafts covered by dressed stone "beehives". Watergrove Mine worked a very rich pipe vein in the late 18th century and horses were used underground. In the 20th century water was pumped from one shaft for use in Cavendish Mill.

From Housley take the next lane on the left and then the next turning left along Thunderpit Lane to reach CAVENDISH MILL (205 752). This is not open to the public but when seen from the roadside it illustrates the contrast in the scale of operations between the small 18th century lead mines and modern fluorspar extraction. Beyond the mill a private road (public footpath) leads past the tailings dams into Coombs Dale to the portal of SALLET HOLE MINE No. 1 (219 741). Here a 19th century drainage and haulage level was re-equipped for 20th century fluorspar mining beneath Longstone Edge: the main activity in recent years has been via SALLET HOLE MINE No 2 up on the Edge and the re-equipped 19th century adit of No 1 mine was used for ventilation and drainage.

Return to the last lane junction and turn left and left again across LONGSTONE MOOR. The lane crosses several rakes – WHITE RAKE, though by some to be named from the occurrence of cerussite (lead carbonate) but by others thought to be named from the abundant white calcite. BLAGDEN GREAT RAKE and the CACKLE-MACKLE MINES are nearby with lines of old hillocks marking their courses (cackle-mackle was very poor quality lead ore). Away on the left of this road there are distant views of the tailings lagoons at the head of Coombs Dale. To the right a turning leads to Sallet Hole No 2 portal, well hidden in a hollow. Where the lane crosses restored ground close to Longstone Edge itself is the site of recent open-pit workings in the LONGSTONE EDGE VEIN system, variously known along its length as DEEP, BOW, HIGH and WATERSAW RAKES. These were worked for fluorspar by dragline in the 1960s and 1970s resulting in deep trenches along the top of the Edge. Mostly back-filled with waste rock to restore the landscape, these operations have obliterated almost all traces of older lead mining.

From where the lane crosses LONGSTONE EDGE (205 730) there are good views over the country to the south. A walk east along the Edge may reveal occasional subsidences into the stopes of Sallet Hole Mine beneath. Well hidden to the west, SALLET HOLE No 2 mine was an inclined adit sunk into Watersaw Rake, working the western end of this major rake complex. The workings of Sallet Hole No 1 and No 2 mines were linked underground. Various branch veins were worked for lead ore along the steep southern side of Longstone Edge but the relics have mostly been destroyed by modern fluorspar operations.

Return to Housley and take the road north through Foolow village and up on to Bretton Edge near the Barrel Inn (200 779). BRETTON EDGE is an eastward continuation of Hucklow Edge; both comprise an escarpment of Millstone Grit, which here lies almost directly above the Hucklow Edge vein. Laporte Industries plc have mined fluorspar from this vein from MILLDAM MINE near Great Hucklow village, with workings reaching almost beneath the Barrel Inn. From the BARREL INN there are wide views southwards over the mining field, which forms lower ground towards Bakewell, Ashford-in-the-Water, Great Longstone and Monsal Dale. Immediately below the Edge the fields are crossed by several lines of waste hillocks marking minor veins, and it is worth pausing and looking down on to the ground just crossed. Along the foot of the Edge a line of workings of 18-19th century lead mines mark the courses of the OLD GROVE and OLD EDGE veins, formerly worked from Ladywash Mine. A line of small hillocks at right angles to the veins marks the position of an early sough driven to Old Grove Mine. Others were driven to Middleton Engine, Bradshaws, Slaters and Silence Mines but there is little trace of them today. They were not true soughs but shale gates, i.e. driven in shale, to serve as pumpways where water was raised up the shafts before flowing away by gravity to the south. The shale gates also served to locate traces of mineralization in the shale above deeply buried veins in the limestone below.

Take the Edge road eastwards for about a mile (1.5 km) and the chimney of LADYWASH MINE can be seen up a private drive on the left (219 775). Ahead lies NEW ENGINE MINE (224 774) with its recently repaired engine house. The shaft was the deepest of the Peak District lead mines: it was sunk through many hundreds of feet of sandstone and shale eventually terminating in the limestone at 1092 ft (c330 m). The engine was made by Davy Bros in Sheffield and installed in 1863. The engine pumped water from the deepest workings up to the level of Stoke Sough. New Engine Mine was last worked in 1884.

On the return towards Eyam the waste hillocks of SHAW ENGINE MINE, mainly shale, are visible at the road junction about 1/4 mile (400 m) southwest of New Engine Mine (222 771). Shaw Engine was on Old Edge Vein and both the Magclough and Stoke Soughs were focussed on this eastern end of the Hucklow Edge vein complex; the latter still provides drainage for the Hucklow Edge mines. Below the road at the next bend are the hillocks of BROOKHEAD MINE (221 768) and from them there are good views over Eyam and the heights above the near side of Stoney Middleton Dale, with lines of hillocks marking the veins.

Return to Eyam.

**Cornish Engine House now demolished at Milldam Mine, Great Hucklow**

# 4 SHELDON & THE MAGPIE MINE

***The ruined engine house and modern head frame of Magpie Mine***

BY L. WILLIES

**Walking Distance – about 4 miles (6 km.).**

**OS 1:25 000 Outdoor Leisure Map No. 24: The Peak District: White Peak Area.**

The history of Magpie Mine can be followed for over 300 years and its story and the remains there are amongst the most fascinating of any mining site in the country. This excursion will take you around the village of Sheldon, with remains of many smaller mines as well as the Magpie Sough tail and the mine itself. It is possible to start near the Sough with parking in a layby on the A6 near Black Rock Corner (181697), or in the village itself, or south of the Magpie Mine where cars can be parked on the roadside (please do not bring cars up to the track to the mine. The whole excursion can also be done in separate sections and can easily be extended on local footpaths.

## MAGPIE MINE (SK172682)

The site contains over twenty shafts and although these are covered, the fields around the site still have open shafts so keep to well marked footpaths. The agent's cottage and adjacent smithy is, nowadays, the field centre for Peak District Mines Historical Society, whose members will be pleased to help visitors. The whole site is very fragile so please ensure that you and your party do not climb on walls, remove stones or clamber up the sides of waste heaps.

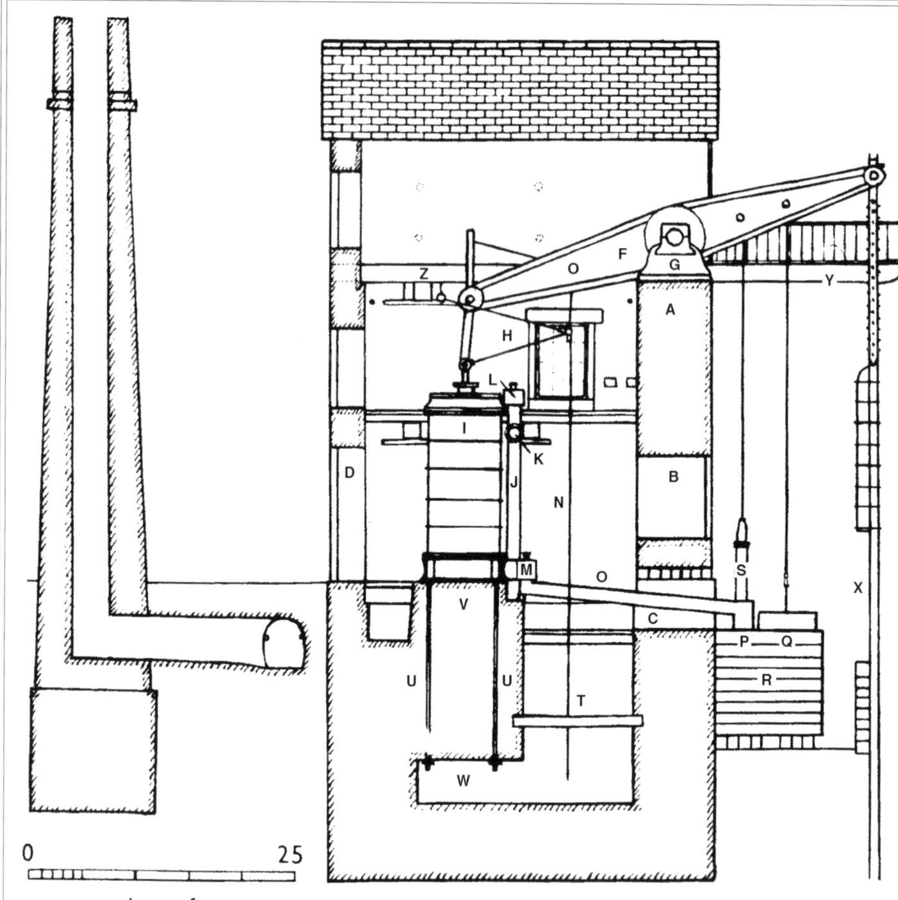


## THE MAGPIE ENGINE HOUSE

### KEY

A. Bob wall
B. Plug rod door
C. Aperture to hot well
D. Cylinder door
E. Boiler house door
F. Bob or beam
G. Stirrups
H. Watts' parallelogram linkage
I. Cylinder
J. Equilibrium pipe
K. Live steam pipe
L. Steam, equilibrium & governor valves
M. Exhaust valve
N. Plug rod
O. Eduction pipe
P. Condenser
Q. Air pump to exhaust condenser
R. Hot well or cistern
S. Feed-water pump
T. Cataract pit or cockpit containing cataracts for governing speed of engine
U. Engine mounting bolts
X. Pump rod in shaft
Y. Bob plank
Z. Spring beams (& side beams)

*The Magpie Mine buildings dominated by the 1868 engine house*

*Start at the small grilled shaft about five metres from the south-west corner of the former cottage and smithy.*

Magpie Mine stands close by the intersection of a number of veins, the first known record of which was the freeing of Shuttlebank in 1674 though most of the veins must have been worked long before this. The Maypitts Mine, near where the horse-gin has been re-erected, was fairly important in the 1740s when around a hundred tons of ore were raised in a year. Otherwise the dozen or so mines once on the site were all very small and insignificant. The mound of the original Magpie Founder shaft is found over the wall just to the south of the cottage. A meer of 29 yards away is the (grilled) climbing shaft. You can see traces near it of a small pond used for washing the ore. The climbing shaft is 110 ft (33 metres) deep and is the first of several shafts and sumps which go down to 50 fathoms depth (300 ft or 90 metres).

*Walk westwardly past the square chimney and its flue and winding-engine house past Bole Shaft and the circular wall of a crushing circle, and on to where the stile crosses to the adjacent field – the site of Shuttlebank Shaft.*

Very little is known of the early mine though it was owned or managed by George Heywood in the 1740s and in the 1760s a deep shaft (360 ft – 108 m) was sunk at the western extremity of the site by George Goodwin of Monyash on which a horse gin was then or later erected. Much fuller information comes from 1786 when Magpie was "given" by the barmaster to Joshua White whose shares then passed to Peter Holme and partners. They worked it, at a small profit, until stopped in 1793 because of

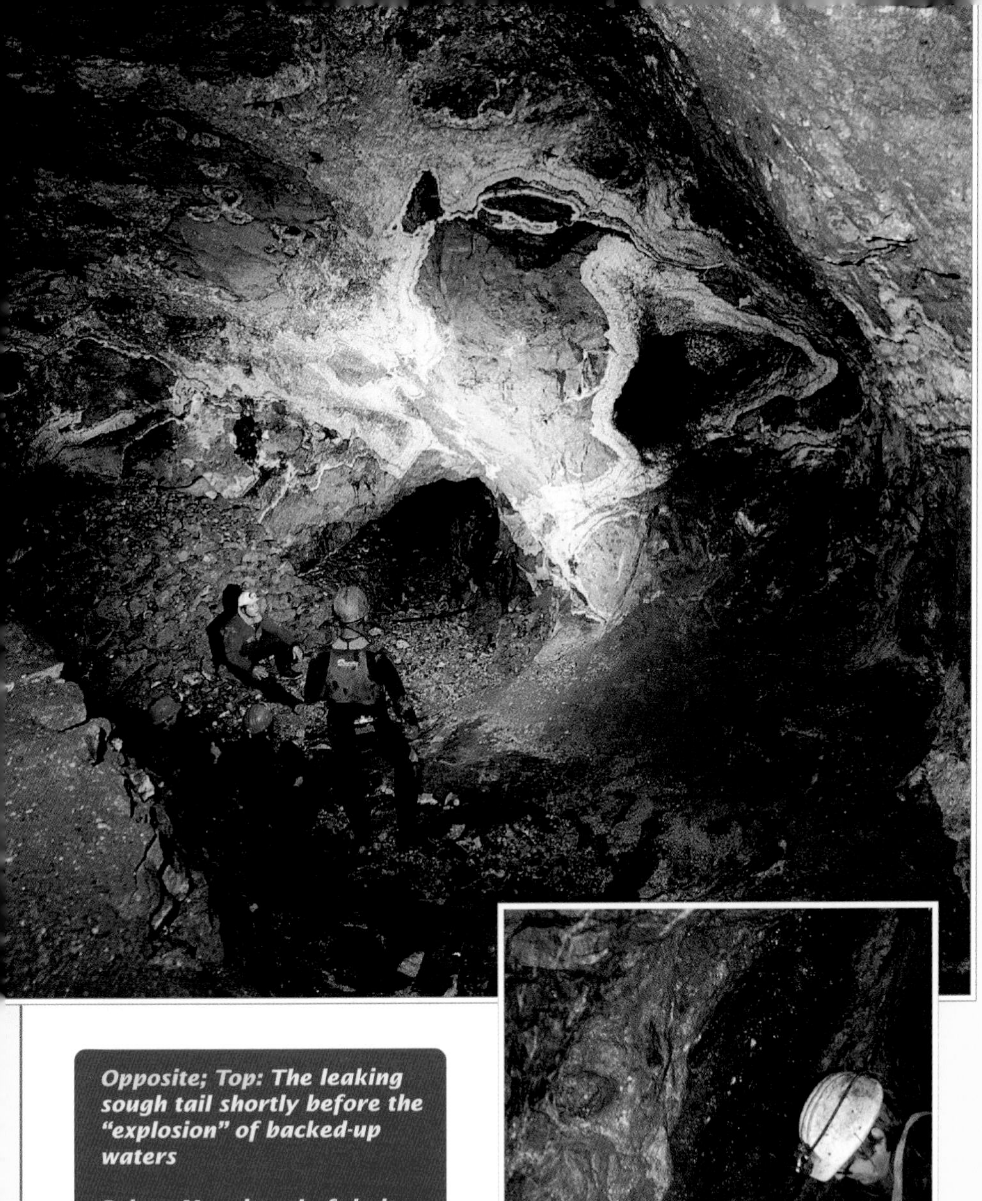

***Opposite; Top: The leaking sough tail shortly before the "explosion" of backed-up waters***

***Below: Maypitts shaft in its ruined coe***

***Above: The Blende Vein Cavern***

***Right: The boil up of water into the sough***

lower prices with the loss of the Dutch market in the Napoleonic War. The main other surface relic of that time is the narrow climbing shaft, Bole Shaft, with projecting stones for footholds sunk 60 feet on Bole Vein about two meers or 58 yards to the west.

In 1801 Magpie Mine reopened and was extended west to the deep shaft sunk by Goodwin. Early efforts proved unrewarding and so a long level, 50 fathoms underground, was driven west, over a period of some five years, under the field beyond the stile adjacent to the Magpie site to just beyond the furthest (north west) corner. High prices allowed a small profit, but only finding old workings at the furthest point made the shareholders very unhappy. Undaunted, they followed another vein, the North Vein, back towards what is the present main Magpie Shaft and about 1810 struck rich ore – the true discovery of what is the modern Magpie Mine. It gave a very comfortable living for the modest group of shareholders until about 1820 – an unusual success for the small men in the business. Apart from the site of the horse gin (on the shaft sunk by Goodwin), little remains to be seen at surface of this last period of profitable working.

*(Walk east to the steel headgear on the main Magpie Shaft)*. This is past the ore coe and other buildings from the 1840s. Look back from the hillock to see the surface grooves of the veins on the adjacent field. The small engine house you pass belongs to a crushing and screening engine which was in use in the 1920s.

By 1820 it was becoming obvious that the mine had to be deepened if working was to continue and that water would have to be removed for this. The first stage was to test the mine at depth – two underground sumps (shafts) were carried down from the then deepest workings at 360 feet to 480 feet, with men working handpumps earning £80 in three weeks (at about two shillings or 10p a man-shift). A survey was then undertaken and in 1823 a rise was made above one of the sumps with a shaft sunk from surface to meet it. The three sections were linked and widened to about 8 by 6 feet to form the first 480 feet of the modern Main Shaft – a fine piece of workmanship, done in six months and duly celebrated in ale. A Newcomen-type engine was erected on the shaft by Francis Thompson of Chesterfield and all seemed set for a further phase of profitable activity under a new agent, William Wyatt of Foolow, and with several new shareholders who financed the activity. Unfortunately the outbreak of hostilities and legal bills in the disputes with neighbouring Maypitts and Redsoil, up the field near the horse gin, removed any chance of profits in the next ten years of working.

The Main Shaft has been the focus of all subsequent working. Up to about 1833 the workings were driven east, intersecting those claimed to be of the other mines at depths of about 420 – 480 feet. The so-called "murders"of 1833 (see below) ended this phase and the mine lay virtually dormant. In 1839 the famous mining firm of John Taylor and Sons were called in to reopen the mine using the then most modern methods in which the firm had excelled in Cornwall. They brought in Cornish pumping and winding engines for which the two chimneys were built, and deepened the shaft. The agent's house, smithy and the round powder house (to the north) all date from this period and Taylor introduced the use of wire rope, cast-steel borers, safety fuse and safety hats, later known as "bradders" and used more efficient layouts and management of the workers. About 14 key miners were imported from Cornwall. All seemed set fair for a time and output rose – until a clay bed was penetrated in the shaft and water flooded in. Taylor wanted a bigger engine. Local shareholders wanted a sough. Others feared the expense and the mine closed again in 1844.

In 1868 a Sheffield stationer, John Fairburn with a new group of shareholders, took over the mine. They bought a bigger engine from Calver Sough Mine and put it in the present ruined engine house. There was a new steam whim, of which the engine and boiler houses and winding drum survives. Notice how each enginehouse is well away from the (older) chimneys. They made a good start, then the shaft was sunk deeper. Huge volumes of water flooded in. It was decided to have a sough too, and driving began from about a mile away, from the River Wye, to intersect the shaft at about 600 ft (180 m.) depth. This was well above existing workings, so the engine, with new pumps was still needed. Driving the sough took place between 1873 and 1881 and, after a slow start, pneumatic drills and dynamite explosives were used for the first time in Derbyshire. It cost about £18,000, then a large sum and though some shareholders turned up their shares, others, encouraged by a quite unscrupulous claim of a 40,000 ton find of zinc ore (40 tons were eventually mined) ensured the sough was completed. Meanwhile the discoveries at Broken Hill in Australia lead to imports of cheap lead and despite the sough, the venture collapsed in 1885, with Fairburn a "ruined man" who died six months later.

The mine did not quite stop. The engine was sold but working went on spasmodically for 30 years, mainly above the level of the sough. From about 1907 Edward Garlick was the mainstay of the mine, using money from his Sheffield saw manufacturing business. He attracted money from other Sheffield men and later from a Glaswegian, Mr McGwistan. Working until 1925 using a variety of small pumps and driving east several hundred yards to the True Blue Mine just above sough level, he succeeded only in losing his own and the other's fortunes. The main effect visible from all this money is the waste heaps visible around the shaft.

There was one further attempt at working Magpie Mine. In the 1950s Waihi, a New Zealand company, reopened the mine using men mainly from Youlgreave. They built the corrugated, sheet-steel winder house and the present headstocks and reopened the shaft. Electric pumping was introduced and the shaft pumped to bottom. Some work was also done above sough and some lead and zinc ore raised, but in all, little was accomplished and the mine closed in 1959 having made a loss of some £80,000.

*(Walk behind the engine house to view the inside)*. Note the two types of crushing stones and pump pipe, which have been brought in recently, by the chimney.

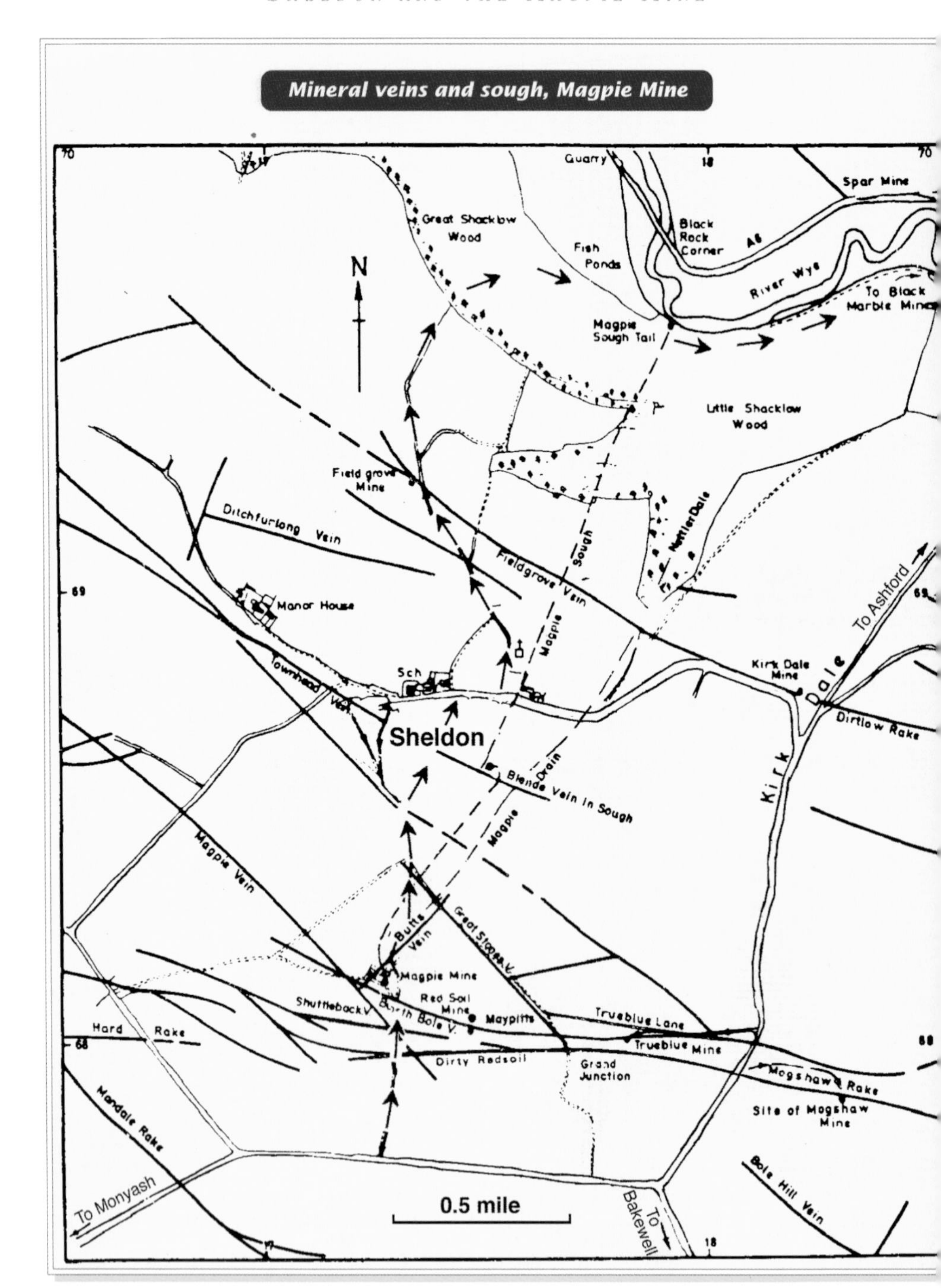
Mineral veins and sough, Magpie Mine
N
Quarry
Spar Mine
Great Shacklow Wood
Fish Ponds
Black Rock Corner
A6
River Wye
To Black Marble Mine
Magpie Sough Tail
Little Shacklow Wood
Field grove Mine
Ditchfurlong Vein
Fieldgrove Vein
Sough
Nettler Dale
Manor House
Magpie
To Ashford
Kirk Dale Mine
Dale
Dirtlow Rake
Townhead Vein
Sch
Sheldon
Drain
Blende Vein in Sough
Kirk
Magpie
Magpie Vein
Butts Vein
Great Sloaes V.
Magpie Mine
Red Soil Mine
Shuttlebock V.
Maypitts
Trueblue Lane
Trueblue Mine
Hard Rake
Dirty Redsoil
Grand Junction
Mogshaw Rake
Site of Mogshaw Mine
Mandale Rake
Bole Hill Vein
To Monyash
0.5 mile
To Bakewell
70
18
69
68
17

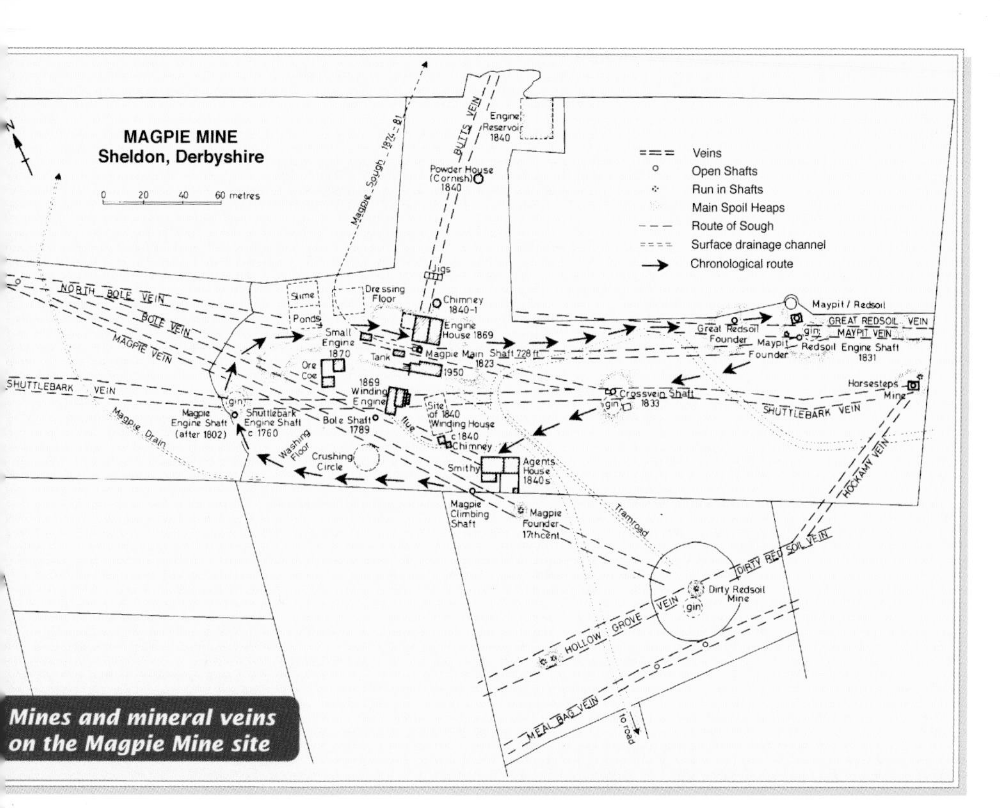


Mines and mineral veins on the Magpie Mine site

Magpie Mine Sough showing Lock gates

*Up the field the disturbed ground is over Butts Vein, which passes near the round powder house – the adjacent footpath can be followed to Sheldon village past the engine reservoir just over the wall: the sough follows the line of Butts Vein some 600 feet below, but first, proceed to the wooden frame of the horse gin on Maypitts and Redsoil Mines.*

## THE MAGPIE MURDERS.

The disputes of the 1820s and 1830s between first Maypits and Magpie, then the same people at Redsoil with Magpie took place under this area. Part of the problem was that the disputed veins lie roughly at the boundary of their titles and also, since unlike other areas of Derbyshire where severe fines were levied for trespass, in Sheldon, part of Ashford Liberty, the only penalty for a losing side was to pay for the dinners of the Barmoot jurymen.

Soon after the 1825 engine began work, the Magpie miners broke through into Maypitts workings and the latter quickly complained to the Barmaster. Meanwhile Magpie's cunning lawyer, William Brittlebank of Winster, freed their veins with the Barmaster for the first time. Eventually the Barmoot Jury awarded the disputed vein to Maypitts, but on appeal to an outside Jury, Maypitts were unable to produce evidence they had freed the mine (the Barmaster, a Magpie shareholder was supposed to keep the documents!) and Magpie won the day. In a similar "thurling through" to Redsoil in 1829, Redsoil were able to find the freeing evidence (from 1780 – earlier than Magpie's), but it was impossible to prove the continuity of their vein without much more work. For some three years the two sides obstructed each other, with juries called in to make decisions, pulling-in the gates, blocking shafts and fighting underground.

To smoke out the Magpie men in 1833, Redsoil lit a fire underground of straw and tar from the gasworks, but the wind blew the wrong way, smoking Redsoil out instead. Magpie then lit their own fires and the shafts at Redsoil *(next to the horse gin)* smoked like "factory chimneys" for a whole weekend. On Monday morning at five o'clock the Redsoil men came back to work. The Redsoil agent descended the first 140 feet into the mine, found the air clear and sent in his men.They went 140 feet down, then descended further by the 20 fathom sump, the 16 fathom, the eight fathom and the Little Sump to about 420 feet depth, at which point, affected by gases, they began falling off the climbing stemples. Someone got out – a bucket chain was set up from the pond in Fairmeer Piece (the next field) and water was poured down the horse gin-shaft to drive air down and miners from both sides began a rescue. But three Redsoil men from Sheldon died.

Police arrived from Derby a couple of days later and arrested six of the twenty four Magpie men thought to be involved. An angry miners'court in Ashford (no outside coroner was allowed to interfere in mining deaths) declared it murder. But at the Derby trial six months later, at which all twenty four men appeared, all but three were immediately released whilst the three, charged with manslaughter, were found "not guilty". Being there did not make them guilty – it was not possible just to leave; fires after four o'clock were legal under the mining customs and the Maypitts agent had been negligent in not examining all the mine. The Redsoil miners widows were not consoled and the bitterness remained for many years. Both mines closed.

Since the 1950s the mine has lain unworked. In the 1960s PDMHS took over the site. In the 1970s and 80s they carried out emergency repairs and raised money to restore the buildings, which were declared the Ancient Monument it is today.

## THE WALK THROUGH SHELDON VILLAGE AND ON TO MAGPIE SOUGH

*Use the footpath from the north end of the site across the fields to the village, paralleling the route above the sough.*

**Sheldon village is part of the Manor of Ashford, belonging to the Dukes of Devonshire, which accounts for the style of some of the houses. Its original pub has closed (another is currently operating) but the position of its sign can be seen. It was formerly the Devonshire Arms and was the "House of Mary Gyte" of the late 18th century when she was a Magpie shareholder and the mine shareholders used to meet there. Her descendant, Alice Gyte, still kept the pub in the 1960s. The village is small, as is its chapel. In the churchyard are the graves of several former mining families – the Naylors and Brocklehursts amongst them. The epitaph engraved on Ephraim Brocklehurst's gravestone is worth seeking out, and will be better understood when you know he died by falling from a plank in Magpie Shaft in 1864.**

The lane past the Churchyard leads towards other mines operated by William Wyatt in the 1830s and 40s, notably the Fieldgrove whose shaft mounds can be found alongside the track. Before these are reached, however, a (signed) path to the right (north) leads across fields into the trees of Shacklow Wood, down a steep log-stairway to the valley and River Wye below. Magpie Sough can be found by following the path down-valley and will be easily recognised by the strong stream which pours out from under an arch into the river.

Driving of the sough began in 1873. The rock here is basalt which can be very tough. It can be seen in the waste heap above the sough tail and gives its name to Black Rock Corner on the A6 road nearby. The miners expected to drive out of the basalt quickly, into the easier going of the Butts Vein. But this was not to be and the going remained slow. Some years later, when almost under the village, the sough cut the Townhead Vein and released an enormous amount of water in what

**The drum on the 1868 winding engine**

became known, and still is known, as the "boil-up" – most of the water today is from this rather than the mine itself.

Somewhere near the tail, perhaps down where the Shacklow Mill is now, a waterwheel was set up to drive a compressor and Schram pneumatic drills, made by Olivers of Chesterfield were installed, and nitroglycerine explosives were used for the first time, which speeded progress. Exploration in the sough is difficult (and for environmental reasons should not be attempted without permission), but the change in profile caused by these new methods is easily seen. Well up the sough is the cavern called Blende Vein, lined with calcite. Here was the small amount of the fortuitously found, claimed 40,000 tons of zinc ore which persuaded some shareholders to complete the project.

A shaft a few yards from the tail ran-in in 1966, blocking the tunnel until, after heavy rain, the shaft blew out, causing thousands of tons of debris to run down the slope and half-blocking the river. This was remedied by PDMHS in 1973 and the present arched entrance was put in place then. Over the river is a stone block. This was used to moor a boat which brought out calcite from the Blende Vein – to facilitate its passage the sough has lock gates underground.

From the sough the walk can be continued downstream to the two mill-buildings and the adjacent, third water wheel which drove pumps to provide water for Sheldon village. Their supply had been lost when the boil-up was cut and it is possible the sough compressor was earlier installed here. The path from the sough to here follows an older leat which was filled-in when the modern dam was built in the final years of the 19th century. The other wheels and mill were used for a succession of purposes including the grinding of barite for paint, a bobbin works and, in the Second World War as a scrap tin can crushing plant for which the concrete pillars were erected.

From here you can either regain the road near Black Rock Corner via the bridge, or continue on the downstream path to Ashford village. In the 1950s it is rumoured that the Magpie men came to work from Youlgreave, went down the shaft, walked along the sough, down this very footpath, spent lunchtime in the Devonshire Arms (now the Ashford Arms) in Ashford, before retracing their route back home. I cannot verify this story, but you may wish to follow their example – the Devonshire Arms, the "House of Mr Frost" is where the Ashford Barmoots were held and the Magpie disputes contested.

# 5 THE ASHFORD BLACK MARBLE MINES & MILL

*Above: Roof support packs in the Black Marble Mine*
*Below: Black Marble beds in the Rookery Mine*

BY T. D. FORD

Maps: 1:25000 SK 16 & 26; 1:10000 SK 16 NE and SK 26 NW.

Conveniently situated near to Sheldon and the Magpie Mine, the Black Marble mines of Ashford-in-the-Water may also be visited to provide a contrast in mining style. Cars may be parked in Buxton Road at the western end of Ashford (not on the A6) or at the foot of Kirk Dale, whence the walking distance is little more than 1/4 mile (400 m).

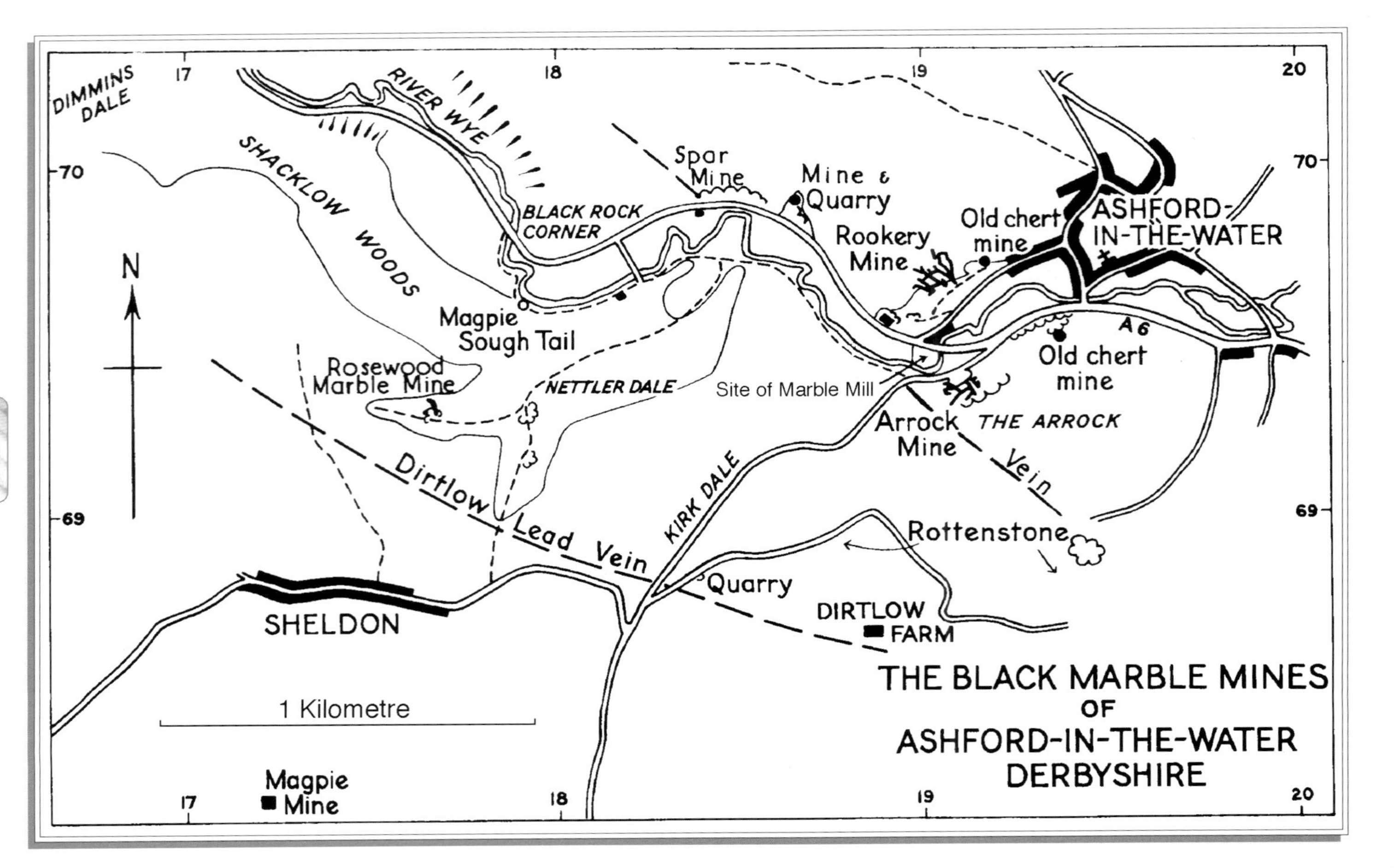

DIMMINS DALE
RIVER WYE
SHACKLOW WOODS
BLACK ROCK CORNER
Spar Mine
Mine & Quarry
Rookery Mine
Old chert mine
ASHFORD-IN-THE-WATER
N
Magpie Sough Tail
Rosewood Marble Mine
NETTLER DALE
Site of Marble Mill
A6
Old chert mine
Arrock Mine
THE ARROCK
Vein
Dirtlow Lead Vein
KIRK DALE
Rottenstone
Quarry
DIRTLOW FARM
SHELDON
1 Kilometre
Magpie Mine
THE BLACK MARBLE MINES
OF
ASHFORD-IN-THE-WATER
DERBYSHIRE
17
18
19
20
70
69

The Black Marble mine workings are a nearly horizontal network of galleries in gently dipping, dark, fine-grained limestones and contrast with the generally vertical lead mine workings. The Black Marble was mined underground from at least the mid 18th century, though its use in stately homes and mediaeval tombs in churches indicates that it was quarried at least from the 13th century. When polished the dark grey limestones are jet black though exposure outdoors soon returns the marble surface to a dull grey and indoor use only is recommended. Its polish can be maintained with natural wax polishes, but modern synthetics should not be used. From the 18th century onwards its principal use was in ornaments for stately homes. These ranged from vases, urns, obelisks, bowls, paperweights and jewellery to fireplaces, floor panels, window ledges, and table tops. The Black Marble was inlaid with various coloured stones to give geometrical, patchwork (sometimes called scrapwork) and floral designs. The last came into favour about the 1830s and some of the finest workmanship was in tables inlaid with floral patterns. Fine examples were displayed at the Great Exhibition of 1851. Etching and engraving were also popular; the latter gave pictures composed of grey lines scribed into the polished black surface yielding "moonlight sketches". Inlaid Black Marble was particularly popular in the late 19th century but the craft died out soon after Queen Victoria died.

There are two main series of mine workings for Black Marble. The ARROCK MINE lies at the back of a much-overgrown quarry at the foot of the Kirk Dale Road in a hill called the Arrock (191 694). There are two gated entrances: the obvious one leads into collapsed workings after only a few metres. The other, somewhat hidden behind rocks about 3 metres up to the right, leads into a gallery about 100 metres long, with several branches. Both worked about 2 metres of beds. Similar dark limestones outcrop in the adjacent quarry but the frequent chert nodules made most beds unsuitable for polished marble. The thin slabby limestones were, however, useful as building stone.

The second and much more extensive series of workings are high in the Rookery Plantation across the valley (190 696). Reached by a track through the wood above the Buxton Road, the ROOKERY MINE entrance is gated for safety*. About 1000 metres of galleries are accessible radiating from an entrance in a long disused quarry near the top of the wooded hill slope. Working faces show that about 2 metres of beds were extracted but there was much waste used in packs to support the roof. Blocks were levered on to rollers and dragged out by horses and down to the mill yard. Two other entrances to the east are now blocked.

The marble mill (190 695) was established by Henry Watson in 1748. He used water-power to drive saws, grinders and polishing devices. The mill was built on the north bank of the River Wye and there were at least three waterwheels; traces of the mill-races can still be seen. Water-turbines were introduced in the 1880s and the mill was in use up to 1905. In the early 1930s several mill buildings were demolished to make way for the A 6 highway. Most of the remaining buildings to the south of the A6 have been removed since then though outlines of foundations and water courses can still be made out. The much-altered manager's house still lies across to the north of the A 6. Since 1905 the mill has been a baryte mill, a saw-mill and lumberyard, a water-authority store and it is now a storage depot for the Peak Park, from whom permission to visit should be sought.

Trials for Black Marble mines also occur in NETTLER DALE about half a mile (1 km) to the west and in LATHKILL DALE but none was worked for more than about 15 m. Nettler Dale also had a small mine for ROSEWOOD MARBLE, though its entrance is difficult to find (177 693) and the galleries are barely 60 cm high. Rosewood Marble was a grey-brown limestone with fine banding rather like wood grain and it was mainly used for inlay work. Another small quarry in Nettler Dale yielded a black limestone with widely scattered, white fossil crinoid fragments known as BIRD'S EYE MARBLE (179 693).

Coarse crinoidal limestone from several small quarries around Monyash was also brought to the Ashford mill for sawing and polishing. It was usually known as encrinital or figured marble and was widely used for floors and window sills in large buildings such as Chatsworth House.

Further details of the Black Marble craft may be found in DERBYSHIRE BLACK MARBLE by J.M.Tomlinson (1996), available from the Peak District Mining Museum, Matlock.

The highest beds of limestone around Bakewell and Ashford contain a thick bed of CHERT. Up to 6 m thick it was mined from both banks of the Wye near Bakewell. Many thousands of tons of chert were sent to the Potteries for grinding the china-clay mixture. North of the river the HOLME BANK MINE (214 692) has several hundred metres of galleries separated by packs of waste. Across the river to the south of Bakewell, the PRETORIA MINE was high up by the Monyash road (211 682). Last worked in the 1950s it too has extensive galleries. It is in the care of the Peak District Mines Historical Society from whom enquiries should be made about visits. Further details of the chert industry may be found in HARD TIMES by Gordon Bowering and Roger Flindall (1998) available from the Peak District Mining Museum, Matlock.

* Permits for the Rookery Mine may be obtained by prior application to Peter Mellors, "Fairview", Station Road, Eardingley, Newark, Nottinghamshire NG22 8BX. Applications should be made at least two weeks before the proposed visit.

# 6 THE LATHKILL DALE MINES

By J. H. Rieuwerts

*In Mandale Sough*

**Maps: 1:25000 SK 16; 1:10000 SK 16 NE and SK 26 NW.**

**Walking distance 5 or 9 km according to the return route.**

N.B. Much of Lathkill Dale is a National Nature Reserve and collecting plants, animals, fossils and mineral specimens is forbidden.

**A great deal of work was undertaken in this area by the old lead miners, and the dale is particularly interesting in the unusual lay-out of the watercourses and aqueducts constructed to provide power to drive water wheels for pumping purposes. The River Lathkill was harnessed and a portion of its water used to drive at least three wheels, one no less than 52 ft (16 m) in diameter. Steam power was also used and the dale vividly illustrates the miners' ceaseless struggle with their major enemy – water. Some workings are still accessible but should not be entered by the inexperienced.**

Cars may be parked in the village car park in OVER HADDON. There is also limited parking part way down the hill into the Dale.

From the car park, proceed down-hill into the Dale. Nestling in the valley floor is LATHKILL LODGE (203 661); the adjacent buildings were formerly a corn mill operated by a water-wheel. A ford (sometimes dry!) and footbridge lead across into Meadow Place Wood; hidden away up on the hilltop is Meadow Place farm, once a monastic settle-ment like its neighbours Conksbury Grange and One Ash Grange.

Do not cross the footbridge but turn left over a stile and follow the river (or its dry bed) downstream. Where the path begins to rise up the bank turn right on to the river bed and the first disturbed ground marks the site of LATHKILL DALE SOUGH. Water still issues from the collapsed tail (205 661), close to the impressive BUBBLE SPRINGS where the main flow of the River Lathkill emerges into daylight from beneath a sheet of calcareous tufa. The history of the Lathkill Dale Sough will be noted later.

Retracing the route back to Lathkill Lodge, inconspicuous grassy mounds, best seen in winter when the vegetation is low, mark the positions of shafts sunk on the sough. Another shaft in the Lodge's garden is now marked by a manhole cover. A little west of this shaft the sough changes direction and passes beneath the footbridge. The Lathkill Dale Vein and Sough extend south-westwards under Meadow Place Wood, though relics are mostly hid-den in the undergrowth (the Wood is part of the Nature Reserve).

Proceed westwards along the main footpath along the north bank of the river passing the remaining buildings of Over Haddon Mill. Soon two small trial levels can be seen by the path side but neither penetrates more than a few metres. Somewhat hidden in the under-growth to the left are the embank-ments round former mill ponds. On entering the wood some 500 metres west of the Lodge, a level, usually partly flooded, is obvious immediately left of the path. This is the tail or outfall of MANDALE SOUGH (197 661) which extends over a mile northwestwards into the hill. It was driven mainly between 1797 and 1820, and extended later. The derelict mine building visible amongst the trees to the right was part of MANDALE MINE, where there were large scale efforts in the mid 19th century to keep the lower workings dry by pumping up to the sough. Mandale Mine is reputed to be one of the oldest in Derbyshire and was certainly working by the 13th century when the famous Inquisition into the Laws and Customs was held in 1288. In 1585 Over Haddon Field Rake was described as containing the best ore in the Peak and this rake is almost certainly that now known as Mandale Rake. Mandale Rake was recorded as being in work in 1615, 1665-6, 1677 and around 1700. At the latter date the workings were said to be 380 ft deep (110 m) and 2 miles (3 km) in length.

The large remaining mine building is the ruined MANDALE ENGINE HOUSE; roofless, only the bob-wall is complete enough to demonstrate the former position of the machinery. Behind it is a deep hollow which once housed a 35 ft (10.5 m) diameter water-wheel directly over the pumping shaft, now filled in. Climbing to the shelf above the wheel pit, one crosses a leat through which water was brought from further up the river, and straight ahead is the entrance to the "Inclined Plane", now the principal means of access to the mine workings. The entrance is gated to discourage entry by inexperienced persons as some of the workings are in an unstable condition. Above the entrance the vein can be seen in the cliff face. Close to the entrance is a concrete cap on a shaft into a short branch level to the sough. Standing with the inclined plane entrance on one's left and looking across the small branch dale an opening on the opposite hillside is part of a flue from the engine's boiler house (now completely destroyed) to a chimney high on the hillside.

The Mandale Mining Co started their sough in 1797 and after 23 years of toil with little return, the miners found a rich body of lead ore, followed by a second in 1823. The first brought a profit of £1155 in 6 months whilst the second yielded £584 profit. The company was anxious to work the vein below river level as they were convinced that a large amount of ore remained untouched by former miners who had used only small hand pumps. During 1839 John Alsop became agent in succession to William Wager who had held the post since 1808. A water-wheel was installed in 1840 and pumped from a depth of 90 ft (27 m) below the sough. The wheel was about 35 ft (10.5 m) in diameter and the pumps were cylinders 14 inches (31 cm) in diameter. However, by 1847 the mine was again in serious difficulties with water. With two levels driven along the vein below the sough it was decided to install a steam engine. The engine house was built of limestone quarried a little further up the dale. The engine was constructed on the Cornish principle at the Milton Ironworks, Elsecar near Barnsley. Its cylinder was 65 inches (163 cm) diameter and it developed 165 horsepower. It was planned to pump

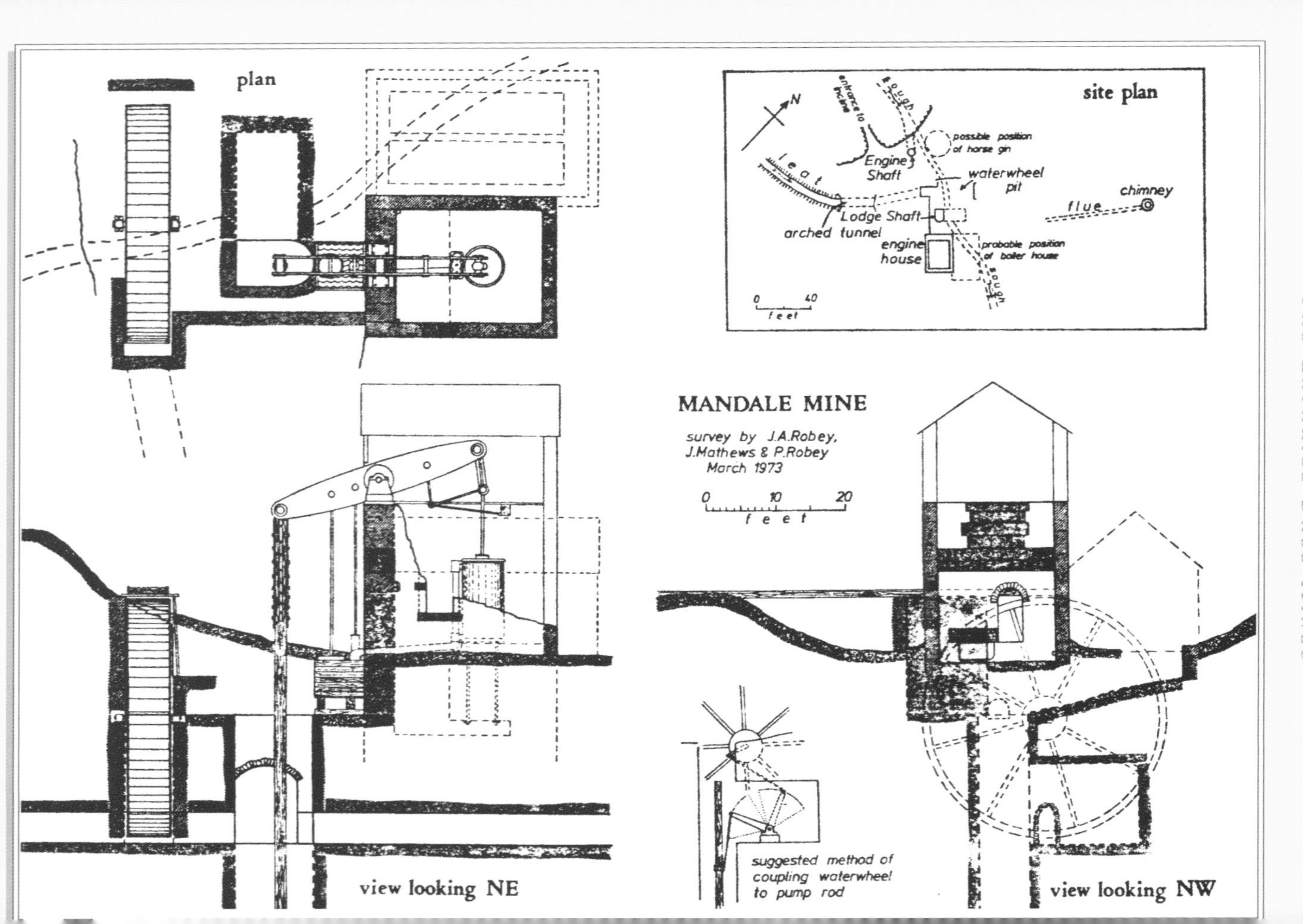
plan
site plan
N
entrance to incline
sough
possible position of horse gin
Engine Shaft
leat
waterwheel pit
chimney
flue
Lodge Shaft
arched tunnel
engine house
probable position of boiler house
0 40 feet
MANDALE MINE
survey by J.A.Robey, J.Mathews & P.Robey March 1973
0 10 20 feet
suggested method of coupling waterwheel to pump rod
view looking NE
view looking NW

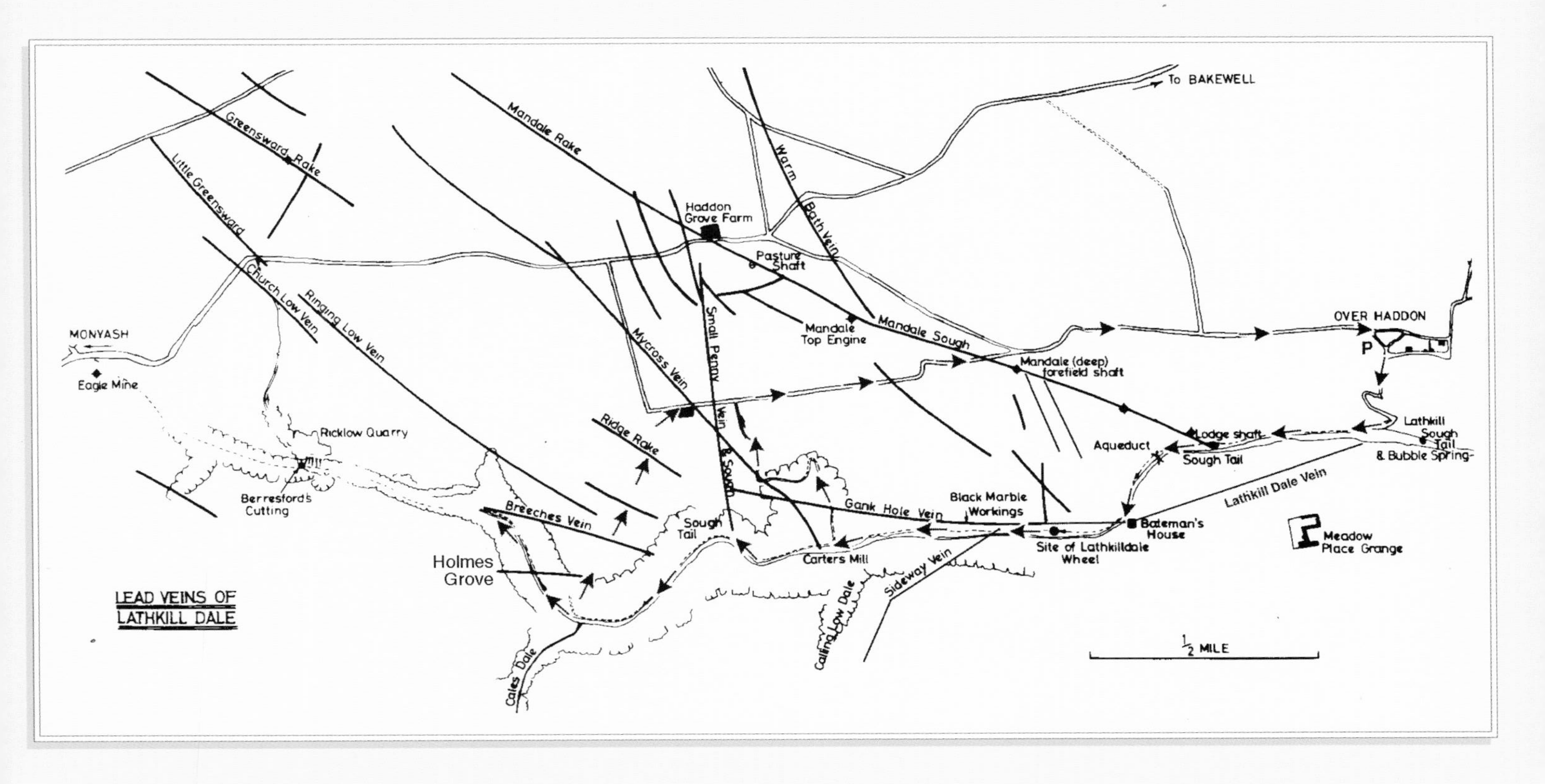
LEAD VEINS OF
LATHKILL DALE
To BAKEWELL
Greensward Rake
Little Greensward
Mandale Rake
Warm
Bath Vein
Haddon
Grove Farm
Pasture
Shaft
Church Low Vein
Ringing Low Vein
Mycross Vein
Small Penny
Vein
& Sough
Mandale
Top Engine
Mandale Sough
OVER HADDON
P
MONYASH
Eagle Mine
Mandale (deep)
forefield shaft
Ricklow Quarry
Berresford's
Cutting
Ridge Rake
Lodge shaft
Lathkill
Sough
Tail
& Bubble Spring
Aqueduct
Sough Tail
Lathkill Dale Vein
Black Marble
Workings
Gank Hole Vein
Bateman's
House
Breeches Vein
Sough
Tail
Meadow
Place Grange
Site of Lathkilldale
Wheel
Carters Mill
Holmes
Grove
Sideway Vein
Calling Low Dale
Cales Dale
1/2 MILE

from 160 ft (53 m) below the sough but it is doubtful if the pumping shaft ever went below the 90 ft (27 m) level. Mandale Mine ceased work in 1851 after, it is said, a loss of £36000. The engine and boiler were removed in 1852 and there is an unsubstantiated tradition that some parts were used at Calver Sough Mine.

Returning to the main path and proceeding westwards following the river, the remaining pillars of an AQUEDUCT are soon seen. Formerly a wooden trough on top of the pillars conveyed water from a leat on the southern hillside across to work the water-wheel at Mandale Mine. The aqueduct was built in 1840, not as a date 1810 carved into one of the stones suggests (it may have been defaced from an original carving of 1840). Within a short distance westwards the path enters more woodland and on the right there is a row of deep hollows. In wet weather these may be flooded as they mark the course of an old unnamed shallow sough driven to LATHKILL DALE VEIN.

Shortly, a ruined building on the south bank is BATEMAN'S HOUSE (194 658). James Bateman was agent to the Lathkill Dale Mining Company from 1836 until its closure in 1842. Two large shafts, one directly below the house, are generally known as Bateman's Shafts, though their correct name is unknown. They were the site of a unique pumping engine designed by the Dakeyne brothers, flax spinners of Darley Dale. It was described as a disc engine though really it was a primitive form of water turbine. Its mode of operation was complex and surviving technical descriptions are difficult to follow. The main parts were made at the Adelphi Foundry in Chesterfield in 1831. In 1833 the engine was working satisfactorily using a head of 66 ft (19 m) of water to supply power and generating 130 horsepower.

Adjacent to Bateman's House, the Lathkill Dale Vein, which has ranged through Meadow Place Wood, plunges steeply down the hillside and its westward extent is mostly beneath the river bed. The Lathkill Dale Sough runs along the sole (lowest accessible level) and during the drought of 1959 it was explored for some 500 metres downstream from beneath the house. Deep water precluded further exploration; upstream the sough was found to have been bricked up beneath the north bank of the river. This is said to have been done in 1854 to prevent the river sinking into the sough and so depriving Over Haddon Mill of its power supply.

LATHKILL DALE VEIN was worked from at least 1765 to 1776 by the London Lead Company who were possibly responsible for driving at least part of the sough. They may also have installed a hydraulic pumping engine situated approximately on the site of the later 52 ft (16 m) diameter water-wheel. The hydraulic engine was invented both in Hungary and independently by William Westgarth and may have been installed about 1765-1770. A plan of 1826 refers to "where the old engine stood" (possibly one of Westgarth's engines) with a surface water course bringing water from higher up the dale, with the old shallow sough taking the water away. The London Lead Company gave up the mines about 1776-7 and little further work was done until 1825 although in 1779 the Hill Carr Sough partners took title to several veins hereabouts. Hill Carr Sough at this time had not reached the mines southeast of Alport and never came anywhere near Lathkill Dale.

In 1825 John Alsop and Thomas Bateman bought part of the Lathkill Dale Vein for £25 and from then up to 1842 it was worked on a fairly large scale. John Alsop was a lead smelter and had shares in several other Derbyshire lead mines. In 1830 a lease was obtained from Lord Melbourne to take water from the river to turn a water-wheel. The large wheel was not erected until 1836 but at least one other operated at the mine. The large one was 52 ft (16 m) in diameter and 9 ft (2.7 m) wide and was said to be "the largest but one in the Kingdom". It was a colossal piece of machinery working six sets of pumps, 18 inches (45 cm) in diameter, and said to be capable of raising 4000 gallons of water per minute from a depth of 120 ft (36 m). Richard Page, an engineer with the Alport Mining Company, was paid £30 "for his attendance and planning from the commencement", suggesting that he was brought in to advise whilst the wheel was being erected. By 1832 John Sheldon was the agent but on his death in 1836 James Bateman took over until the mine closed in 1842. The wheel was offered for sale along with other equipment in 1847 but its fate is not known. The present quiet woodland contrasts sharply with bustle of the industrial operations of the 19th century.

Adjacent to the path opposite Bateman's House a small ruined building was the POWDER HOUSE. Flood water sometimes resurges from a back-filled shaft close by. Shaft hollows now become evident, at first at on the north and later between the path and the river. They mark the course of the Lathkill Dale Vein up to the site of the giant water-wheel some 280 metres to the west, where little can be seen except a water-filled hollow and the remains of the breast wall. The pillar of a small aqueduct can be seen across the river with its counterpart on the north bank. The south bank also has an adit entrance to SIDEWAY MINE in a vein branching southwest from the Lathkill Dale Vein.

During the winter months when the vegetation is low, the leat which conveyed water to the wheels can be made out above the southern river bank.

After about 300 metres further west a steep scramble for some 10 metres up the right-hand hillside leads to two trial levels for dark limestones once tried for use as black marble.

About 600 yards beyond the wheel pit, a well-defined vein can be seen ranging northwest out of Lathkill Dale Vein and obliquely up the northern hillside. This is GANK HOLE VEIN (186 658), the site of Gank Hole Ochre Mine, worked in the 1880s for both lead and iron ore. It was planned to drive a long level along Gank Hole into Mycross Vein and so to Greensward Mine, but the project did not live up to early promise and was abandoned. It was intended as both drawing level and sough as both Greensward Mine and others on these veins were said to be very rich.

About 100 metres east of the Gank

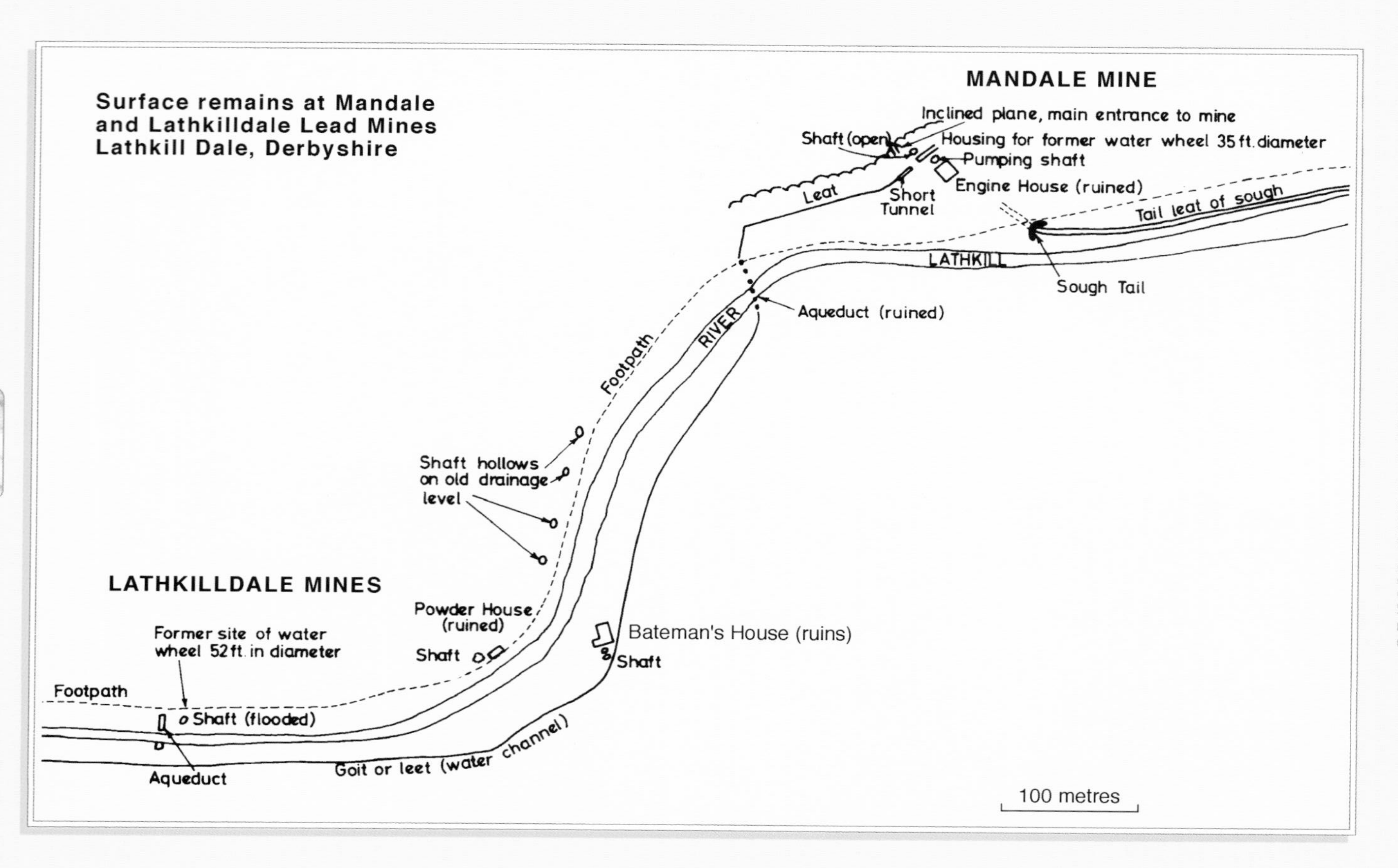
Surface remains at Mandale
and Lathkilldale Lead Mines
Lathkill Dale, Derbyshire
MANDALE MINE
Inclined plane, main entrance to mine
Shaft (open)
Housing for former water wheel 35 ft. diameter
Pumping shaft
Engine House (ruined)
Leat
Short Tunnel
Tail leat of sough
LATHKILL
Sough Tail
Aqueduct (ruined)
RIVER
Footpath
Shaft hollows
on old drainage
level
LATHKILLDALE MINES
Powder House
(ruined)
Former site of water
wheel 52 ft. in diameter
Shaft
Bateman's House (ruins)
Shaft
Footpath
Shaft (flooded)
Aqueduct
Goit or leet (water channel)
100 metres

The Bob-wall of the Mandale Engine House

Hole vein intersection was the site of Lathkill Dale Sough forefield shaft as it stood in 1782. No evidence has been found to suggest that the sough was ever extended beyond this point, though it is possible that a branch level was driven into Sideway Vein by the London Lead Company. A branch level referred to as Mandale and Lathkill Company's Deep Level was also driven towards Mandale Vein but no distances are known.

The path emerges from the woods at the site of CARTER'S MILL (184 657), a demolished corn mill. In the angle of the two paths there is another trial level though it is uncertain whether it was for black marble or for chert.

From Carter's Mill the excursion may be continued by either of two routes. For a short return turn right up the steep side valley to reach the road by Haddon Fields Farm and turn right back to Over Haddon. Close before the junction with the Monyash road, the line of hillocks and disturbed ground marks the course of Mandale Rake (190 664) up towards Haddon Grove Farm on the left. Parts of the vein have been worked opencast for fluorspar in recent years and the section down towards the Dale has been largely removed.

For a longer return route continue westwards along the footpath up the Dale past banks of tufa once worked for rockery stone at the PUDDING SPRINGS waterfall (181 657). The extensive scree slopes nearby have partly covered the tail of SMALLPENNY SOUGH. Beyond the footbridge into Cales Dale, the path reaches HOLMES GROVE (173 656) where large springs rise from mine workings about which little is known. Further on is the gaping entrance to LATHKILL HEAD CAVE (171 659) with some 2 km of passages, liable to flooding in unsettled weather and recommended only for experienced cavers. In very wet weather the river sometimes flows out of the cave.

To complete the excursion, return to the Cales Dale junction and take the steep path up the northern hillside to the farm turning right along the road back to Over Haddon.

**Above: The entrance to Gank Hole Mine c. 1884**

**Opposite page: Miners outside Gank Hole Mine c. 1884**

# 7 HILLOCKS AND KNOTLOW MINES, MONYASH

By J. A. Robey and T. D. Ford

Map: 1:10000 SK 16 NW

*Hand picked shaft in Hillocks Mine*

These two old lead mines northwest of Monyash have extensive workings which can be visited by properly equipped explorers. Although access is limited to those having suitable ropes and wire ladders, a description is included here to give an impression of the underground features typical of many smaller mines. The two mines also have a fascinating history dating from the earliest record in 1670 to the late 19th century when the Derbyshire lead industry collapsed.

The two mines worked the same two parallel veins trending northwest to southeast. Hillocks Mine and the entrance series of Knotlow Mine were worked in the WHALF PIPE, whilst the further reaches of Knotlow Mine worked CRIMBO PIPE. Early mine documents suggest that Hillocks Mine was also worked in Crimbo Pipe but no route into such workings is known today. Whalf Pipe is in fact a complex series of scrins and small pipes branching from them. Crimbo Vein in Knotlow Mine is a typical rake, but it may have developed into a pipe in the currently inaccessible workings. The long lower levels were driven as soughs, Whalf Old Sough was driven before 1740 probably from Crimbo Swallow, Whalf Sough was driven between 1748 and 1755, whilst Crimbo Sough was driven between 1764 and 1769. An underground water-wheel, installed in 1765, lifted water from 60 ft (18m) beneath the sough. The long Chapeldale Level (not to be confused with Chapeldale Sough near Flagg) dates from 1765-1771. It was connected to Crimbo Swallow by a short section of Whalf Sough and was driven along Crimbo Pipe for nearly 1750 ft (525 m) between 1825 and 1844. None was really successful as the costs of driving were in excess of the ore obtained.

Both mines are easily accessible from a parking area adjacent to a barn at the junction of two "green roads" some 600 yards (1 km) northwest of Monyash (143 673). Hillocks Mine

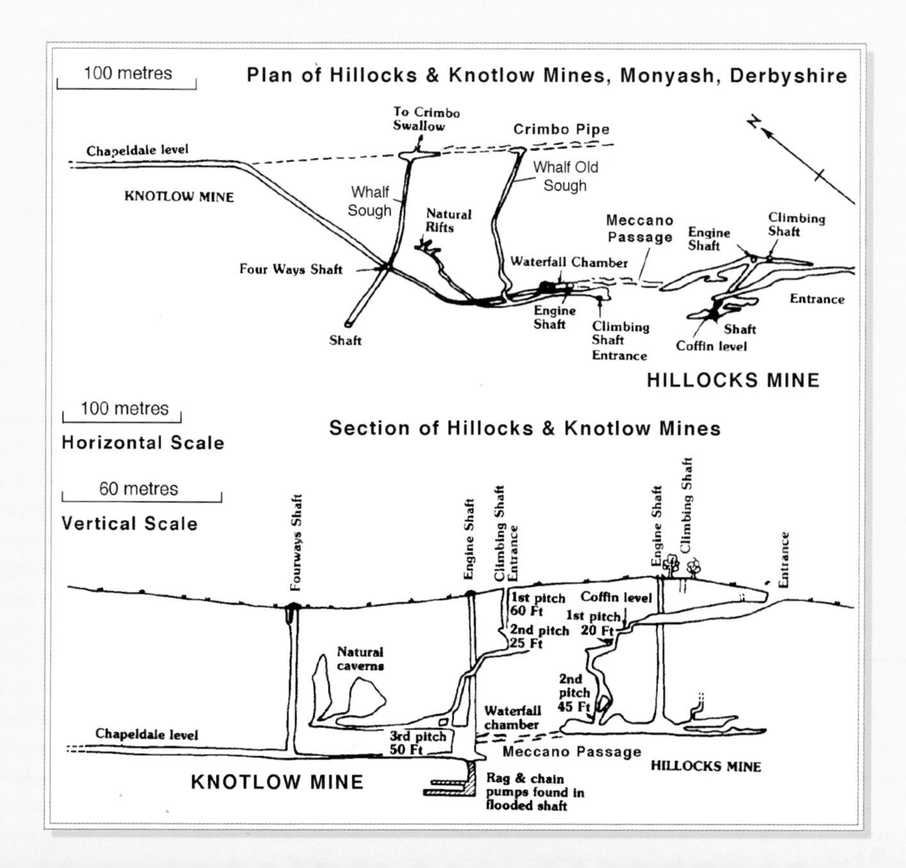

entrance is in the field immediately to the southeast of the junction (143 672) whilst Knotlow Mine climbing shaft is in the second field NNE of the junction (144 674).

**HILLOCKS MINE:** climb the stile and the entrance is in the cutting ahead, by crawling through an oil drum with a gate to exclude animals. No key necessary. Inside is a roomy passage for some 90 m with mineral matter clearly visible in the walls. When first entered by the miners this was apparently a cavern full of broken rocks, calcite, baryte and galena in a matrix of clay and sand. Most of this was cleared out and the galena separated on the surface, making much easier work than hacking through solid rock or vein-stuff. Such mining may be much earlier than the first documentary mention in 1670, and probably took place before the days of explosives. There are small climbing shafts in the roof and a few stacks of deads (waste rock) before the passage lowers to a flat-out crawl. This leads to a short climb down (3 m) and a right-angle turn into a short cross-cut level in limestone. Roughly a metre high and 60 cm wide this was picked out by hand with sweeping pick-marks on the walls. It is barrel-shaped in cross-section so it is not really a coffin level. After some 9 m is the first pitch – a vertical hand-picked shaft 7 m deep, requiring a ladder or rope. Below, short scrambles lead to the second pitch where a 15 m ladder is required for a corkscrew shaft with several short drops and steep slopes.

A low arch at the bottom of the Second Pitch leads to a junction of three larger levels of walking height. Left and right do not go far but straight ahead a large 19th century cross-cut level was cut into the floor of an old coffin level still clearly visible in the roof. After a branch on the right leading to the lowest workings in Hillocks Mine, the main level reaches the Main Chamber with an engine shaft coming in through the roof (the shaft was the depository for unwanted army ammunition in 1945 and occasional bullets may still be found in the mud!). The Engine Shaft is 58 m deep but is grilled for safety at the surface. To the right is a level 103 m long with a climbing shaft system in the roof – now blocked by a collapse. Several small scrins and pipes can be seen. To the left of the Engine Shaft is an undulating passage for 85 m following an irregular pipe via Pool Chamber. About halfway along a small hole on the right leads to a low series of muddy crawls eventually emerging in Meccano Passage in Knotlow Mine. Hillocks Mine is effectively in two parallel veins about 20-30 m apart; together they make up Whalf Pipe.

**KNOTLOW MINE:** the usual entrance is the original climbing shaft in the second field NNE of the green road junction (144 674). The shaft is fitted with a lid requiring a large adjustable spanner key to open it. Other entrances are the nearby Chapel Dale Engine Shaft (64 m deep) and the Crimbo (Fourways) Engine Shaft (53 m deep), both are suitable only for those with appropriate expertise.

> *N.B. Inflows of sewage occasionally cause build-ups of carbon dioxide in the lower levels. If there is any suspicion of such bad air, leave the mine immediately.*

The climbing shaft (First Pitch) is 15 m deep passing through ginging built on the principles of a dry stone wall to retain loose ground, and then into solid rock. It is followed quickly by the Second Pitch of 8 m into Pearl Chamber. Here the vein is visible though obscured by stalactitic deposits. The route slowly descends through natural caves along the bedding with stacked deads filling much of the space. A hole on the right opens into Chapel Dale Shaft, but ahead a scramble down reaches the lip of the Third Pitch of 9 m into the large stope of Waterfall Chamber (liable to be rather wet). At the far end of this chamber fixed ladders lead up to Meccano Passage and the tight, muddy link to Hillocks Mine, 107 m away. A flooded shaft in the floor of Waterfall Chamber was pumped out some years ago to reveal workings 12 m below. Two rag-and-chain pumps were recovered. These devices used wads of rags at intervals along a chain to lift water up hollowed-out tree trunk pipes.

By-passing the Third Pitch, the passage ahead leads into a series of natural caverns and on the right is the Whalf Old Sough, a coffin-level 380 m long which leads to Crimbo Vein. A difficult descent down the vein to the left, following a stream of water, eventually reaches Rift Chamber. N.B. In wet weather this link is usually impassable.

From the bottom of Waterfall Chamber a coffin level 150 m long, is part of Whalf Sough, with moderate to deep water, leads to Crimbo Hollow (Fourways) Engine Shaft, where there is occasionally bad air. To the left a level leads to another deep engine shaft in Whalf Pipe. Ahead a large level was driven from 1827 to 1844 towards Flagg in order to drain the Chapel Dale Mines though it was never finished. It leads to a dead end after 700 m when there was another 1.5 km still to go. With a triangular cross-section it followed a narrow scrin, which the miners hoped would "belly out" into a rich vein. Over £6000 was spent with very little return.

From Crimbo (Fourways) Shaft, to the right another coffin level is the initial portion of Whalf Sough, was driven between 1748 and 1758; it leads after some 90 m to Rift Chamber in Crimbo Vein, where a water-wheel was installed in 1765 to lift water from workings 19 m below, now completely submerged. Crimbo Vein is up to a metre wide and there are deads stacked on timbers overhead, now cemented into position by stalactite deposits. Crimbo Inlet comes in at the right from a difficult scramble up the vein to the East Level, noted above. The scramble is against the flow of a substantial stream which is liable to back up above the explorer and so the route is not recommended except in dry weather.

From Rift Chamber the combined waters flow into Crimbo Swallow. This is a natural passage partly enlarged by the miners, but after some 40 m of scrambling through several small chambers it reaches a final sump. The water reappears in LATHKILL HEAD CAVE nearly 3 km away to the east and the passage between still remains to be explored.

On returning to the surface it is worth reflecting on the great battle the miners had with the water pouring down to the Crimbo Swallow. It wet weather the lower levels of Knotlow Mine become inaccessible as the Swallow cannot take all the inflow. In flood conditions it has been known for the water level to rise by as much as 12 m almost to the lip of the Third Pitch into Waterfall Chamber.

# 8 THE ALPORT MINES

The water pressure engine of 1819 in situ in Wills Founder Mine


BY L. WILLIES

(Based on an earlier account by A. E. Marsh)


Walking Distance – about 3-4 miles (4.5-6 km.), but car and walking can be combined.

**OS 1:25 000 Outdoor Leisure Map No. 24: The Peak District: White Peak Area.**

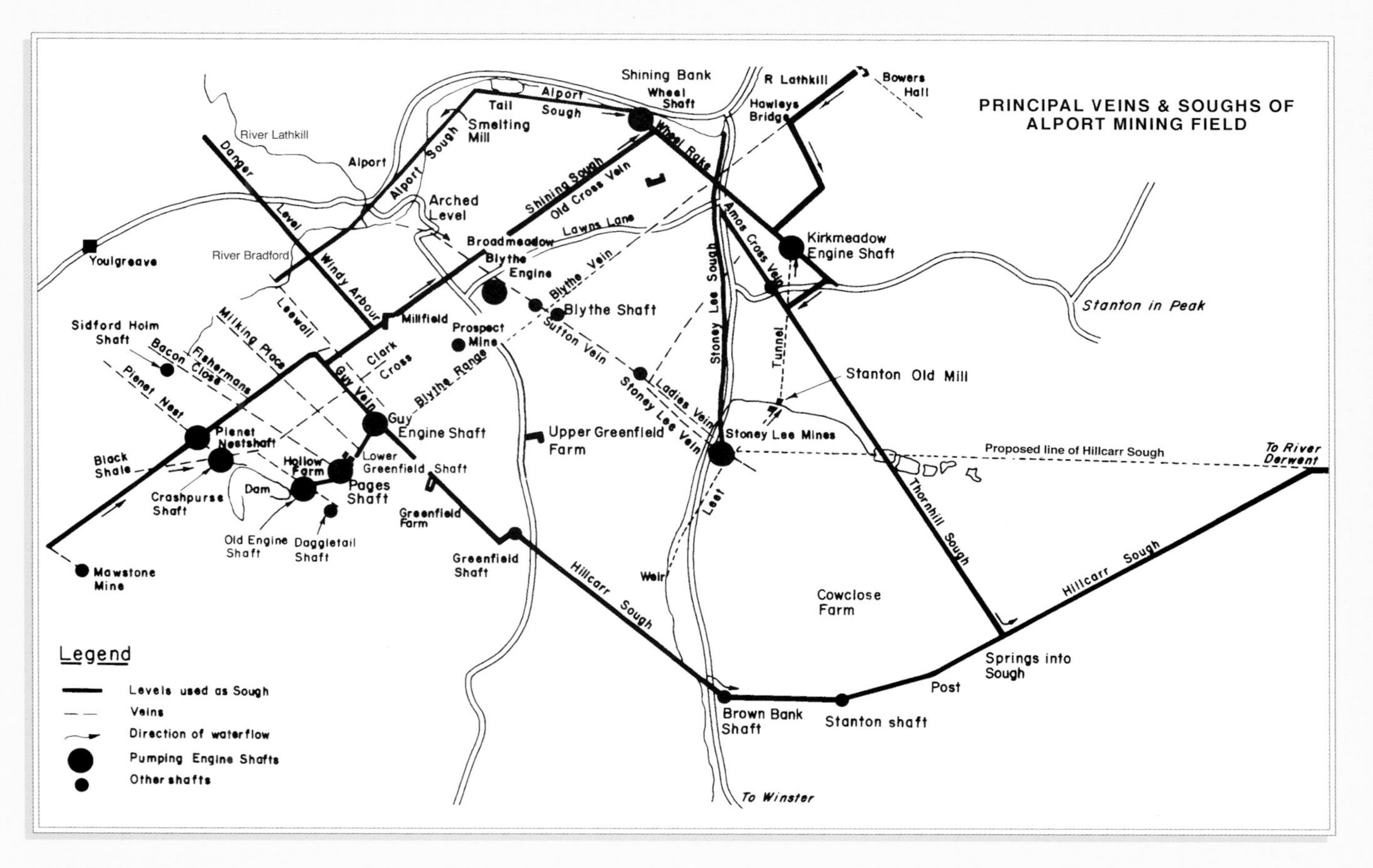
PRINCIPAL VEINS & SOUGHS OF
ALPORT MINING FIELD
Shining Bank
Wheel Shaft
R Lathkill
Bowers Hall
Hawleys Bridge
Tail
Alport Sough
Smelting Mill
River Lathkill
Alport
Danger Level
Alport Sough
Arched Level
Shining Sough
Old Cross Vein
Wheel Rake
Amos Cross Vein
Kirkmeadow Engine Shaft
Stanton in Peak
Youlgreave
River Bradford
Broadmeadow
Lawns Lane
Blythe Engine
Blythe Vein
Blythe Shaft
Windy Arbour
Millfield
Stoney Lee Sough
Tunnel
Sidford Holm Shaft
Milking Place
Leewall
Prospect Mine
Sutton Vein
Bacon Close
Fishermans
Clark Cross
Blythe Range
Stanton Old Mill
Pienet Nest
Guy Vein
Ladies Vein
Stoney Lee Vein
Stoney Lee Mines
Pienet Nestshaft
Guy Engine Shaft
Upper Greenfield Farm
Proposed line of Hillcarr Sough
To River Derwent
Black Shale
Hollow Farm
Lower Greenfield Shaft
Crashpurse Shaft
Dam
Pages Shaft
Greenfield Farm
Leat
Thornhill Sough
Old Engine Shaft
Daggletail Shaft
Greenfield Shaft
Weir
Hillcarr Sough
Mawstone Mine
Cowclose Farm
Hillcarr Sough
Springs into Sough
Post
Brown Bank Shaft
Stanton shaft
To Winster
Legend
Levels used as Sough
Veins
Direction of waterflow
Pumping Engine Shafts
Other shafts

**Alport-by-Youlgreave is a small hamlet about two miles south of Bakewell on the road from the A6 to Youlgreave, at the confluence of the Bradford and Lathkill rivers. The antiquity of mining in the area is attested by the name Youlgreave, *Auld Grove* or "Old Mine", but its mining fame dates mainly from the 18th and 19th centuries with the driving of many small and one great sough; the use of water from two rivers and a stream off Stanton Moor were used to power underground water-pressure engines for pumping. These were introduced by the Cornish mining engineer Richard Trevithick in 1803 (who rather casually also invented the first locomotive at about the same time). Larger engines were used in the 1830s/40s far surpassing those in use anywhere else.**

## EARLY HISTORY

The 17th century history of the area was sometimes tumultuous, with repeated mass invasions of miners between 1641 and 1657 anxious to protect their mining rights against the Earl of Rutland This resulted in mounted and armed attacks on the miners in Haddonfields (near Haddon Hall) by military forces and mounted gentry and yeomen. Further "battles of Haddon Fields" took place in 1657 and 1658 when men using the authority of the Mines Royal tried to seize the mines on the pretext that the (very small) content of silver made them Royal. The Duke was not amused and his men saw the intruders put to flight. Despite the recording of mining customs in 1647, the usual freedoms of the miners were severely restricted and as a result the Alport mining field was drained and exploited by large mining concerns and finally as a single unit in the 18th and 19th centuries.

Before 1700 the heavily watered Haddon – Alport – Youlgreave mining field had witnessed the driving of at least sixteen soughs, of which two were of considerable extent. In addition water-powered, or horse-powered, engines had been installed at eight sites. Most notably this was at Wheels Rake, Haddon, where mining was financed by the Earl of Rutland and less successfully at Youlgreave where attempts at drainage by 'wheeles and trickes' in 1679 – 1680 resulted in failure.

After 1700 slightly more ambitious drainage projects were started at Harthill Sough, Blythe Sough, Stoneylee Sough, Shining Sough and Black Sough. These were moderately effective until the mid 18th century when a 'fire-engine' was installed at Stoney Lee Mine. The general lack of success must have contributed to the decision to drive Hillcarr, the longest of the Peak Districts soughs, between 1766 and 1787 with later extensions.

### HILLCARR SOUGH

The two and a half mile long Hillcarr Sough followed the practices established by John Gilbert at the Duke of Bridgewater's Worsley coal mines in Lancashire. He became a shareholder with the Barker family, Peter Nightingale and other local people including members of the Duke of Rutland's entourage. The portal is on the east side of Stanton Moor and a considerable outflow drains into the River Derwent. The tunnel size is much greater than usual, allowing boats to be used to convey spoil out and to provide space for ventilation pipes using boy-powered fans to let it pass for a mile without shafts under the Moor. Events included the first strike known in Derbyshire, by Stanton Lees men over Sunday working, with defeat and sacking of the miners. Deaths and severe burning took place amongst the new workers from a firedamp explosion soon after. Once on the west side of Stanton Moor in 1778-79 a shaft was sunk, 2994 yards in and a second, at Brown Bank in 1780 (3358 yards) in which a water-blast ventilation system was installed. Effective relief came with completion to Greenfields Shaft (4218 yards) in 1783 and Guy Vein, the main objective, two and a half miles from the portal, was reached in 1787, after 21 years of mining and about £20,000 expenditure. Its arrival was celebrated with much rejoicing and a roast ox and two sheep, much ale and over 400 guests. Though the sough never repaid its shareholders' capital, the mines, with only slightly different owners, were successful over the next few decades.

## WATER PRESSURE ENGINES

By 1800 most of the field above sough level was nearly worked out, and the next phase of drainage using hydraulic engines began. The first of Trevithick's engines was installed on Crashpurse Shaft in1805 (later moved to Old Engine Shaft) and by 1819 three engines were at work, needing a complex of surface and underground pipes and channels and the large dam near Hollow Farm, with all the water draining to the Hillcarr Sough. A generation of larger engines began installation with the replacement of the 1819 engine (nowadays to be seen at Peak District Mining Museum at Matlock Bath) with the Broadmeadow engine of 1836. John Taylor (see also the Magpie and Sheldon section of this book) took over in 1840 when the three major mines of the area, long worked in conjunction, were consolidated. Under Taylor the huge Guy Engine was installed in 1841; another was placed in Pienet Shaft in 1845 and yet another at Kirkmeadow Shaft at Stanton in 1848. The 2000-6000 gallons a minute pumped was the largest amount to that time. But still the water was too powerful for complete success and the mines had to be abandoned in 1851 with the mine equipment sold the following year. Losses were tremendous, though some mining and small profits were made in succeeding years from above-sough working.

## LEAD SMELTING

About 1840 it was also decided by the Barker family, part owners of the mines and lead smelters, to open a cupola at Alport, at a site alongside the river. This had a much longer life than the mine, only closing about 1876. It developed extensive slag smelting as well as for ore and to cope with fumes, established a long and complex flue system, much of which still exists in semi-ruined form.

**Above: Hill Carr Sough**

**Opposite Page: Wills Founder Engine, Peak District Mining Museum, Matlock Bath**

## THE END OF MINING

From 1878, the formation of the Mawstone Mine led to extension of the Hillcarr Sough to that mine along Clay Vein, south west of Alport, with working under various owners, including small steam engines, up until the 1932 disaster when five miners and three rescuers were killed there in a firedamp explosion. Another venture, the extension of Danger Level northwards, at one time destined for Magpie Mine (where it would in fact have come in *above* their sough) into Youlgreave was less deadly but no more successful.

## A TOUR OF PRESENT DAY REMAINS

*The tour can be walked throughout, or by a combination of car use and walking.*

**Use of the White Peak 1:25000 map is recommended. A useful place to start is Picory Corner (239688), the junction of the road to Winster and Youlgreave from the A6). Haddon Hall, near the corner was once the seat of the Dukes of Rutland. Before trees overwhelmed views, it looked out southwards over Haddonfields which extend over the hill to Alport: thus the intrusion of rioting miners must have been especially galling. Low relief remains of mining can be seen in the fields from the road. At Picory Corner the powerful Ladies Rake passes under the valley and the limit of mining is marked by a stone in the field next to the roads and river (240657).**

At Hawley's Bridge (232 649) the road divides, the left branch going towards Winster. Up the sides of the valley can be seen remains of Grimes and Stoneylee Soughs, with low mounds of shafts at frequent intervals (231 646). Kirkmeadow Shaft in which the last water pressure engine was placed can be seen across the field from the side road leading to Stanton (234 644). Shallow tunnels delivered water to Kirkmeadow from Stanton Mill (233 639), which is a little higher up the Winster Road. Water to (and earlier for) the mill came off Stanton Moor and from a long leat which crosses the road near the gatehouse or lodge (230 634) – it can be seen leaving the Ivy Bar Brook a little further upstream on the west side. Hillcarr Sough passes under the road about a hundred yards north of the junction at Eagle Tor to Birchover, far below the surface. Brown Bank Shaft is partly beneath the road and partly under the bankside (232 628). A section of wall on the east side marks the position, in which a small hole sometimes exudes air. Opposite to Brown Bank Shaft, over the wall and a little upstream, the fine stonework for the embankment and lined spillway, with a small dam behind, form a part of the installation made for the ventilation water-blast in Brown Bank Shaft.

The right hand road, towards Alport and Youlgreave, follows the Lathkill/Bradford river. On the far bank of the river from the road, low mounds reveal the site of Wheels Rake (228 648), where there was a water pumping wheel of some size (private land and dangerous drops – keep out) and a little distance away Shining Sough commences. Just below the village of Alport, a hump-back bridge crosses the river (private land) and in winter the remains of the smelting works can just be seen in the trees (223 648). Alport Sough started just below the works.

Alport village (222 646) is on the ancient Portway, an early medieval name for a road which probably goes back to Bronze Age times and which served as a main artery between the Roman fort of Anavio (Brough) in the north and the settlement of Lutudarum in the south of the mining field. Today it is a lovely place of expensive houses, some converted from miners' cottages, a corn mill and the road bridge. In the 1840s it was straddled with a giant pipe or box on trestles carrying water from the River Bradford into a tunnel on the far bank leading to Guy Shaft for the engine there. The change from industrial to rural scenery, when the proximity of the smelting works is remembered, challenges the imagination.

At Youlgreave (212 644), the church reminds us of the wealth mining generated – the church also drew its revenues from the important nearby mining settlements of Elton and Winster. If the hill is followed southwards down below the church, it leads to the River Bradford and it is possible to walk past the remains of Pienet and Crashpurse Shafts (216 638), and the Hollow dam which maintained the water supply as far as Hollow Farm (219 637). Here the remains of a wall of the Old Engine Shaft can just be discerned, whilst the farm itself was the home of Richard Page, one of Trevithick's engineers who took care of the hydraulic engines. Reputedly the Old Engine here had a balance bob at surface worked by a rod down the shaft to the engine, which screeched at every stroke – silence must have been disturbing for Page if no-one else.

Mawstone Mine (212 634), again on private land, can be seen about half a mile away to the south west, alongside Mawstone Lane which leads to Elton. Only the buildings remain, though the mine is again producing, though only water for the local water supply.

Earlier editions of this book included several other sites, including a stone post at the turn of the sough at Greenfield Shaft, remains of the shaft and a modern but primitive fluorspar washing plant in Guy Plantation, but the only site now worth visiting around here is the huge Page's or Great Shaft near Lower Greenfields (220 638). This is now safely gridded over: here was installed the smallest of the engines, about 1809. Finally, one other site is the Broadmeadow Counting House and Smithy (224 644), now converted to cottages. A stone post here marks the sough junction. The Broadmeadow shaft with its engines was to the left of the cottages (as seen from the road). It is still possible, though very dangerous, to get to the engine position via a climbing shaft behind the cottages, though the engine shaft was filled-in early in the 20th century – two men, with shovels and a wheelbarrow took six months for the task.

# 9 THE LEAD MINING VILLAGE OF WINSTER

*The Market Hall in Winster. The original Moot Hall at Wirksworth looked like this*

## By L. Willies

Walking Distance – about 2 miles (3 km.) – five miles (8 km.) with diversion routes.

OS 1:25 000 Outdoor Leisure Map No. 24: The Peak District: White Peak Area.

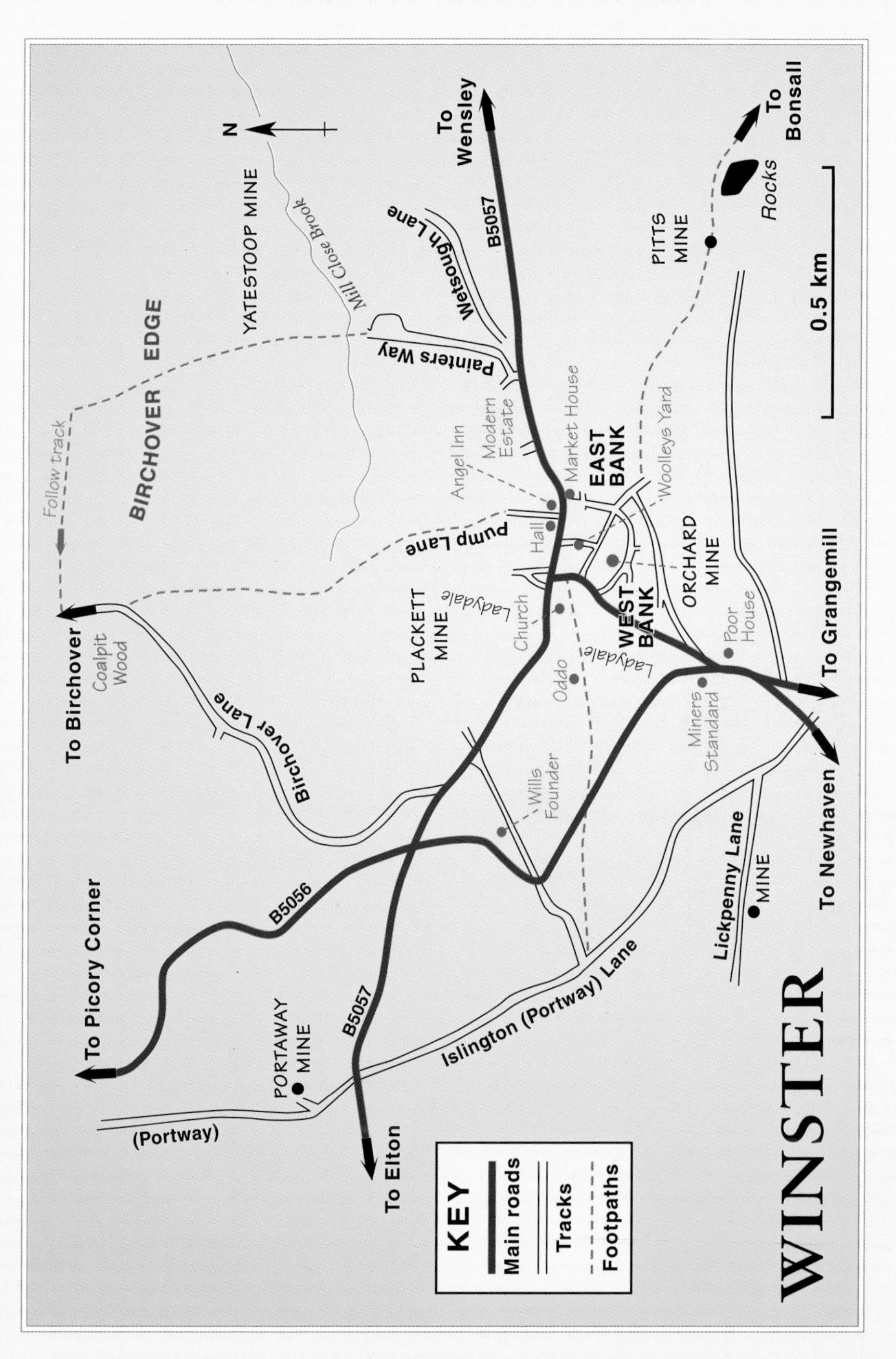
WINSTER
KEY
Main roads
Tracks
Footpaths
N
To Wensley
To Bonsall
Rocks
PITTS MINE
0.5 km
To Grangemill
To Newhaven
To Birchover
To Picory Corner
To Elton
B5057
B5056
YATESTOOP MINE
Mill Close Brook
Wetsough Lane
Painters Way
BIRCHOVER EDGE
Follow track
Modern Estate
Angel Inn
Market House
EAST BANK
Woolleys Yard
Pump Lane
Hall
ORCHARD MINE
PLACKETT MINE
Ladydale
Church
WEST BANK
Poor House
Oddo
Miners Standard
Coalpit Wood
Birchover Lane
Wills Founder
Lickpenny Lane
MINE
PORTAWAY MINE
Islington (Portway) Lane
(Portway)

**Of all the lead mining villages, Winster (241 606) is probably the best preserved. In the late 17th century it had some 375 inhabitants but by 1750 this had grown to around 2000 – with some 24 inns and alehouses supplying the needs of the miners and tradespeople who served them. Nowadays the village, at about 900 ft (270 metres) altitude, seems remote, but in times past it was adjacent to the crossroads on the north-south (pre-Roman) road, known as the Portway, and the Saltersway crossing over the Pennines from Cheshire to the bridges at Cromford, Matlock and Darley Dale. In the late 18th century the new turnpike from Nottingham to Newhaven came through the village, which for a time was, perhaps, the third largest settlement in the County.**

*N.B. Parking can be a problem in season. Sometimes you can park on the Main Street, but better to go to the top of the village and park opposite the Miners' Standard inn from where the following tour commences.*

The Miners Standard dates from the early 17th century when the mines nearby were active. It was adjacent to a now nearly disappeared hamlet called Islington, at the crossroads and bordering the former commons. Its name may reflect the measuring dish kept for lead ore, but, perhaps more likely, it refers to Charles I's Standard or flag raised at Nottingham by the miners, who, promised relief from tithes on their lead ore, flocked to his aid. The green lane a couple of fields to the west, and slightly uphill is the old Portway. At the intersection of the roads is a former orehouse with chutes at the rear, used to store ore bought from small mines, whilst almost opposite you can see the remains of two large meers, once important for local water supply. The fine building with arched windows opposite the inn was the Poorhouse until 1841, It is also near an old ropewalk, one of the necessary trades for a mining community. The Duke of Devonshire's Barmaster, Thomas Roberts, during the 1760s, lived in one of the houses downhill by the main road, opposite the deep valley which is the top of Ladydale.

Follow the lesser road alongside Ladydale then down Westbank into the village. On the north side is the converted stables of Oddo, the house lower down and west of the Church and the home of a succession of lawyers who thrived on mining litigation. One of these was the wily William Brittlebank who was involved at Magpie Mine before and in the period of the "murders" – his son had previously been involved in a scandalous murder in Winster, in the garden of the house next to the stables and bordering the churchyard. The son disappeared, and supposedly never returned.

Go down to the Main Street. Here there is a fine vista of the houses of the once more-important occupiers – tradesmen like whitesmiths and blacksmiths, mine agents, shopkeepers, more lawyers, the list includes a remittance man and minor gentry.

Return uphill a few yards and take the small path or gennel between the houses to get into the middle of the village. This climbs over the hump of the Orchard Mine waste hillock and soon reaches an open grassy area – another shaft hillock of the same mine.

The row of houses below you is Woolley's Yard – typical homes of the miners and small businesses such as a candlemaker – which was not a pleasant trade to have next door. Woolley was a man with many varied interests who went bankrupt in the 1840s. His successors were the Heathcotes whose yard-name has unfortunately been lost by the recent thoughtless renaming as "The Courtyard", just off the Main Street. Regain the Main Street at the bottom of Woolley's Yard.

Almost opposite is the Hall, rebuilt in Palladian style for the younger Francis Moore on the occasion of his marriage, about 1710. The Moores were then the major family of Winster, lawyers, of course, and Francis Moore senior had been also overseer of Winster Sough or Lousey Level. The younger Moore died without issue, and his nephews seem to have dissipated most of the money by the 1760s.

At the centre of the village is the Market House, built in the early 18th century as the mining boom developed. Within fifty yards (metres) or so, were the Angel (on the north side of the street opposite – where the Barmoot Court used to meet), the Bull, the Wheatsheaf, The Crown, The Derbyshire Sally and, still open, The Bowling Green. Miners were paid every six or seven weeks when the Barmaster had measured and the ore was sold. "It were so thronged you could walk on th' heads" was a contemporary description of market day which undoubtedly would have followed a pay.

Go down the Main Street (eastwards). At the last house in the row on the south side, it can be seen, from the side, that the fine front has, in fact, been put on a much older house. The thin gritstone "tiles" are held on with iron cramps. Several other houses can be seen with similar add-ons, again a reflection of the rich years after 1700 and before about 1780.

Where were the mines? The greatest was Yatestoop. Its site can be seen from the rough track, heading north, at the east end of the village, known as Painters Way (just past the modern housing estate). The mine extended from the bottom of the valley to beyond the top of the far hill, as indicated by trees today. Painters Way Farm was probably the count house and it was also the site of a dam, used for water power before deep soughs cut off most of the flow. Yatestoop Mine had the first steam engine used in Derbyshire, by 1719, soon after their invention by Thomas Newcomen, and perhaps three by 1730. The long Yatestoop Sough was driven under Birchover Edge between 1751 and 1766. Two other engines had been installed by 1780, including one underground at Birchover Edge. Two other great mines, Placket and Portaway, were at the west end of the village, towards Elton. Like Yatestoop, these were worked on a great scale, underneath the shales where water had defeated earlier generations of miners. It is possible to divert to follow a footpath north from Painters Way to Birchover over the former Yatestoop workings, passing the shaft over Yatestoop Sough in the field beyond Birchover Edge. Return is possible by using the track, to

Birchover Uppertown, down Birchover Lane, then over the fields near Coalpit Wood (site of a shaft on Yatestoop Sough), to Pump Lane, opposite the Market House. Both are former miners' paths with some gritstone pavers remaining (walking conditions can be poor in winter).

The Market Hall contains a small display of Winster history – try the local shop if closed. Go uphill on the East Bank. This was also largely inhabited by working miners – many of whom also had a small farm (sometimes just one of the multitude of small barns seen in the local fields) to keep a beast for milk and a couple of pigs. Note the Methodist chapel, favoured by many miners over the church.

Take the left or east fork and at the bend follow the footpath sign for Bonsall in a narrow gap between the houses. This goes out over the fields. (In inclement weather you may prefer just to follow the road round and uphill, which leads back to the Miners Standard). From the fields there is a fine view back over the village. About a third of a mile out, beyond a couple of stiles, and just before the prominent rocks are reached, can be seen the waste heaps of Winster Pitts Mine, a Scheduled Ancient Monument. Careful observation will reveal a system of trenches and troughs lined with stone. These are the remains of substantial buddling or washing operations for lead ore during the 1850s onwards, possible since the Spanish slag hearth could cope with very low grade feed. The unusual flat-topped spoil heaps had slimes dams on top of them to settle mud and clarify the water. The range of Yatestoop Mine can be seen across the valley and, on a clear day further down-valley, the ruined engine-house of the old Millclose Mine and the modern chimneys of the Enthoven's lead smelter are visible.

From here you can walk back to the Miners Standard via the track at the top of the field, or return via the village. A further diversion can be made down the former Portway, now called Islington Lane, past Lickpenny Lane (Lick-or-Luckpenny Mine) to the former site of Portaway Mine, perhaps returning via the roads or footpaths past Wills Founder Mine. The 1819 hydraulic engine, previously installed on the Alport Mines, was found deep underground at Wills Founder and was recovered by PDMHS in 1976 for exhibition at the Peak District Mining Museum at Matlock Bath.

***Descending a shaft on Coast Rake, Elton***

# 10 THE WENSLEY-DARLEY AREA AND MILL CLOSE MINE

The ruined Watts Shaft engine house

BY N. GREGORY
AND T. D. FORD

Maps: 1:25000 SK 26: 1:10000 SK 26 SE

To the north of the two contiguous villages of Wensley and Darley Bridge lie the very extensive mine workings of the old and new MILL CLOSE MINES. Partly beneath the valleys of Mill Close Brook and the River Derwent, these mines have had a long history dating back at least into the 17th century. The recently re-discovered workings of Old Mill Close Mine were among the first to be driven in the limestones under the shale cover and the accessible workings alone total some 15 kilometres in length. The later "new" Mill Close Mine was extended northwards from the earlier mine under the shales in 1859 and continued working until 1939. About 500,000 tons of lead ore and 120,000 tons of zinc concentrates came from Mill Close Mine and the waste heaps yielded about a quarter of a million tons of fluorspar and some baryte during re-processing in the 1970s. The latter mine is now totally flooded.

OLD MILL CLOSE MINE lies to the northwest of Wensley, with shafts in the fields west of the Red Lion. The maze of workings extends northwards beneath Cambridge Wood where there are further shafts. The miners extracted ore from a complex of scrins and pipes of which there is no surface expression. Starting in Wensley Dale the miners followed the ore bodies down the dip of the strata northwards, steadily getting deeper beneath the shales. The workings became troubled with water and to remedy the situation no fewer than five soughs were driven into the hill between 1658 and 1678. Soon after 1700 a long drainage level was begun from near Darley Bridge and which reached the veins about 1711-1712. It was then continued westwards and after the London Lead Company bought the mine in 1743 it was extended for thousands of feet to mines lying between Wensley and Winster.

The London Lead Company worked the vein north of Millclose Brook, firstly with the aid of two water wheels sited underground in the mine and in 1748 a Newcomen FireEngine was installed. After 1778 the London Lead Company gradually sold their interests and little further development took place for 80 years.

In 1859 Edward Wass re-opened the mine and erected a new Cornish type engine at Watts shaft. Made by Thornewill & Wareham of Burton on Trent this had a 50 inches (125cm) diameter cylinder. Watts Shaft was deepened by a further 120 ft (40 m) and the workings were extended northwards to discover the massive ore-body complex of the new MILL CLOSE MINE. Warren Carr Shaft was sunk to 300 ft (90 m) in 1874 and fitted with an even bigger engine, known later as Jumbo; it had a 60 inches (150 cm) diameter cylinder with a 10 ft (3.3 m) stroke. It was followed by Lees Shaft sunk in 1881. Finally deepened to 73 fathoms (438 ft, 130m) in 1901 two further pumping engines, Baby and Alice, were set to work in 1887.

Mill Close Mine's workings followed a main joint northwards for about a mile (1.5 km) with numerous branches northwest and southwest. The workings were entirely beneath the shale cover and, with the aid of internal shafts, the miners cut through seven toadstones interleaved with the limestones. The mine finally reached more than 1000 ft (330 m) depth and the distant workings were approaching Pickory Corner near Haddon Hall. Most of the mine was beneath the River Derwent or its floodplain and the pumps were raising over 5000 gallons per minute. The outflow was disposed of down YATESTOOP SOUGH, whose portal can still be seen in the river bank adjacent to the waste heaps. In spite of investments in a rope-and-bucket system for waste disposal and an early form of flotation cells for separating ore from waste a shortage of proven ore reserves meant that the end was in sight. The costly haulage system and a pump failure finally resulted in the closure in 1940 of what, in its day, had been one of the world's richest lead mines.

During the 75 years of working some 500,000 tons of lead concentrates and 120,000 tons of zinc concentrates were produced. Some was smelted at Wass's own smelter at Lea, near Cromford.

After the closure of Mill Close Mine in 1940, it soon flooded up to sough level and the most extensive and interesting mine in Derbyshire is now totally submerged. The engines and processing plant were dismantled for war-time scrap metal and the remains of the transport systems around Lees and Warren Carr shafts were removed. Some of the buildings were later converted into a scrap lead recovery works which is still operated by H.J.Enthoven & Sons plc., but all that remains of the mine buildings are a coe, an engine house and the base of a chimney. Much of the waste has been re-processed to recover fluorspar.

## ITINERARY

In spite of the long history and vast complexes of workings there is relatively little to see on the surface today. A short walk will take in most of the surface remains. Roughly midway between Wensley and Darley Bridge, directly opposite the lane to Snitterton, a path goes northwards across the fields to Mill Close Brook. About 100 m downstream from the footbridge, on the north bank, is the tail of MILL CLOSE SOUGH (265 618), still discharging a little water. From the footbridge keep on the path northwards to reach the narrow Oldfield Lane, whence there is a view of ENTHOVEN's works, occupying the site of Mill Close Mine. Turning left and continuing uphill on Oldfield Lane it is soon reduced to a track. The left fork is Clough Lane, leading towards Clough Wood and a short way ahead is the ruined WATTS ENGINE HOUSE (258 618). Around it are the remains of extensive waste heaps from Wass's first operations in 1859 to 1874. Across the brook to the left CAMBRIDGE WOOD rises steeply towards Wensley. Within the wood are several capped shafts which were sunk into OLD MILL CLOSE MINE. Both Wass's and the Cambridge Wood waste heaps were largely reworked for fluorspar in the 1970s, so that many relics were destroyed. However, a footpath leads steeply southwards up through the wood. The field at the top has several more capped shafts adjacent to the path which leads back to the road west of the RED LION public house. Turn left (east) along the road back into Wensley and the start of the walk.

The excursion may be extended by driving north from Darley Bridge village, past Enthoven's works. Park at the end of the waste heaps on the right (261 624) and take a rough path alongside the brook to the river bank where the arched tail of YATESTOOP SOUGH is visible (265 626). This major sough was started in 1751 with the objective of unwatering the rich Yatestoop Pipe about a kilometre west of Old Mill Close Mine. Mostly driven through shales it reached its target in 1766 but the mine had already been carried some 50 m below the sough intersection using Newcomen engines. A larger engine was installed in 1782 in an artifical cavern some 500 ft (150 m) below the surface, but it failed to remove enough water to make the enterprise profitable. After 1766 Yatestoop Sough was continued westwards to drain the PORTWAY MINES near Winster and eventually reached COAST RAKE near Elton, more than 4 km from the

tail. Much of the Wensley-Winster area is now drained by this sough and a steady stream discharges from the tail.

In contrast to the limited surface relics, a tour through OLD MILL CLOSE MINE is possible. It involves the descent and re-ascent of shafts 25-30 metres deep by bosun's chair or by abseiling, with several hours of stooping or crawling through the maze of workings. Meets are organized usually at biannual intervals by the Peak District Mines Historical Society, to whom enquiries should be made. A separate underground trip is possible through the first 500 m of Yatestoop Sough, wading in knee-deep water. Again, enquiries should be directed to PDMHS at the Mining Museum, Matlock Bath.

*Opposite page: A pipe working in Old Mill Close Mine*
*Above: One of the drainage levels in the same mine*

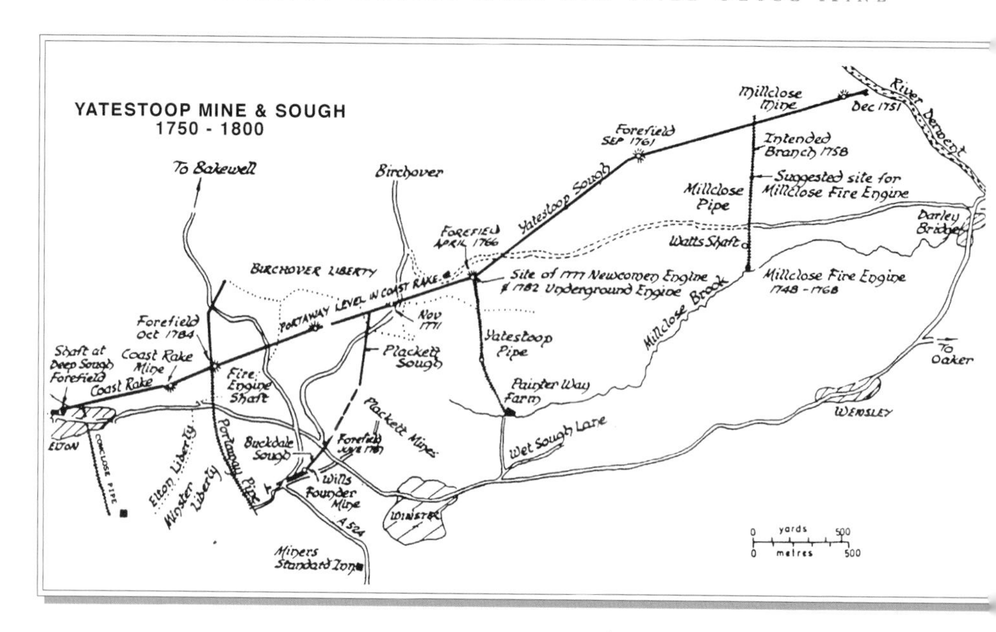
YATESTOOP MINE & SOUGH
1750 - 1800
To Bakewell
Birchover
Millclose Mine
Dec 1751
River Derwent
Forefield SEP 1761
Intended Branch 1758
Suggested site for Millclose Fire Engine
Millclose Pipe
Yatestoop Sough
Darley Bridge
FOREFIELD APRIL 1766
Watts Shaft
BIRCHOVER LIBERTY
Site of 1777 Newcomen Engine & 1782 Underground Engine
Millclose Fire Engine 1748 - 1768
PORTAWAY LEVEL IN COAST RAKE
Nov 1771
Millclose Brook
Forefield Oct 1784
Yatestoop Pipe
To Oaker
Shaft at Deep Sough Forefield
Coast Rake Mine
Coast Rake
Fire Engine Shaft
Placket Sough
Painter Way Farm
WENSLEY
Placket Mines
Wet Sough Lane
ELTON
COWCLOSE PIPE
Elton Liberty
Portaway Pipe
Buckdale Sough
Forefield JUNE 1787
Wills Founder Mine
Winster Liberty
WINSTER
A 524
Miners Standard Inn
yards
metres
0
500

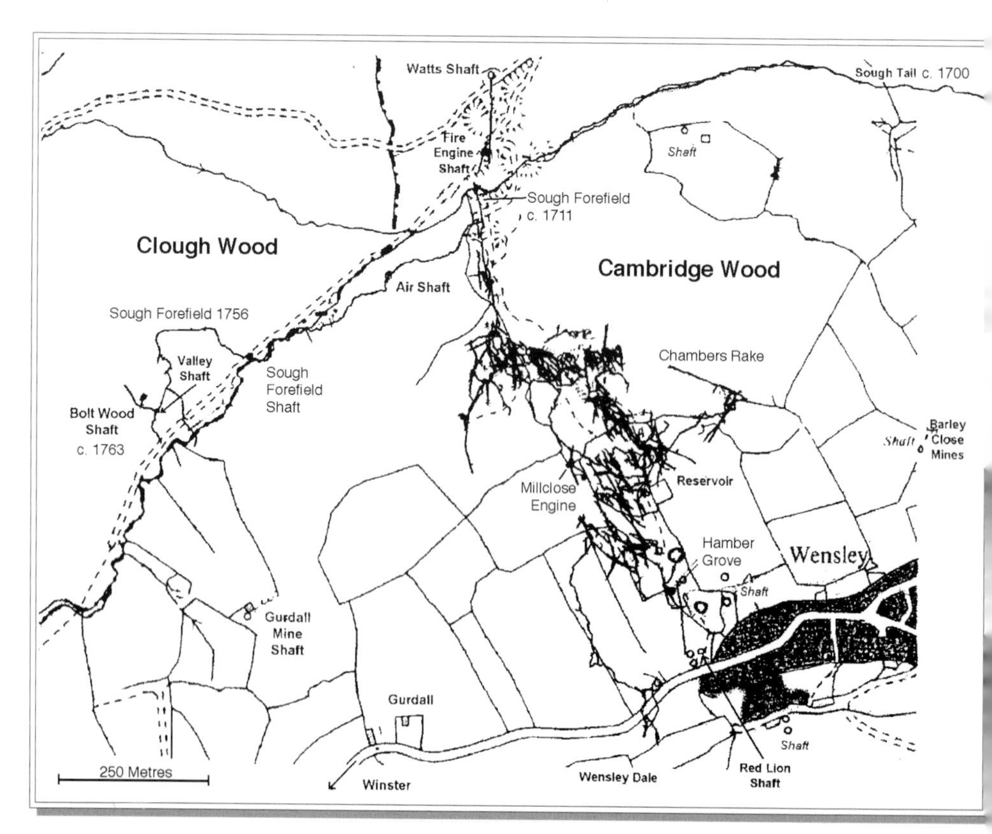
Watts Shaft
Sough Tail c. 1700
Fire Engine Shaft
Shaft
Sough Forefield c. 1711
Clough Wood
Cambridge Wood
Air Shaft
Sough Forefield 1756
Valley Shaft
Sough Forefield Shaft
Chambers Rake
Bolt Wood Shaft c. 1763
Barley Close Mines
Shaft
Reservoir
Millclose Engine
Hamber Grove
Wensley
Shaft
Gurdall Mine Shaft
Gurdall
Shaft
250 Metres
Winster
Wensley Dale
Red Lion Shaft

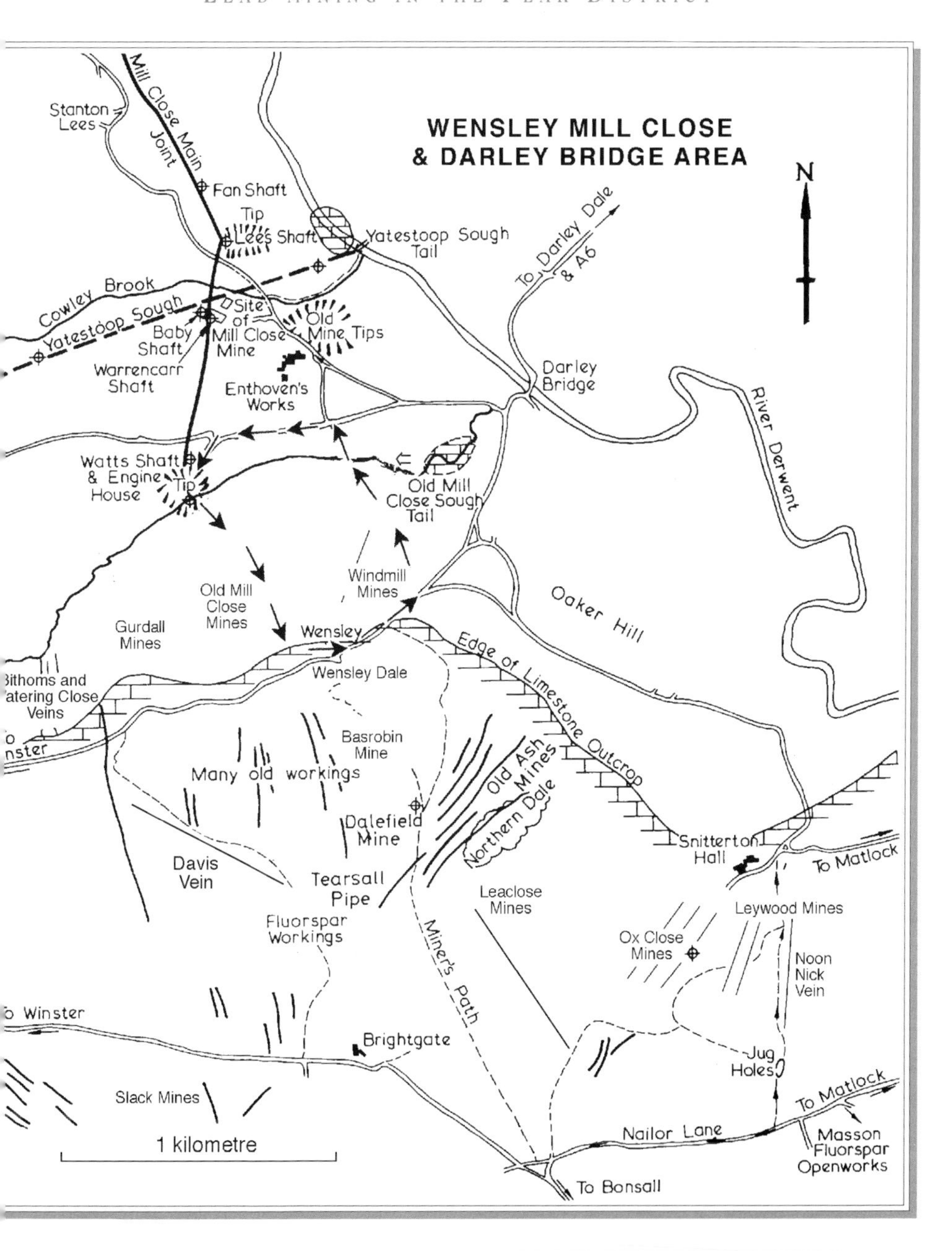


***Opposite page; Below: The complex workings of Old Mill Close Mine***

# 11 THE MATLOCK AREA

*Part of the Black Ox workings in "Masson Mine"*

By N. Gregory and T. D. Ford

Maps: 1:25000 SK 25; 1:10000 SK 25 NE & SE

Matlock has been associated with lead mining since Roman times. Several lead pigs with Latin inscriptions have been found in the area; one found in 1783 weighed 84 lbs whilst another found nearby in 1787 weighed 173 lbs. Early mining took place on the BACON and the associated NESTUS PIPE and COALPIT RAKE where pick-work indicates mining before explosives. The earliest documentary evidence is in 1470 though mining was in progress long before. Lead mining continued into the 20th century with an unsuccessful venture at RIBER MINE in the 1950s. In more recent times there have been several mines extracting fluorspar and baryte. Apart from the well-known large mines, there were dozens of small mines which produced little more than a ton or so of lead ore per year. Much of the evidence of mining has been swept away by modern building, roadworks and flood control schemes. Fourteen old lead mines have been open as tourist "caves" at one time or another and five are still open to the public. Some of the others are still accessible to cave and mine explorers.

Starting from Cromford Market Place (see also chapter 12) it is worth driving up the VIA GELLIA (A 5012) for about a mile to park by the former Pig of Lead Inn (284 575). Walking back down the road for 200m one can view the waste heaps and relics of the BALL EYE MINES on the northern hillside (286 574) opposite the mill buildings. Now gated for safety, these mines once yielded galena with a much higher proportion of silver than elsewhere in Derbyshire, up to 20 ounces per ton (the usual figure is about 2 ounces per ton). The upper levels of the Ball Eye Mines start in a cave-like opening once known as Rugg's Hall after a mine proprietor Wiiliam Rugg who lived nearby. The cave walls are now much shattered by blasting in the adjacent quarry. The sediments just inside yielded the skull of an "elephant" in the 17th century, probably some form of the prehistoric woolly mammoth. The lower levels of Ball Eye Mines were not far above road level in a series of pipe veins, drained by FOUNTRABBEY SOUGH which tapped a thermal spring. The water was used by Simon & Pickard's paper mills for a time, but now the water is sold as bottled spa water.

Return to Cromford cross-roads and proceed north along the A6 towards Matlock Bath. The road passes through SCARTHIN NICK, an artifical cutting blasted out in 1815 to improve access to the Matlock warm springs and spa. The Nick has been widened several times, the last being in 1960. Prior to 1815 it had been necessary either to take a circuitous route to the west over Harp Edge to Upperwood and thence down to river level near the present Matlock Bath station. Alternative routes were by a ford near Cromford Bridge at

"Woodpecker" pick work in "Masson Mine"

Willersley leading to a toll road over Starkholmes into Matlock town, or a track from near St Mary's Church along the riverside (the original road to the Bath). This narrow track survives as a footpath on the right (east) of Scarthin Nick and from it one can gain views of WILLERSLEY CASTLE, the home Sir Richard Arkwright built for himself across the river from his mills, though it was incomplete at the time of his death in 1792.

Some 400m further north on the A6 are the MASSON MILLS, recently converted into a shopping complex. The oldest part was built in 1783 but it was much extended later. It was powered by water-wheels erected by a weir on the Derwent and boosted by a sough bringing water from the Ball Eye area. Arkwright's son, Richard Arkwright II, continued the texile mill operations with a long legal battle with the lead miners which held up the completion of Meerbrook Sough for 30 years. Arkwright needed the outflow from Cromford Sough to drive his mill but Meerbrook Sough eventually diverted the water away from the former. Iron doors erected in the sough under Cromford Moor ensured that Arkwright got some water from Cromford Sough but it was not enough. He tried to buy the mineral rights of much of the area so as to gain control of the water from the soughs, but was unsuccessful. His son Frederick inherited the business in 1843, but the textile operations gradually declined and he sold out. English Sewing Cotton operated the mills through much of the 20th C.

Another local family involved with lead mining were the Nightingales, whose daughter Florence is alleged to have absorbed lead when playing in the smelter yard. Though she lived to a ripe old age she suffered ill health through much of her life, possibly from lead-poisoning.

Immediately north of the Masson Mills one can see the weir across the River Derwent to the right, whilst across the road is the remains of the Wapping track climbing to the left, just south of the New Bath Hotel (access via the hotel approach). A house here was once the home of George Newnes, son of the chaplain to the mills, who later founded the publishing empire in London.

Some 200 metres up the Wapping track, in a cutting in the rough ground to the left is the entrance to WAPPING MINE (294 575) which worked a westerly continuation of MOLETRAP RAKE. Wapping Mine was worked for lead ore in the 1750s and there are large, partly collapsed stopes. Further into the hill a series of pipes yielded fluorspar until the 1950s. Wapping Mine links up underground with further pipe workings which were opened as a tourist attraction in 1797 called the CUMBERLAND CAVERN (292 577), after an 18th century Duke of Cumberland. The entrance has recently partly collapsed.

Further north along the A6, banks of tufa can be seen on the roadside below the New Bath Hotel. Tufa is a calcareous deposit precipitated by the warm springs which appear at intervals for some 600 m along the hillside. Though only 20°C, the warm waters led to the development of a spa town which attracted visitors from far and wide. The first bath was built in 1696 and several others followed. The site of the former Royal Hotel, burnt down in 1927, is now a car park with a grotto over a warm spring on one side and a rock garden on the other with water cascading over moss-covered tufa. The discharge from the springs flows into a roadside fish pond near the Pavilion, and the overflow from this drains beneath the car park to a tufa cascade on the river bank. Another spring bubbles up through the floor of a pond in the Derwent Gardens nearby. Tufa coats any object placed in the waters and there were once several "petrifying wells" though only one survives and that is now closed. Across the river, on the east bank is HAGG MINE, fitted with a water-wheel in the 1760s.

The PAVILION was built in 1885 and now houses the PEAK DISTRICT MINING MUSEUM with many relics and demonstrations of the former lead mining industry. The Museum was set up by the Peak District Mines Historical Society in 1978 as a joint venture with the Derbyshire Dales District Council and Derbyshire County Council. It contains a mock-up of a lead mine which is very popular with school children. The centrepiece is the water-pressure pumping engine rescued from oblivion down the 60 fms deep shaft of the WILLS FOUNDER MINE near Winster in 1976. Based on an original design by Westgarth, improved by the Cornish mining engineer Richard Trevithick, it was built in 1819. It was powered by the force of water falling from a level 25 fms (45 m) higher into a piston system which worked pumps drawing water from 100 ft (30m) lower down. The enormous cylinder is 3.5 m long and 45 cm in diameter. At four strokes per minute it raised some 200 litres per stroke. The combined power and pumped waters ran away down a sough, eventually reaching Yatestoop Sough and thence the River Derwent near Darley Dale. The weight of the pump rods was counterbalanced by a beam with a large box of rocks on the end and this has been reconstructed in the Museum. The whole pump, beam and counterbalance were once housed in an artifical cavern 120 m below the surface.

Other exhibits in the Peak District Mining Museum include several models or replicas of mining machinery, various mining tools, a collection of 18th century lead pigs, choice mineral specimens from both Peak District and elsewhere and a selection of plans, photographs and paintings of Derbyshire mines. A bookshop specializing in mining history is also in the Museum.

Across the A6 road from the Mining Museum, a short walk up Temple Road is TEMPLE MINE (292 581). Worked for fluorspar in both the 1920s and 1950s it is now open as an extension to the Museum to demonstrate the minerals in place and various sorts of mining equipment. The mine level penetrates both dolomite and toadstone and examples of small pipe veins lined with fluorspar are present. Also visible are small caves filled with sediments washed out from Ice Age glaciers.

Part of the hillside above Temple Road has been developed as GULLIVER'S KINGDOM, a theme park with dinosaurs and rides. Between this and Temple Mine a long series of steps leads to Upperwood. Adjacent to the steps about halfway up a manhole cover conceals the entrance to OWLET MINE, once known as Victoria Cavern. A key is kept at the Mining Museum. Access is down a mine shaft some 15 m deep fitted with iron ladders. It leads into a single long stope where a vein of fluorspar with some galena has been worked on top of a toadstone layer. A thin parallel vein has been worked by fire-setting.

High up above Gulliver's Kingdom is ROYAL MINE (292 579). Once known as Pavilion Mine, this can be reached by a separate road up past the theme park. A tour with taped commentary is now available. Royal Mine was merged with the old Speedwell lead mine in the 1950s and the latter can no longer be distinguished as a separate set of workings. Royal Mine was last worked for fluorspar in the 1950s and has underground links with Tear Breeches Mine and Hopping Mine at Upperwood, high above Matlock Bath. Started as lead mines, both the latter worked fluorspar up to the 1950s and are now sealed for safety. These mines worked a complex of pipe veins and replacement ore bodies with large calcite crystals up to 30 cm long (12inches) in places.

Returning to the A6 in Matlock Bath, some 200 m further along on the left is HODGKINSON'S HOTEL. At the rear of the restaurant is an old wine cellar which leads into a mine level with another warm spring (now closed off). The hotel was built over it in 1773-6. Following improvements to the road south through Scarthin Nick in 1838, Hodgkinson's Hotel became the main stage coach stopping place. Adjacent to the hotel is a shop with a large bay window at first floor level, once the leading mid 19th century "Museum" or shop for the sale of spar and marble ornaments and collections of minerals and fossils.

At the next corner, opposite the turning to Matlock Bath station, a sharp turning up to the left is Holme Road. It climbs steeply towards the village of UPPERWOOD. Partway up is the entrance to the HEIGHTS OF ABRAHAM pleasure grounds (limited parking), landscaped during the 19th century. The grounds include two ancient mines still open to the public – Rutland Cavern and Great Masson Cavern. The latter, situated at the top of the grounds, can also be reached by cable car from near Matlock Bath Station.

RUTLAND CAVERN (293 586) was opened as a tourist cave in 1810 and named after the Duke of Rutland. It lies in part of Bacon Rake and NESTUS PIPE in Masson Cavern (see below). Rutland Cavern's entrance adit goes through a toadstone layer into the underlying limestones. Cavernous chambers have resulted from large scale removal of minerals but good examples of fluorspar and barytes are visible. Workings beyond the tourist route have yielded the unusual copper-zinc carbonate minerals, aurichalcite and rosasite, as well as traces of the mercury mineral cinnabar. These old workings extend to below the entrance adit of Masson Cavern, and nearby there is a covered shaft 60 fms (108m) deep into a lower complex of old mine workings with another warm spring at the bottom.

GREAT MASSON CAVERN (292 587) lies at the top of the Heights of Abraham grounds. It can be reached by walks up through the grounds past Rutland Cavern or directly by cable car from near Matlock Bath station. The Victoria Tower, a shop and cafe are close by. The entrance passage to Great Masson Cavern follows part of the worked out BACON RAKE with stopes high in the roof. Traces of this rake may also be seen across the valley on the south side of HIGH TOR. The underground route then turns northwards through a long series of linked pipe vein cavities. Each cavity is

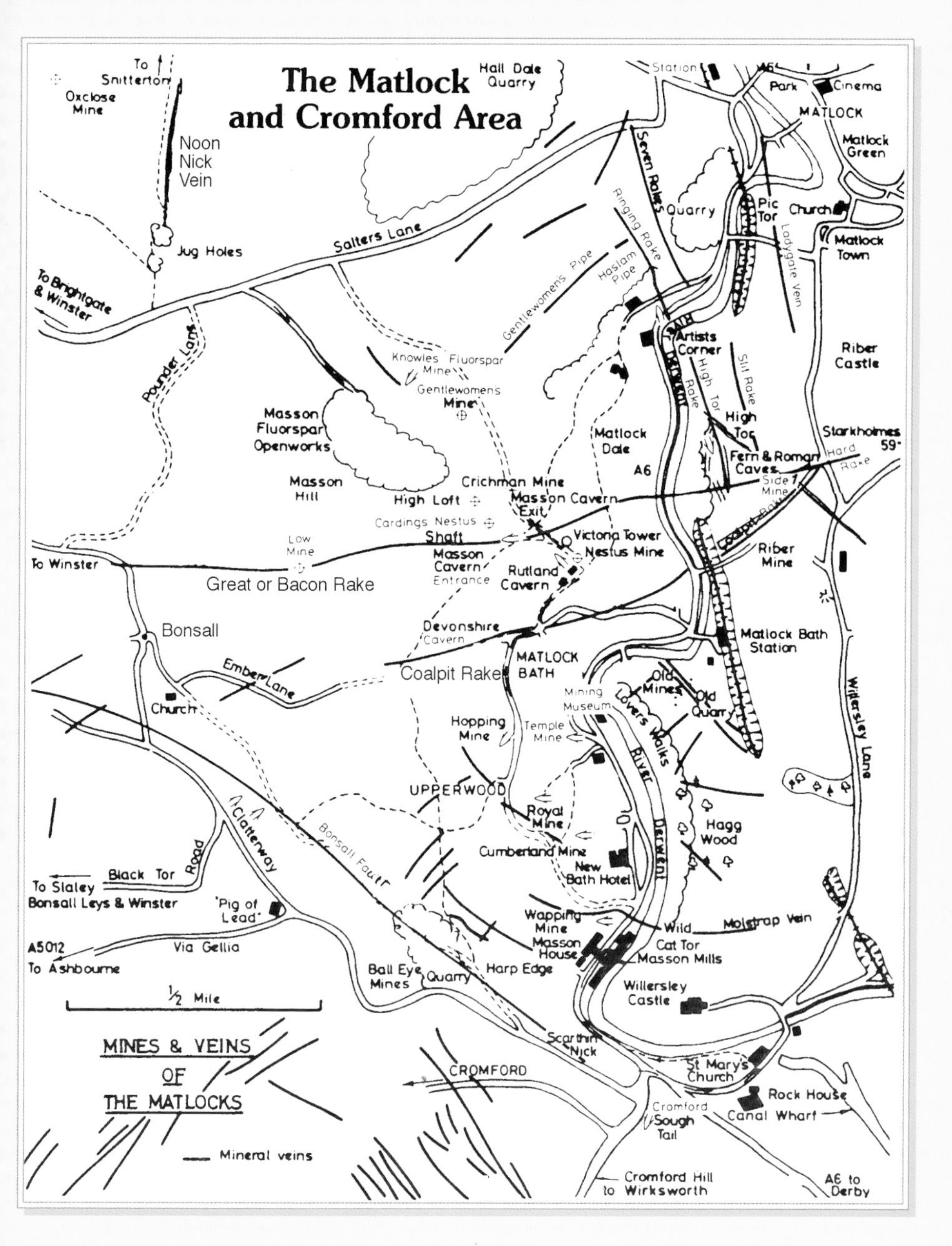


around 2 m long and is characterized by numerous pick marks, sometimes known as "woodpecker work". Before the days of using explosives in mining this was the usual means of extracting minerals. Some of the smaller pick-marks may date back to Roman times and it has been speculated as to whether this area of ancient workings could have been the "lead work at Mestesford" listed in Domesday Book in 1086. However, most of the visible woodpecker work is probably Mediaeval. Galena lined the walls of the cavities and was carefully picked off with long chisels. Much waste fluorspar was left behind and has been removed in more recent times. These ancient workings are part of NESTUS PIPE, recorded as the Breakholes as early as 1470, it yielded ore worth £2400 in 1671, equivalent to a million pounds in today's money. The visitors' route ends in Masson Cavern, a large "self-open" or natural cavern, recorded as early as the mid 17th century. As with several other caverns in Masson Hill this is thought to have been dissolved out by natural processes only to be re-filled with sediments washed out of melting glaciers. The sediments contained lumps of lead ore from the pipes so most of them were removed by lead miners and sieved on the surface. Tinker's Shaft, operating in the 1640s, can be seen high in the roof where the date of 1699 inscribed in an inaccessible position shows that the cavern was once nearly full of sediments. At the far end of Masson Cavern the mineralization comes to a sudden end at a "hard forefield" of solid limestone. A nearby stairway leads to an upper chamber with inscribed initials and the date 1705 and beyond further stairs climb to the exit doorway.

Off to the west of the passage leading to Masson Cavern is a maze of old workings once nearly a mile long, which are not normally open to the public. If arrangements can be made with the Peak District Mines Historical Society and with the owners, it is sometimes possible to visit these interesting workings. They constitute the northwesterly extension of NESTUS PIPE, here known as Carding's Nestus Pipe in the 19th century. It was worked from several separate mines now linked underground, with the transfer of names between them over the years raising uncertainties in disentangling their history. Immediately inside the link passage is a shaft usually known as BLACK OX though earlier it was called CARDING'S NESTUS MINE, which may have incorporated Walkers Grove at some stage. The shaft is so narrow that it is difficult to see how the miner could extract rock from beneath his feet whilst sinking the shaft. Modern fluorspar and calcite workings lie to the south of Black Ox shaft and they also lead to some further woodpecker work.

Two further parallel pipe veins lie to the west and there is a long link passage through to HIGH LOFT MINE, last worked for fluorspar in the 1960s. The miners even had a logwasher underground to process their spar, driven by compressed air brought down Dale Shaft from an engine on the surface. Off to the east side is HIGH LOFT CAVERN, said to have been found in 1779 with many "petrifactions". This is often taken to mean stalactites but no evidence has been found of these, and the petrifications were probably good cubic crystals of fluorspar. They have long ago been stripped out, but the remains of timber platforms and candle smoke marks can still be seen high in the roof. A fluorspar flat vein lies on one side, roofed by a thin clay wayboard. Behind High Loft Mine's Dale Shaft a short branch passage leads into a stope with a fine mineral vein clearly exposed in the roof. To one side is a walled-off "snap cabin" where the 1950s miners ate their lunch. Branching off to the left (west) is a "coffin level" picked out by hand. Uphill from

High Loft Mine is the SAND CAVERN where banks of glacial outwash sand and clay are still present. Beyond, a large chamber was once part of CRICHMAN OLD FOUNDER MINE. A scramble ahead leads to partly collapsed workings at the present limit of access. The workings of King Mine, Knowles Mine and Beck Mine beyond were unroofed and ripped out by the Masson fluorspar opencast mine in the 1970s. Knowles Mine was opened in the 1750s but much enlarged in the 1940s when an adit was driven in from the hillside to work fluorspar. It penetrated an area of almost total replacement of limestone by yellow fluorspar. This area was unroofed by the opencast operations and both it and further sand-filled caverns were destroyed. One sand-filled cavern can still be seen in the roof above the partly collapsed workings of Crichman Mine. There was formerly a link from here to another complex of pipe-workings extending northeastwards down the hill through GENTLEWOMEN'S PIPE and OLD JANT MINE to MASSON SOUGH, a branch off RINGING RAKE SOUGH (see below) but it has been destroyed.

Together, the Rutland and Masson Mines workings, including the parts now destroyed, totalled some 10 kms in length and ranged from the summit of Masson Hill down to river level, a height of 240 m. They indicate a complex geological history. The beds of limestone between two lavas were partly converted to dolomite. Both limestone and dolomite were later dissolved away along fractures and replaced by a network of scrins, pipes and flats with galena, fluorspar, baryte and calcite. Later, during the early stages of the Ice Age the pipes became overflow routes for melt-water and the mineral fill was deeply eroded to leave a mineral gravel in the bottoms of the cavities. Finally outwash sand from the glaciers partly filled the caverns. The lead miners found the weaknesses provided by the pipe veins, caverns and sand fills much easier to excavate than cutting through hard limestone and it is not surprising that early mining seems to have been concentrated here.

From Masson Mine entrance several footpaths lead to further mining relics. Westwards, uphill, a track leads to Ember Farm and Bonsall alongside the surface workings and waste heaps of BACON and COALPIT RAKES. Or, northwest-wards, past the cavern exit, a track leads past the Masson fluorspar opencast pit to the summit of Masson Hill. A road across the northern end of this is SALTER LANE, once the route for pack mule trains carrying salt from Cheshire to the growing industrial cities of Nottingham, Derby etc. Across Salter Lane a few metres to the west a gate opens to the right and a short walk away among the trees is JUG HOLES (279 596), a gaping cavern on Noon Nick Vein, worked as early as 1629. Under the right-hand (west) wall of the cavern openings lead into a series of fluorspar pipe workings.

Leaving these digressions, return from Masson Cavern to the A6 at the bend leading to Matlock Bath station and proceed northwards along the main road. After about 300 m a wicket gate on the right leads down a few steps to the river bank and the entrance to LONG TOR GROTTO (296 587). The partly flooded adit leads back under the A6 to a small series of vein and pipe workings beneath a long-disused quarry. A landslide occurred here in 1965 and two houses were ruined.

Some 200 m further north, across a foot bridge to the right is a paint works, behind which is a concealed entrance to HIGH TOR GROTTO; once a show cave, all that remains is a short flooded series of pipe veins lined with calcite. Also hidden behind the paint works is SIDE MINE, an adit along Hard Rake used in the 1820s and 1840s as a pumpway from mine workings beneath High Tor. Outside on the river bank a large waterwheel worked a rod system along the Side Mine adit to raise water from 120 ft (40 m) below river level in the distant workings. Nothing is left of this machinery. The Side Mine workings were intersected in the 1950s by the RIBER MINE'S inclined adit at Starkholmes (see below).

Continuing north along the A6 after some 500 m another foot bridge over the river leads to HIGH TOR GROUNDS. High Tor itself is a massive mound of reef limestone best seen from the A6 road. Up in the grounds behind High Tor are two tourist "caves", FERN CAVE and ROMAN CAVE (297 589). Neither is a true cave: instead they are roofless open workings in two mineral veins, High Tor Rake and Hard Rake. The former is a continuation of Seven Rakes, high on the western slopes above Matlock Town, whilst the latter is the easterly continuation of Bacon Rake, seen in Masson Cavern. Fern and Roman Caves are very old mine workings with numerous pick marks. They give a good idea of the way narrow rakes were worked in the days before explosives. To the east of Roman Cave, near the village of Starkholmes, SHALEY VEIN was the subject of a major mining speculation in the 1950s. Following a series of inclined boreholes in search of the eastern extension of Coalpit Rake, an inclined adit 3 m wide was driven at RIBER MINE (299 588) in 1952. Some 500 m long it revealed that the 17th and 18th century miners had penetrated much further beneath the shale cover than had been anticipated and that most of the expected ore had already been mined! Yielding small quantities of lead and zinc ores, the mine closed in 1959 and the adit entrance has since collapsed.

Continuing north along the A6, just past the bend to the right at ARTIST'S CORNER, there is a public car park on the river bank to the right. At the south end close to a toilet block a manhole cover is over the entrance to RINGING RAKE SOUGH (295 595). A key is available at the Mining Museum. Also known as Youd's level (from the owner of the house across the road whose yard collapsed into the sough) an arched level goes back under the A6 into a short series of workings in Seven Rakes on the lower slopes of Masson Hill. Branching left from Ringing Rake Sough is MASSON SOUGH, where a flat-out crawl in the stream leads into a long series of pipe workings climbing nearly 2 km and rising almost 240 m to near the summit of Masson Hill. Passing through HASLAM PIPE, OLD JANT MINE and GENTLEWOMEN'S PIPE this had a connection via QUEEN MINE into the Crichman/Beck section of the Masson mine workings until it was destroyed by the fluorspar opencast on the summit of Masson Hill. Ringing Rake Sough is a fine example of a "coffin level". Old Jant Mine has a cavern filled with glacial outwash sands, whilst Gentlewomen's Pipe has a cartoon of an Overseer, possibly the rather tyrannical mine agent Roger Jackson, scratched into the wall.

# 12 CROMFORD AND BOLE HILL

Longe or Cromford Sough

BY P. NAYLOR

Maps: 1:25000 SK 25;
1:10000 SK 25 SE

**The Cromford area encapsulates much of Derbyshire's mining history within a day's walk. Artefacts found around Cromford suggest that mining started in Roman times.**

The itinerary starts in the village of Cromford, made famous by Sir Richard Arkwright who was one of the pioneers of the Industrial Revolution. He built the first water-powered cotton spinning mill in the world at Cromford.

It is best to start at the County Council car park off Mill Lane, opposite ARKWRIGHT'S MILL (299 570). The buildings nearby are the original wharfage for the CROMFORD CANAL terminus. The canal extended 14 miles (22km) from here to Langley Mill in the Erewash Valley, whence it gave access to the River Trent and to Nottingham. The canal was built from 1791 to 1794, a remarkably short time considering it had to cross roads and rivers, and involved two short tunnels. One has collapsed isolating the Cromford stretch of waterway. It cost twice the original estimate of £42,697, and was partly financed by Arkwright, who used barges to export his cotton thread to the framework knitters and lace makers of Nottingham and other Midland towns. Other financiers were Francis Hurt of Alderwasley, a landowner and lead smelter, and the Gell family of Hopton who also had extensive lead mining interests.

Cross the road to ST MARY'S CHURCH, built by Arkwright as a private chapel for his family. It stands on an area called The Green which was once the site of a lead smelter powered by a water-wheel on the Derwent. Two pigs of lead were found on The Green in 1918: identical except for being inscribed XXX and XV, they weighed 51 kg each. The smelter was surrounded by the hamlet of WILLERSLEY, all swept away to enhance the view from Arkwright's newly constructed "Castle" across the river. Owing to a disastrous fire, the Castle had to be refurbished in 1792 after Arkwright's death.

Proceed down Mill Lane away from Cromford to the BRIDGE over the River Derwent. Dating from the 15th century it has pointed arches on the downstream side but rounded arches upstream due to a later widening. The bridge replaced a ford often assumed to be of Roman origin on the former Hereward Street. The bridge chapel has a "squint" window where a candle would be placed to guide travellers across the ford. The squint faces towards the ford, not the bridge.

Turn back along Mill Lane towards Cromford, noting the canal feeder stream on the left, until an IRON AQUEDUCT across the road is reached (298 569). Stone steps lead up to it but it is now dry. It once carried water to Arkwright's mill. Note that the mill has no windows on the ground floor in order to discourage Luddite machine wreckers and industrial spies.

Cross the A6 (beware traffic!). To the right (north) the A6 goes through a cutting known as SCARTHIN NICK, built to divert traffic from Willersley and widened in 1960. During the original excavation a human skeleton was found with a cache of Roman copper coins from the time of Licinius and

Constantine (4th century A.D.).

Continue into CROMFORD MARKET PLACE, dominated by the Greyhound Hotel, built by Arkwright in town hall style to accommodate business visitors. Adjacent single-storey buildings were once the market shambles. A tunnel beneath the square conveys the Bonsall Brook to the mill. Across the road are ancient lead miners' trials in the limestone crag at the end of Allen's Hill. At the foot of this cliff is a leat which once conveyed water to the mill from Cromford Sough, but it is now dry.

Bear right of the hotel along a narrow road to SCARTHIN PROMENADE in the separate village of Scarthin, part of Matlock Parish, not Cromford. Below the Promenade is the mill pond and in the far corner a low arch admits water from Bonsall Brook by the water wheel pit. Continue along the Promenade to reach Water Lane leading to the Via Gellia road (A 5012).

Proceed along WATER LANE to a low dam. Climb the steps and cross along the dam wall to a small building with a wheel pit. This was the CORN MILL built by Arkwright for the benefit of the village. It replaced an earlier mill of 1720 where calamine (zinc carbonate) was ground and roasted by the Cheadle Brass & Copper Company who sent their product on to Cheadle in Staffordshire for brass manufacture. Most of the calamine came from nearby Bonsall; together with calamine from Wirksworth and Cromford the output reached 500 tons per annum. The houses opposite are Staffordshire Row, built to house workers from Cheadle.

Across the road near the pond another mill still has a WATER WHEEL in working order. Though now occupied by a wholesaler in basket ware, it was originally a grinding mill for pigments raised in local lead mines. The water in the mill race is joined by a flow from Alabaster Sough which drains the mines in the hill to the south.

Return to Cromford village along Water Lane to reach the foot of CROMFORD HILL (the B 5036 road to Wirksworth), once the line of Hereward Street. A silver/copper alloy coin found here in the 1950s was of Roman origin though minted in Constantinople (today's Istanbul). It was inscribed FEL. TEMP. REPARATIO (= Felicium Temporarum Reparatio, which translates as "a return to secure and happier times").

At the foot of Cromford Hill, enter a passageway between a cafe and a dress shop on the left (east) side to reach an enclosure locally known as the BEAR PIT, which is a junction of several watercourses. Ahead, a low arch with a gentle flow is the tail of CROMFORD or LONGE SOUGH (295 568). Started in 1657-8 it was extended at intervals for over a century and a half and drained most of the Bole Hill area: branches extended almost to Wirksworth. About 300 m are still accessible and a branch near the tail has examples of some of the earliest-known gunpowder blasting in British mines dating from 1662-3. To the right of Cromford Sough tail is a slightly higher arch discharging a steady flow of water.

This is mostly surface drainage from Cromford Hill but there may be some contribution from early soughs under Dean Hollow and its quarry (also spelled Dene in many old documents). There are two exit portals in the Bear Pit; one takes a little water to the leat feeding the mill, whilst the other feeds into Bonsall Brook beneath the Market Place. The original outlet for Cromford Sough was in the middle of the square but the buried watercourses have been adapted from time to time. Cromford Sough was later superceded by the lower Meerbrook Sough.

Cromford Sough is one of the reasons why Arkwright chose Cromford for his mill. In his day the flow was substantial and slightly thermal and, mixed with Bonsall Brook, it provided him with all the power he needed. He was wary of the river for it was capricious and liable to flooding, which damaged Nightingale's mill nearby. Cromford also supplied plenty of cheap labour.

A path beyond the Bear Pit leads up past the school to NORTH STREET, named after Lord North. On both sides are classic Arkwright houses, three storeys high, the top floor being for the knitters' frames. His mills only produced thread and were operated by women and children whilst the men were framework knitters in their own homes.

It is a long steep walk up Cromford Hill so it is best to retrieve cars and drive up for about three quarters of a mile (1200 m) and fork left to reach the top level of the BLACK ROCKS Picnic Site car park (291 559). En route the road passes the entrance to Dean Quarry, near to the tail of Vermuyden's Sough. Started in 1631 it was the earliest major sough in Derbyshire, designed by the Dutch canal engineer, Sir Cornelius Vermuyden. However, it was not long afterwards that the miners realized they could drain the veins to a much greater depth by driving firstly BATES SOUGH. Started in 1657, the tail is concealed between the houses on the east side of Cromford Hill. But almost immediately CROMFORD SOUGH was started at a much lower level. Commenced about 1657-8 Cromford Sough and its branches total nearly 4 miles (6km) in length. Water-wheels were installed in the sough to raise water from still lower workings around 1800-1820.

At Black Rocks car park, adjacent to the small visitor centre and toilet block are the ruins of an engine house on the Godbehere section of the GANG VEIN (also known as Dovegang). This was the principal mineral vein hereabouts and extended east-west for about a mile across Bole Hill where the disturbed ground marks its course. It was worked from several shafts in the CROMFORD MOOR MINES and was drained by Bates and Cromford Soughs until the later driving of the Meerbrook Sough.

At the far end of the Black Rocks car park a gate leads on to the track of the former High Peak Mineral Railway, now the HIGH PEAK TRAIL. Across the trail a path leads up to BLACK ROCKS, with a waste heap and run-in shaft on the Cromford Moor Mines alongside. Black Rocks are part of the Millstone Grit series of sandstones. Beneath them are black shales and fragments of both sandstone and shale can be found on the waste hillock, for the shaft was sunk through both to reach the vein in the limestone.

MEERBROOK SOUGH has a branch under this area. Driven from a portal near Whatstandwell, downstream from Cromford from 1772 to 1813 at a cost of £45,000 with a further extension 1841 to 1882 costing £70,000, it is more than 100 ft (30 m) lower than Cromford Sough and greatly reduced the flow in the latter, depriving Arkwright of his power source. In spite of a lengthy legal battle

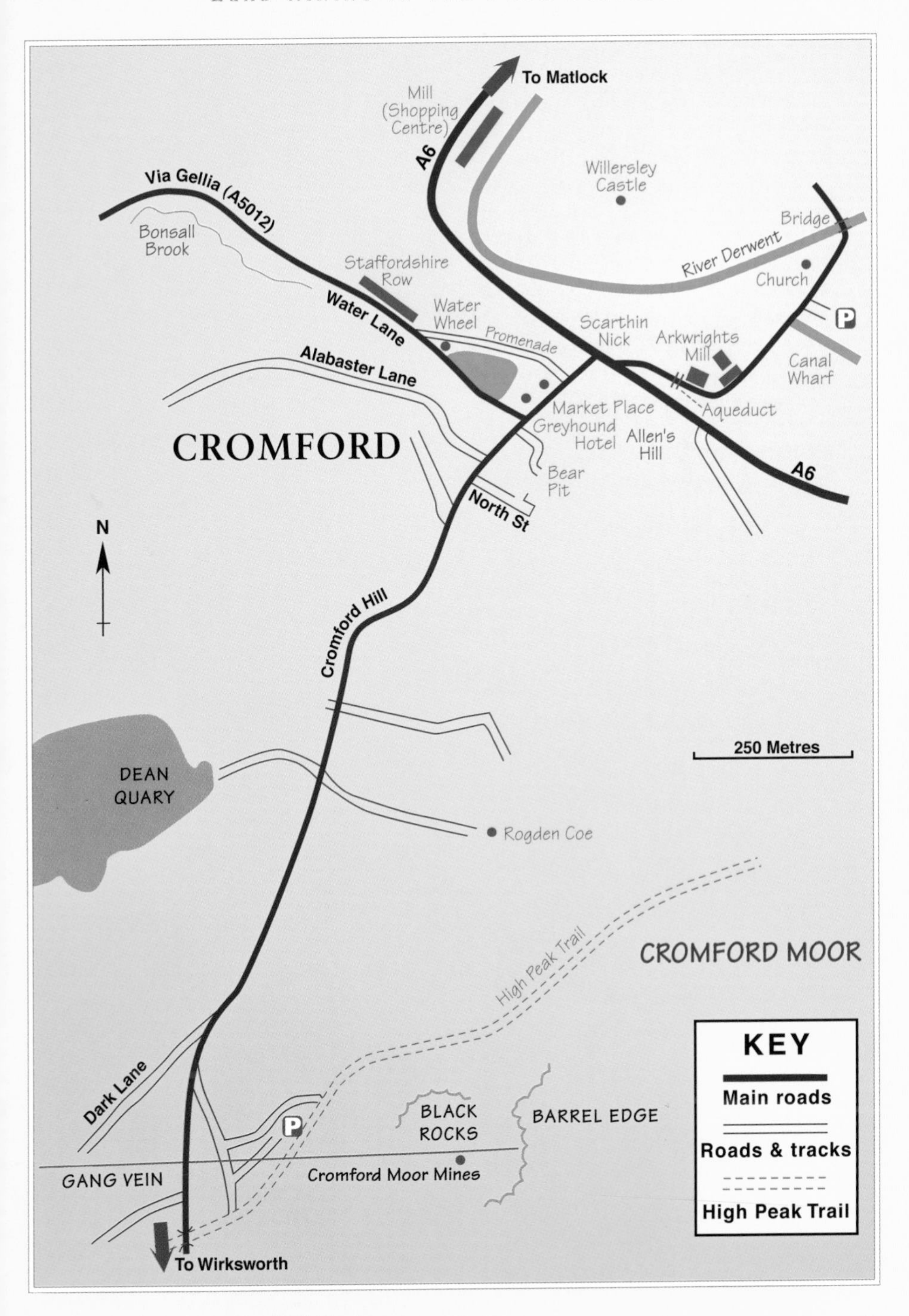

To Matlock
Mill
(Shopping
Centre)
A6
Willersley
Castle
Via Gellia (A5012)
Bonsall
Brook
Bridge
River Derwent
Church
Staffordshire
Row
Water
Wheel
Water Lane
Promenade
Scarthin
Nick
Arkwrights
Mill
Canal
Wharf
Alabaster Lane
Market Place
Greyhound
Hotel
Allen's
Hill
Aqueduct
CROMFORD
Bear
Pit
A6
North St
N
Cromford Hill
250 Metres
DEAN
QUARY
Rogden Coe
High Peak Trail
CROMFORD MOOR
KEY
Main roads
Roads & tracks
High Peak Trail
Dark Lane
BLACK
ROCKS
BARREL EDGE
GANG VEIN
Cromford Moor Mines
To Wirksworth

between Arkwright and the sough proprietors, Meerbrook Sough remains the main drainage today. Together with branches it is over 4 miles (6 km) long and provides 3.75 million litres per day for the Severn-Trent Water company.

Cromford Moor was the source of another Roman lead pig. Found in 1777 it was inscribed IMP.CAS.-HARDIANI AUG.MET.LVT, broadly translated as "from Emperor Caesar Hadrian Augustus metal works at Lutudarum" giving a date between 117 and 138 A.D. Lutudarum was the Roman lead mining centre, though its exact location is unknown. The most likely site is where the Roman road between Buxton (Aqua Arnemetiae) and Derby (Little Chester) crossed Hereward St. though this is now drowned beneath Carsington Water reservoir.

**Pick work in "Masson Mine"**

From Black Rocks there are views over DENE QUARRY, situated in the heavily mined area of Dean Hollow. The ever-changing quarry faces reveal signs of previous lead mining activity. A walk north along the High Peak Trail gives views towards Cromford village and waste hillocks from mines such as Rogden Coe Shaft can be seen. During the driving of Cromford Sough this had a fire-basket hung in the shaft to improve ventilation.

Either return to the cars at Black Rocks Picnic site or, if the cars have been left at Cromford, continue north and then east along the trail for a mile or so and descend the SHEEP PASTURE INCLINE where railway wagons were once hauled up by a stationary engine. The High Peak Railway was built by the canal company in the 1830s to feed goods to and from the limestone country where a canal was impractical. At the foot of the incline is High Peak junction by the canal. Turn left (north) for a tow-path walk back to Cromford.

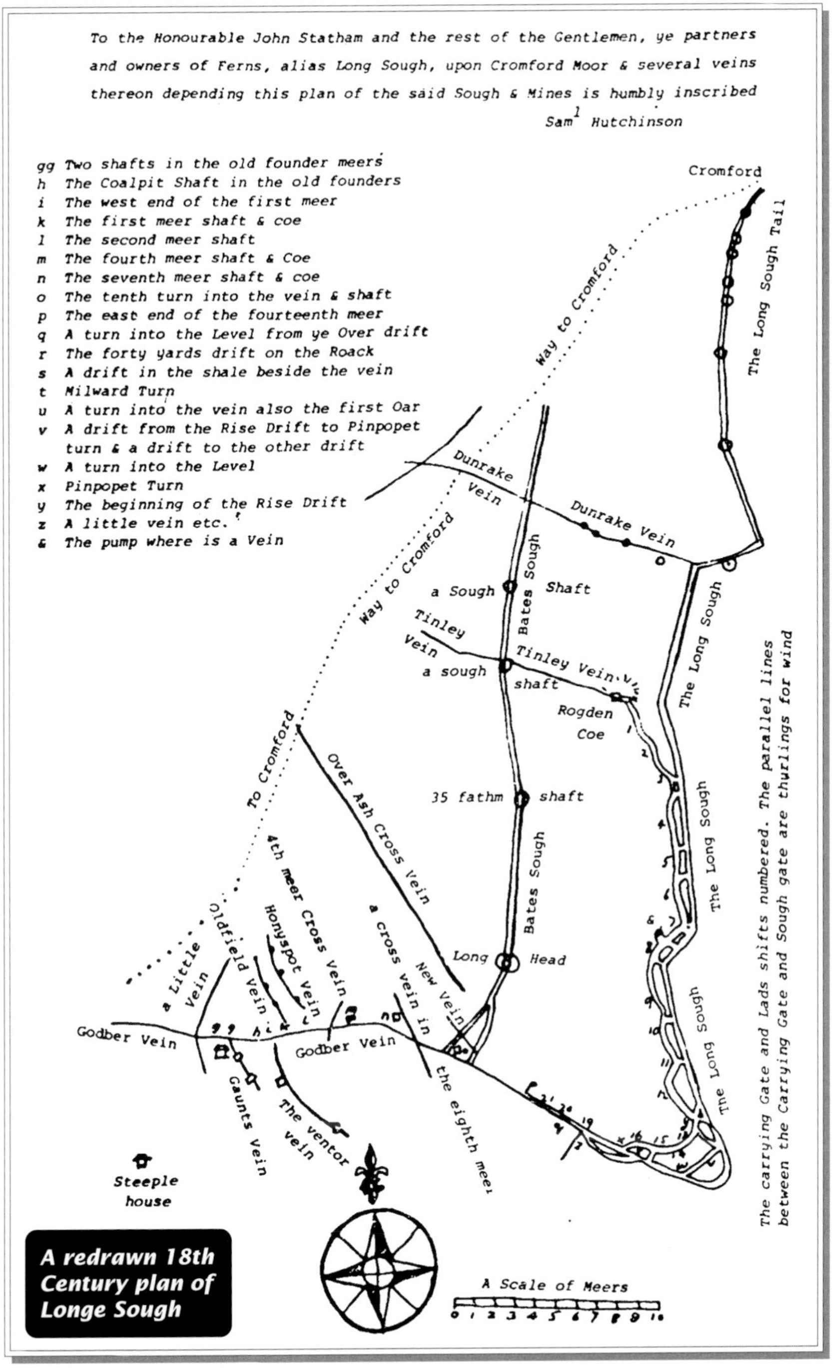
To the Honourable John Statham and the rest of the Gentlemen, ye partners and owners of Ferns, alias Long Sough, upon Cromford Moor & several veins thereon depending this plan of the said Sough & Mines is humbly inscribed
Sam[l] Hutchinson
gg Two shafts in the old founder meers
h The Coalpit Shaft in the old founders
i The west end of the first meer
k The first meer shaft & coe
l The second meer shaft
m The fourth meer shaft & Coe
n The seventh meer shaft & coe
o The tenth turn into the vein & shaft
p The east end of the fourteenth meer
q A turn into the Level from ye Over drift
r The forty yards drift on the Roack
s A drift in the shale beside the vein
t Milward Turn
u A turn into the vein also the first Oar
v A drift from the Rise Drift to Pinpopet turn & a drift to the other drift
w A turn into the Level
x Pinpopet Turn
y The beginning of the Rise Drift
z A little vein etc.
& The pump where is a Vein
Cromford
The Long Sough Tail
Way to Cromford
Dunrake Vein
Dunrake Vein
Way to Cromford
a Sough
Shaft
Bates Sough
Tinley Vein
Tinley Vein
a sough
shaft
Rogden Coe
The Long Sough
To Cromford
Over Ash Cross Vein
35 fathm
shaft
Bates Sough
The Long Sough
4th meer Cross Vein
Oldfield Vein
Honyspot Vein
a Cross vein in
New Vein
Long
Head
a Little Vein
Godber Vein
Godber Vein
Gaunts Vein
The ventor vein
the eighth meer
The Long Sough
Steeple house
The carrying Gate and Lads shifts numbered. The parallel lines between the Carrying Gate and Sough gate are thurlings for wind
A Scale of Meers
0 1 2 3 4 5 6 7 8 9 10

A redrawn 18th Century plan of Longe Sough

# 13 GOOD LUCK MINE, MIDDLETON-BY-WIRKSWORTH

The entrance to Good Luck Mine

BY: P. NAYLOR

**Maps: 1:25000 SK 25; 1:10000 SK 25 NE**

**To the north of Middleton-by-Wirksworth lies the Via Gellia which was named after the Gell family, once the owners of the valley. It is a deeply incised Derbyshire valley trending eastwards and carrying the A 5012 road from Cromford to Newhaven. During the early days of mining many mine shafts were sunk into the veins on the hill tops both north and south. Adits were also driven in from the valley sides.**

From the 18th century further attempts were made to exploit the veins at depth by driving adits into the hillsides, mostly below the Lower Matlock Lava. Soughs were started but few completed owing to lack of investment and poor returns from deep workings. GOOD LUCK MINE (269 566) is one of those adits and is unmistakeable with its prominent spoil heap easily seen to the west of the road above a lay-by west of Marl Cottage, the unusual house built from large blocks of tufa from the nearby Dunsley Springs.

John Alsop and Company acquired the title to Good Luck Mine by consolidating several other titles, the original Good Luck Founder (now lost under the turnpike road built in 1803 from Middleton-by-Wirksworth to Ryder Point), Bals Founder (whose name suggests either a Cornish influence or perhaps a local family name Ball), Bachelor's Venture, Miners Venture and Moore Jepson Mines. The last is now covered by Mountain Cottage, one-time residence of D.H.Lawrence in 1919-1921 when he was ostracized as a pro-German sympathiser. He shared this home with Frieda Weekley, the wife of his ex-professor at Nottingham University College and niece of the air ace Baron Von Richthofen. Lawrence's mother's family, the Beardsleys, originated from Middleton parish.

John Alsop of Lea had considerable mining interests either as an owner or as an agent. He was a typical early 19th century entrepeneur who controlled the capitalisation of mining in the Soke and Wapentake of Wirksworth by the smelting industry, owning smelters at Lea and in Bonsall Dale. The latter mill occupied the site of the original manorial corn mill, later to

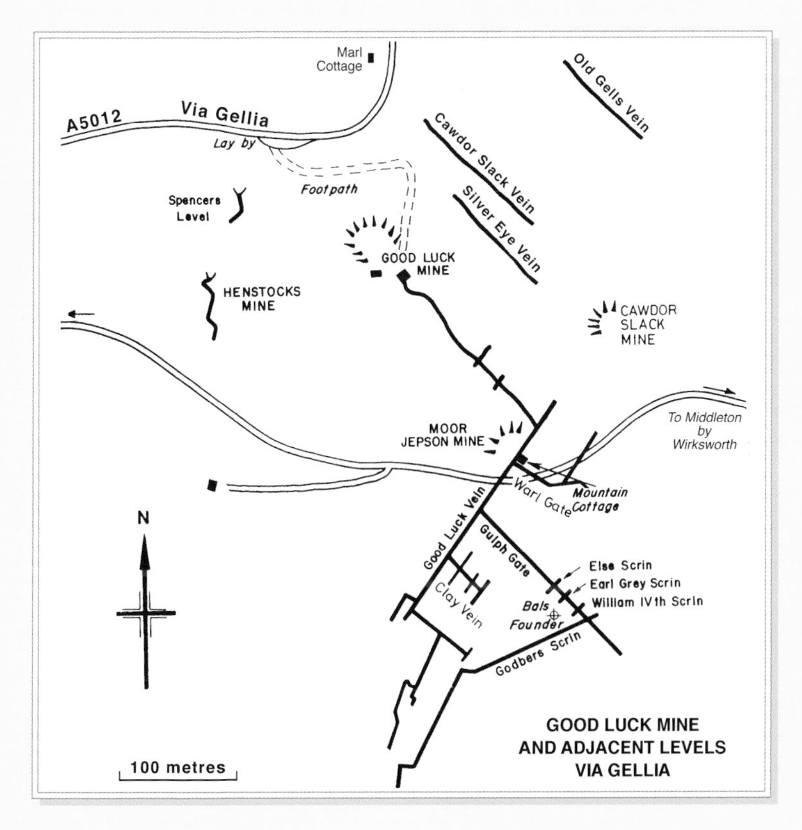

be occupied by Howits, whose brand name is Viyella, a corruption of Via Gellia. The present brick-built mill was erected by Cromford Garnetters and is now broken up into units with different occupiers. Among Alsop's business partners was Joseph Hall of Lea.

Roger Knowles of Bailey's Croft, Wirksworth, agent for the owners, started work on the adit, possibly on Monday, 25th October 1830, for a record in the Barmaster's Book states that by the following day, work had begun, the site had been inspected and the access route marked out as required by customary lead mining laws. The adit was driven into barren limestone, for some unknown reason at the eastern limit of the title, using hand drilling and gunpowder blasting. The spoil was taken out on an 11 inches (282 mm) gauge tramway and tipped on to the hillside. The hillock is estimated to contain over 10,000 tons of limestone.

When they had penetrated 90 m from daylight, the miners intersected SILVER EYE title, then in the possession of Isaac Spencer. An agreement was made whereby Spencer could have access to his vein by the new adit, in return for which he would pay one fifth of the cost of the adit to this point. This vein has been reopened in recent years to provide access to the shaft in order to provide an emergency escape route.

The next vein to be intersected was one of the BLACK RAKES in the possession of William Greatorex and Benjamin Buckley. An agreement was made but this time, in return for using the adit, the miners paid two shillings (10p) for each load which had then to be sold to Alsop at the current market rate. The agreement did not allow for waste rock to be removed through the adit and this had to be "laid within the cheeks of their own veins or scrins". Finally, after about a year's work through "dead" limestone, the GOODLUCK VEIN was intersected at the top of an incline formed to raise the workings above a clay wayboard, approximately 183 m from the entrance, where a winch was installed to raise and lower tubs. They must have been disappointed for the vein below the Lower Matlock Lava was very poor in lead ore.

The lead ore is granular galena in a gangue of baryte, the vein seldom thicker than 50 cm: 25 cm width is more usual. The proportion of galena in the vein averages 5%. It meant a considerable amount of work was expended on cutting away the limestone cheeks to give a working width. The deads were stacked overhead on stone stemples in the traditional fashion. These packs, together with the stemples, are some of the finest to be seen in the area. The stopes were excavated both above and below the wagon gate. Those above are accessible, rising as much as 20 m above the level, but the stopes below went to at least 20 m depth and were later back-filled. They have been partially explored by cleaning out a shaft in the floor. By the shaft top is a branch to the left (south) to WARL GATE with initials and the date 5th December 1831 by the entrance. Amongst others there are the initials of the agent Roger Knowles.

The Good Luck Vein was fully exploited for its length in the consolidated title. Cross-cuts were driven following scrins in the search for further veins. Warl Gate was driven to WARL VEIN(S); an unamed cross-cut was driven through BAKER'S VEN-

TURE title, but the principal drive was GULPH GATE driven to intersect ELSE SCRIN, named after a local mineral agent. EARL GREY and WILLIAM IV SCRINS were named to commemorate the passing of the Reform Act in 1832. The miners then continued to the southeast limit of the title "under Arthur Spencer's barn". They exploited GODBER'S SCRIN intersected by Gulph Gate and trending parallel to Goodluck Vein. This was even poorer in lead than usual and there was no understoping and very little overstoping, so that it was in effect no more than an exploratory level.

GODBER'S SCRIN intersects the only natural rift in the entire mine. Clean water was evident and the miners undertook a little ore-washing. A start was made in the 1840s to extend this level into Bondog Mine in the adjoining title, with a view to making ore-raising more economical, but the scheme was abandoned. Evidence of this venture can still be seen in the furthest reaches of the workings.

By 1840 Goodluck Mine was worked out and it can only be assumed, in the absence of reckoning books, that it was not a profitable undertaking. It has been tried again from time to time for galena and for baryte and a little fluorspar "sand" has been raised. Traces of copper ores in the form of azurite and malachite have also been found.

Surface waste was re-worked for baryte in the 1920s. A little lead ore was raised in the 1950's, after which the landowner blew in the entrance to prevent illegal mining.

On 25th May 1972 the title was given to two members of the Peak District Mines Historical Society by the process of nicking, through the Great Barmote Court, 140 years after the Alsop consolidation. The mine was reopened and is still in the possession of Ron Amner, a member of the Society, who opens it from time to time. Visitors can still experience something of the life of "T'owd man" for there are no concrete pathways or flood-lighting. The Gulph Fault can be seen where the miners tunnelled through it. There are artefacts on display where they were used, and the remains of coes, powder house and bousteads (ore bins) can be seen on the surface. Some ore was still in storage when restoration took place.

**A Stows in Good Luck Mine**

Anyone wishing to visit the mine should contact the owner, Ron Amner, c/o Peak District Mining Museum, Matlock Bath, Derbyshire. DE4 3NR.

# 14 WIRKSWORTH

*The Moot Hall*

## By T. D. Ford

**Maps: 1:25000 map SK 25; 1:10000 SK 25 NE & SE**

**Walking distance about 2 miles (3km)**

Wirksworth town lies at the heart of Derbyshire's lead mining industry. The Roman lead mining settlement of Lutudarum was nearby, now thought by some to be submerged beneath Carsington Reservoir. Wirksworth has had a succession of Moot Halls devoted to Barmote Court business and the current MOOT HALL is hidden away on Chapel Lane (288 542). Now used only once a year for sittings of the BARMOTE COURTS for the Soke and Wapentake of Wirksworth, the High and Low Peaks, and other Liberties held by the Duchy of Lancaster (i.e. the Crown), the court house doubles as a Baptist chapel.

The focus of lead mining around Wirksworth was beneath THE GULF (usually spelled Gulph in old documents) to the northwest of the town, and beneath BOLE HILL to the north, but other workings lay to the west towards Hopton and Brassington. Many mines were sunk on Bole Hill and there is a long history of drain-

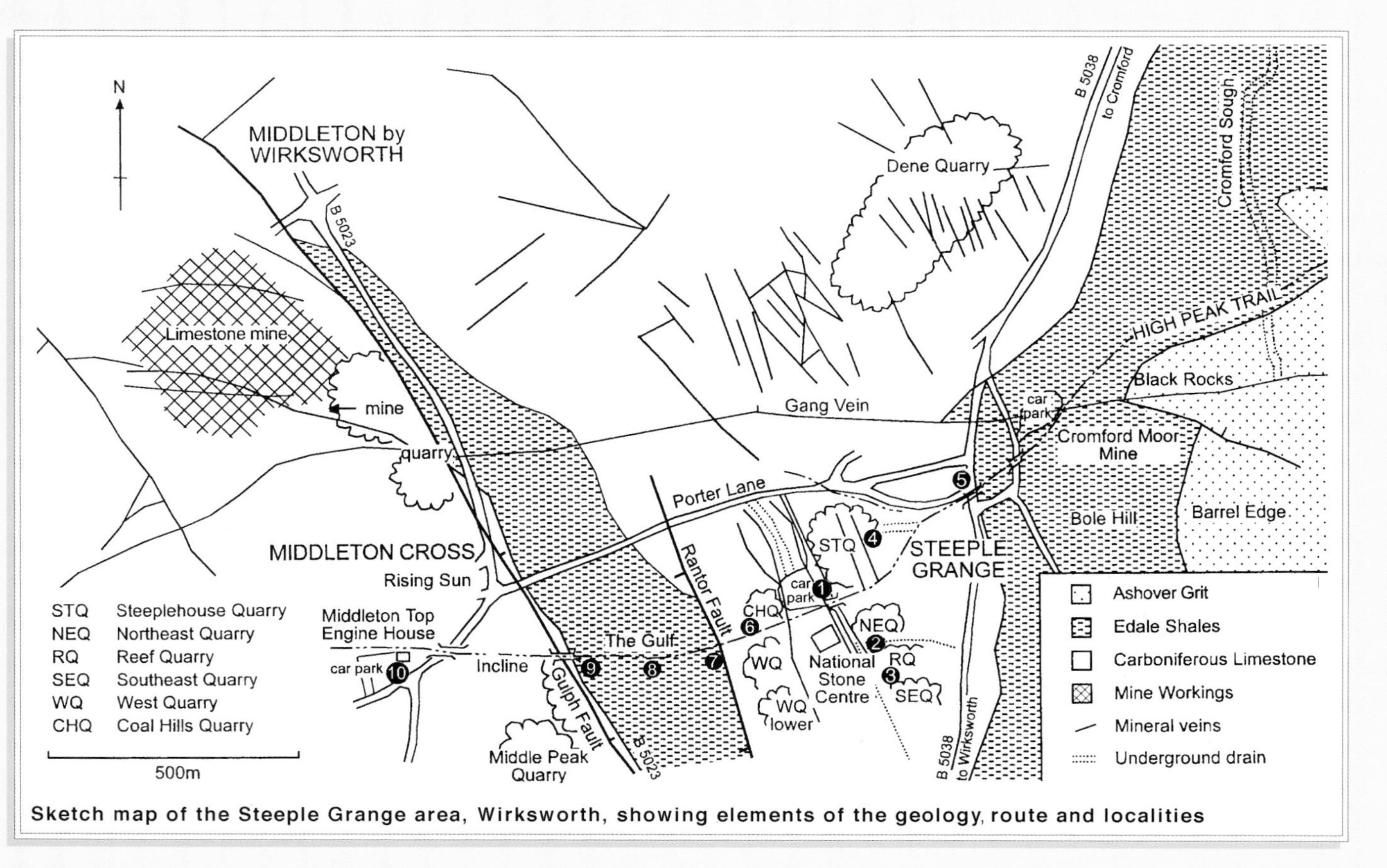


**Sketch map of the Steeple Grange area, Wirksworth, showing elements of the geology, route and localities**

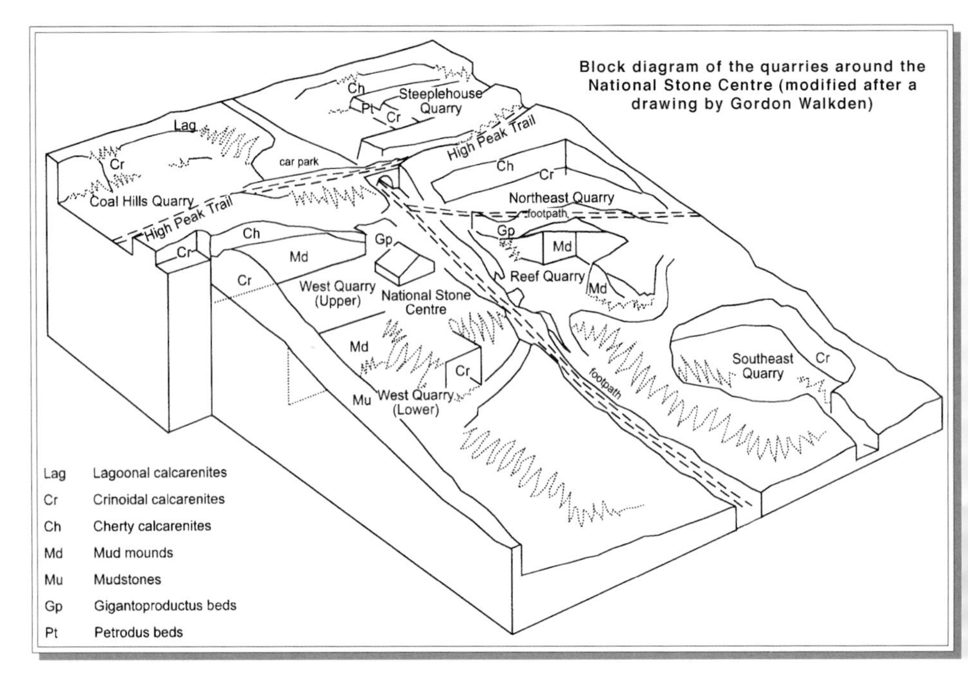


Block diagram of the quarries around the National Stone Centre (modified after a drawing by Gordon Walkden)

age problems as mining went deeper beneath the hill. Quarrying has destroyed many mining relics but there is enough for a short but fascinating excursion. It can be taken as an extension of the Cromford excursion (Q.V.).

## ITINERARY

The itinerary starts in the NATIONAL STONE CENTRE car park (287 553), approached by turning downhill off Porter Lane (locality 1). The Centre focusses on stone quarrying and a short but highly instructive excursion may be had touring the old limestone quarries around the Centre. These show a variety of types of limestone, particularly "reefs" or mud-mounds and the bedded limestones interspersed between them. Many fossil shells can be found in the limestones. Numerous relics of lead mining can be found in the quarries and the surrounding area.

From the car park, walk downhill through the arch under the High Peak Trail and turn half-left to the viewpoint into the NORTHEAST QUARRY (formerly Upper Coal Hills Quarry) (288 522) (locality 2). It is cut into the Cawdor Limestones beds with varying grain size and some instructive sedimentary structures. The far right corner of the quarry face cuts a thin mineral vein and two aspects of mining can be made out. The miners extracted the vein by hand pickwork for the first 3 or 4 metres from the surface and their pick marks can still be seen. Later they sank deeper using drills and blasting and the 1 inch (2.5 cm) diameter drill holes are visible to a depth of some 10 m. The vein below that was too poor and was not worked.

A short digression down the steep path opposite gives a view into the REEF QUARRY (locality 3). The quarry has been cut into one of the classic mud-mounds (reef knolls in older accounts) illustrating the irregular way in which limestone sediments accumulated on the sea floor.

Return towards the arch and just before it take the right-hand path up on to the High Peak Trail. Continue along this northeastwards for about 300 m and then turn sharp left through the bushes into STEEPLEHOUSE QUARRY (also known as Steeple Grange or Smart's Quarry) (288 554) (locality 4). "Steeple" is a corruption of steep hill, and the roads up to Bole Hill explain that connotation very well. The buildings by this turn are the remains of BOLE HILL WHARF, with its name dating from when the canal company built the railway about 1830. The quarry is in the highest beds of limestone and it is crossed by two thin veins. Pick-marks and a few shot holes are visible, as well as veneers of baryte on joint faces. The limestones are packed with fragments of fossil crinoid stems and also have many chert nodules.

Leaving the quarry and turning back to the Wharf it is worth walking a few metres further east on to the bridge over the B 5036 road (locality 5) whence there is a view of the much disturbed ground along the GANG VEIN to the north. The Cromford Moor mines lie below the crag of Black Rocks in the trees beyond. The east-west Gang Vein along the crest of Bole Hill was by far the richest vein in the district and was the focus of intensive mining and many disputes. A branch from the old mineral railway (High Peak Trail) here once led to the Middleton Limestone Mine; its track is now occupied by a miniature railway, open to tourists.

Whilst at this point it is worth stopping to consider the problems faced by the miners. Beneath this area progressively deeper mining in the 16th and 17th centuries required drainage and several soughs were driven in from the north (Vermuyden's Sough 1631; Bates Sough 1657; Cromford Sough 1657 onwards) and from the east (Meerbrook Sough 1772 onwards). There were several other soughs driven northwards beneath Wirksworth town, but little can be seen of these today.

Turn back along the High Peak Trail (the former railway linking the Cromford and Whaley Bridge canals), walking southwest past the National Stone Centre. The left-hand wall a few yards ahead is partly built of square gritstone blocks about 40x40x15 cm which were once the sleepers for the railway. Sockets for the rail ties can be found on some of them. The long-disused COAL HILLS QUARRY on the right (north) (285 553) (locality 6) has an old lead mine shaft in the far right-hand corner, where it was cut into by the quarry face. A little imagination will restore the missing side of the shaft and give an idea of the narrow holes the miners used to get to their workings.

Continuing along the High Peak Trail through a cutting with limestone crags on the left: a short walled section marks the site of a former branch railway going down an incline to Wirksworth. The crags

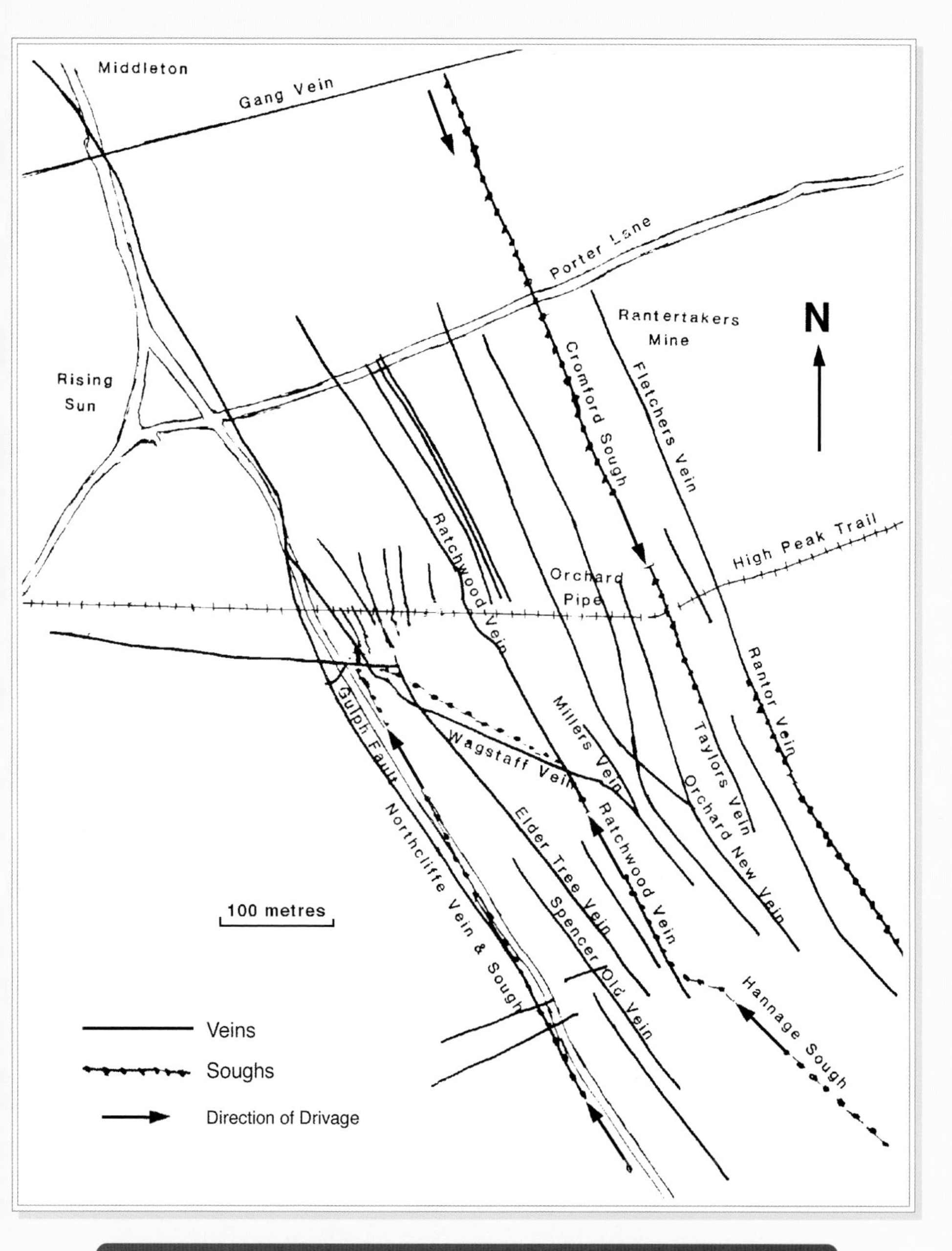


**Opposite page: Top: Much disturbed ground along the Gang Vein**
**Below: A large stope in Godbehere Mine**
**Above: Mineral veins and soughs beneath the Gulph**

on each side have small worked-out pipe veins. Immediately beyond the cutting take the track through the bushes to the left on to a small terrace overlooking THE GULPH (284 552), (locality 7) with the ivy-clad crag of Rantor (=Raventor) on the left. The Gulph is, in effect, a miniature rift valley, where a stretch of ground some 300 m wide has been dropped down between two faults. On the left the Rantor Fault has a displacement down to the west of about 50 m whilst the Gulf Fault along the road ahead raises the strata again by about 150m. Much of the limestone escarpment west of the Gulf Fault has been removed by the Middlepeak Quarry and the fault scarp is no longer the striking feature it once presented. The floor of the Gulph is shales resting on limestone below, and several veins parallel to the two bounding faults lie in these concealed limestones. Large waste hillocks mark numerous mines including Nether Ratchwood and Orchard Mines. The lost mine of Orchard Pipe, noted by Farey in 1811, lies beneath the Trail near the viewpoint.

With the deeper parts of the veins in the Gulph lying under a progressively greater cover of shale towards Wirksworth the mines there ran into drainage problems and several soughs were driven in from around the town. These include Lees, Hannage, Ranter, Northcliffe and Baileycroft Soughs. Cromford Sough was extended beneath the Gulph in the 1770s but was made redundant by the lower Meerbrook Sough in the 1840s and it discharges little water today. Branches of all these soughs lie beneath the Gulph but the bulk of the drainage today finds its way out of Meerbrook Sough into the River Derwent north of Whatstandwell, where some 3.5 million litres per day are drawn off and piped into public supplies.

Returning to the High Peak Trail, continue westwards to the foot of the MIDDLETON INCLINE (283 552) (locality 8) where railway trucks were hauled up by a stationary engine at the top. A timber-framed pit on the left contains the pulley wheel for the endless steel wire cable of which a few scraps are still lying about on the Trail. It was last used in 1966.

Some 20 m up the incline the field on the right (north) has an obvious mine hillock and capped shaft. This is RATCHWOOD FOUNDER MINE (282 552). Worked at least as early as 1696 the complex of passages and stopes linked several mines and extends under the Trail and the nearby coal merchants store and adjacent buildings, with workings eventually going through the Gulf Fault into the limestones beyond. Internal shafts reached as deep as the Cromford Sough but the lowest workings are now flooded.

Continue up the incline as far as the bridge over the Wirksworth to Middleton road (B 5023) (locality 9). At this point it is worth stopping to reflect on the fact that the road is built along the Gulf Fault and in the unlikely event of another earthquake moving the fault again, it might be a case of "tear along the dotted line" in the middle of the road.

Looking north from the bridge towards Middleton, hidden away in the old Hoptonwood Quarry some 500 m to the north is the portal of the MIDDLETON LIMESTONE

***Above: The "reef" quarry at the National Stone Centre, overlooked by the Barrel Edge escarpment of Millstone Grit***

***Right: The former head frame at Ratchwood Mine***

MINE (277 556). Opened in 1959 to extract high purity limestones, the workings have gone in 2 km right under Middleton Moor to reach daylight in Hopton Quarry, a mile away to the west. In so doing they have intersected the workings of several old lead mines, including Bondog Hole. The Middleton Limestone Mine is NOT open to public viewing. A short path off the incline just below the bridge leads on to the road. Turn right and a short distance uphill at Middleton Cross is the ROBIN HOOD, providing suitable refreshment for mine historians. Road-widening a few years ago uncovered a mine shaft in the grass verge by the crossroads but nothing is to be seen now.

The excursion can be terminated at the bridge, with a return along Porter Lane to the National Stone Centre car park. Alternatively, enthusiasts may like to climb to the top of the incline (or drive round) and visit the MIDDLETON TOP ENGINE HOUSE (276 552) (locality 10) to inspect the beam engine, still in working order. It is similar to those used on many mines but was adapted for hauling goods wagons up the High Peak Railway. A small visitor centre and car park are nearby.

# 15 CARSINGTON PASTURE AND BRASSINGTON

*A breccia of baryte and calcite in Golconda Mine*

By R. Slack & T. D. Ford
(based on an earlier version by R. Tune)

**Maps: 1:25000 map SK 25; 1:10000 maps SK 25 SW & SE**

**Walking distance 5 miles (8 km)**

Carsington Pasture has a very long mining history, stretching back at least as far as the Romans, who smelted lead nearby. There are ancient walls on the Pasture, partly obscured by mining waste, marking field boundaries of Romano-British or even earlier times. The Roman mining settlement of Lutudarum was probably somewhere in the vicinity of Carsington but has not been located yet. Evidence of mining between Roman times and the 16th century is sparse but records of the industry thereafter have been researched and published. As Carsington Pasture escaped most of the effects of the Enclosure Acts of Parliament there are few stone walls.

The walk described below gives only a limited view of the mining activity which was intense at times. The route is roughly in the form of a square with sides a mile (1.6 km) long. It is bounded by the villages of Brassington and Carsington to the south and

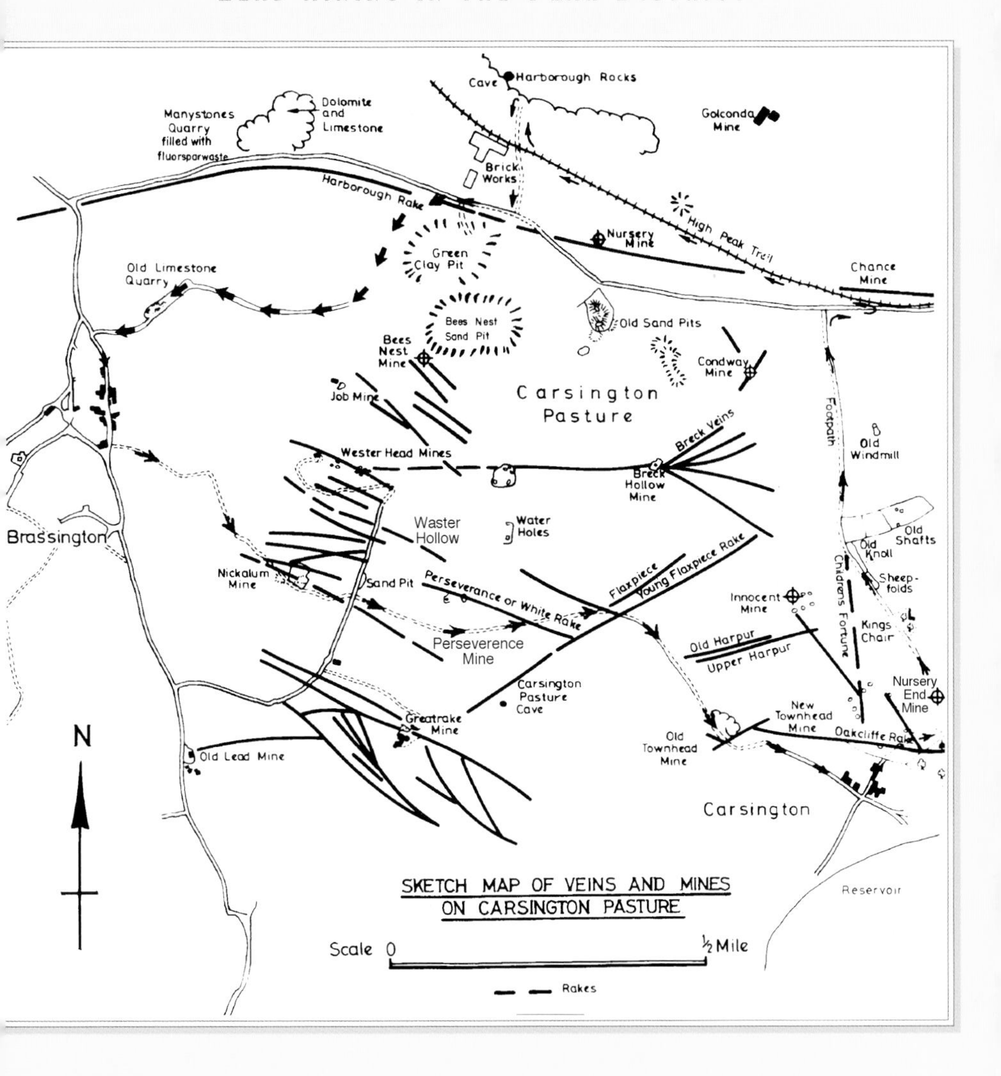


by the minor road between Wirksworth and Brassington on the north. Last worked on any scale were the NICKALUM and GREAT RAKE Mines, both producing baryte in the 1920s. The nearby CONDWAY MINE was worked briefly in 1940-1943 whilst the GOLCONDA MINE finally ceased work in 1953 after two centuries of intermittent activity. Though all these were baryte mines in their final years all had been important lead producers earlier. Many still have ruined coes where the miners changed their clothes and kept their tools. There is a scatter of open shafts, some hidden in long grass so take care!

The limestones around Brassington have mostly been dolomitized, i.e. magnesium has been introduced into the calcium carbonate molecule. The result is a more porous, cream-coloured rock which weathers to a grey-brown, pitted surface, as can be seen on Harborough Rocks. Dolomite thus contrasts with the light grey of the unaltered limestone and is locally called dunstone.

There are also two small caves: one in HARBOROUGH ROCKS yielded evidence of Romano-British occupation. The other cave is well hidden in a hollow in the middle of Carsington Pastures. Harborough Rocks Cave has been occupied on and off since Neolithic times. Either cave could be the cave described by Daniel Defoe when he visited the Wirksworth area in 1731. He wrote of his party meeting a miner's wife and five children who lived happily *"in a natural opening in the rock, wherein her husband had been born. The chamber within was divided by a curtain, had shelves with earthenware, pewter and brass. A hole in the roof served as a chimney. She had a few pigs and a cow enclosed outside. She earned, when she could, a few pence per day washing ore"*. Defoe and his party presented her with half-a-crown ($12^1/_2$p) at which she was highly delighted. Harborough Cave seems the most likely candidate for Defoe's woman's cave as he noted a Giant's Tomb on the rocks above where there is a tumulus today. Defoe and his friends also paid a visit to a nearby mine shaft where he left us a graphic account of a miner returning to the surface: "*We were agreeably surprised to see a hand and then an arm and, quickly after, a head thrust up out of the very groove we were looking at....this subterranean creature...was a most uncouth spectacle clothed all in leather.... for his person he was as lean as a skeleton, pale as a dead corpse, his hair and beard a deep black, his flesh lank, and as we thought something of the colour of lead itself. He drew up a basket of tools the names of which we could not understand"*. The cave where the miner's family lived is usually taken to be the Harborough Rocks Cave but if Carsington Pastures Cave is visited with Defoe's account in hand it fits the description reasonably well so an element of doubt must remain.

## ITINERARY

The starting point for the walk is at the Miners Arms in BRASSINGTON (232 544), a typical lead mining village though the main occupation today is agriculture. The landlord was the local Barmaster who also supplied ale to the miners on measuring days. The village has some interesting old buildings and a fine church and was listed as "Branzincton" in Domesday book which made no mention of lead mines there. It is unknown when lead mining started here but there is documentary evidence of mining in 1305 and by the 16th century Brassington was one of the chief sources of lead ore for the Earl of Shrewsbury's smelters. One of the Earl's buyers referred to the "orr that is got in Brassington lordship ...that is very good orr and great stor". The Gell family had interests there in the 16th century and by the early 17th C there was enough ore being produced to warrant a Deputy Barmaster. The oldest dated building in Brassington, apart from the church, was built in 1615 as an inn and is now known as the Tudor House. The Westerne family who built it had lead mining connections and it was a meeting place for courts and commissions as early as 1620. In 1627 a hearing on John Gell's claim to tithes of lead ore in Bakewell and elsewhere in the Peak District was held here.

From the east end of Town Street there is a public footpath eastwards across the fields climbing towards the western limits of CARSINGTON PASTURES. After passing through a stile on to open grazing land, it is worth turning round for a view back over the village and its setting amongst the limestone hills. Proceeding up the path, just below the crest of the hill two features astride the path may be seen: on the left is a crushing circle with some track stones still in place, though the centre stone is missing. A ruined coe is close by. Below and to the right are the remains of a settling pond; together these remains may have been associated with the nearby Corsehill Mine.

Ahead, where the path levels out are the ruins of the NICKALUM MINE engine house (237 540). The only other mine with an engine house on the Pasture is Great Rake Mine, visible about 500 metres to the southeast. Adjacent to the Nickalum engine house is a shaft covered with a concrete slab. It is said to have three "turns" of about 70 ft (22 m) each, making a total depth below the engine shaft foot of around 210 ft (63 m). Nickalum Mine bought a steam engine from Great Rake in 1860 and by 1862 was emplying more than 100 men. They celebrated the miners' annual holiday, May 13th, with beer and sandwiches in the fields below. Brassington Liberty's production in 1862 was 2658 loads (roughly 880 tons) and most of it came from Nickalum Mine. Also known as Old Brassington Mine, it was still producing a little baryte in 1912. The mine is said to have been in a pipe vein trending northwest with the strata forming a dome rich in lead ore. At one time it produced ore to the value of £13000 in two years, but in 1891 it produced only 35 loads and 3 dishes (about 9 tons), and by 1895 this had dwindled to 5 loads (a little over one ton).

Leaving Nickalum Mine the path descends into WESTER HOLLOW, a picturesque amphitheatre ringed with limestone crags and with the ground much disturbed by shallow mine workings. On the left at the head of Wester Hollow are the remains of the WESTER HEAD MINES (239 542). Some shafts are said to have been sunk here to depths of 18 to 30 fathoms (35-90 m) in white sand and were worked for cerussite (white lead ore). Similar ore has been found in the nearby silica sand pits. It was a hazard of mining here that the "old man" following a vein sometimes broke into pockets of loose sand occasionally containing cerussite.

High up to the south are the ruins of the GREAT RAKE MINE (240 536), now only low walls and concrete engine beds. The earliest date for this mine is 1653 but there is no evidence of high productivity at any time. In the 1820s only 142 loads of ore were mined in four years. There are two shafts, 320 ft (100 m) and 250 ft (80 m) deep, but sumps at the bottom finally reached 70 fathoms

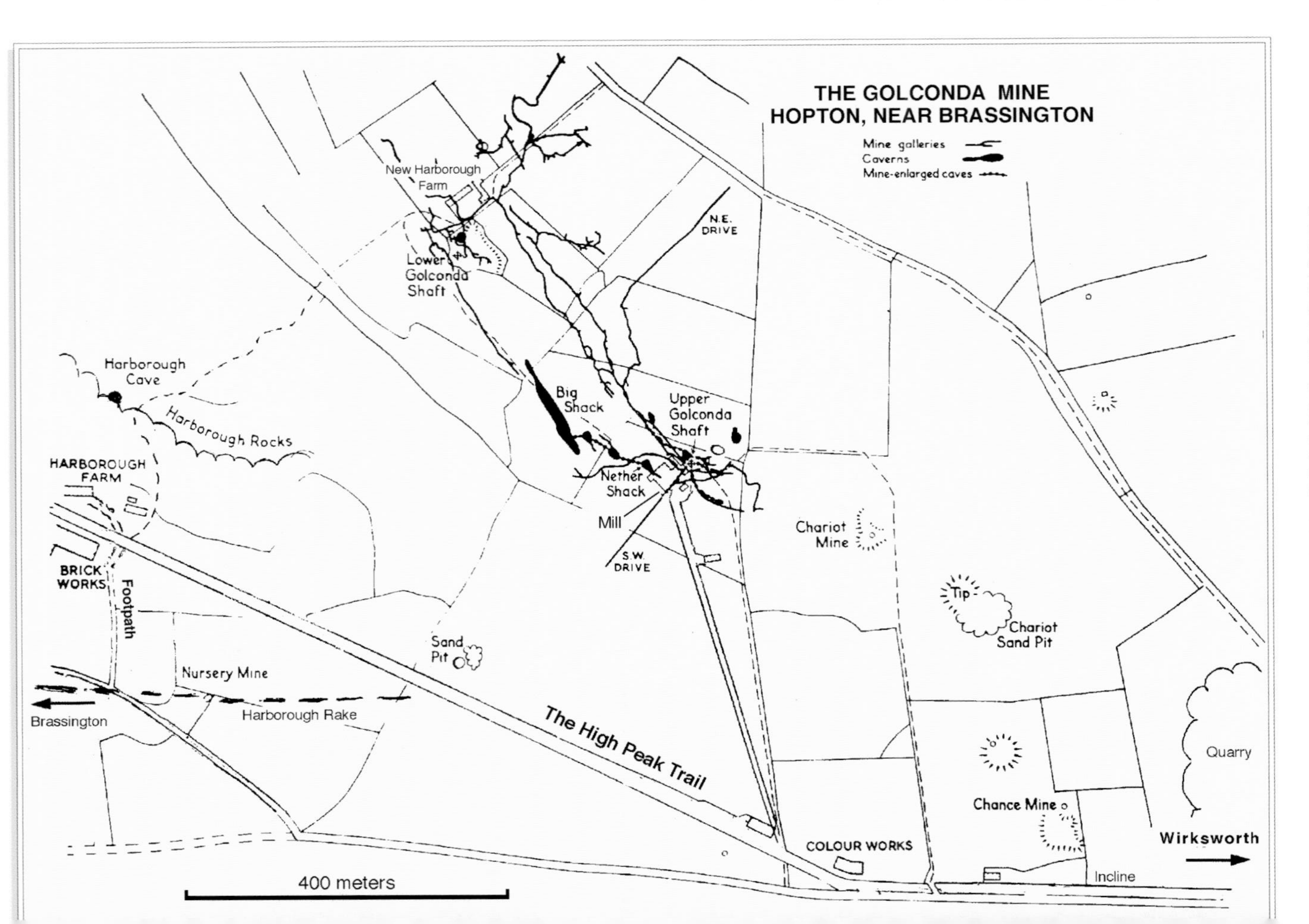
THE GOLCONDA MINE
HOPTON, NEAR BRASSINGTON
Mine galleries
Caverns
Mine-enlarged caves
New Harborough Farm
Lower Golconda Shaft
N.E. DRIVE
Harborough Cave
Harborough Rocks
Big Shack
Upper Golconda Shaft
HARBOROUGH FARM
Nether Shack
Mill
S.W. DRIVE
Chariot Mine
BRICK WORKS
Footpath
Tip
Chariot Sand Pit
Sand Pit
Nursery Mine
Brassington
Harborough Rake
The High Peak Trail
Quarry
Chance Mine
COLOUR WORKS
Wirksworth
Incline
400 meters

**Above: The ruined engine house on Nickalum Mine**
**Below: Layered galena and baryte in Golconda Mine**

(420 ft: 97 m); both are now covered with concrete-filled wheels from the winding gear. In its last years of working during World War I baryte was being produced from a vein from 4 to 11 ft wide (1.3 – 3.5 m) but "robbing" the walls around the shaft led to partial collapse. The mine site was used for iron oxide processing in the 1920s. A winch and ramp for wagons survive as does an iron-tyred gritstone crusher wheel. The washing trough is still in place, and remains of a thick-walled magazine for gunpowder survive.

Adjacent to the cart road in Wester Hollow is one of a series of sandpits of which more later. Following the footpath up the east side of the hollow, pass slightly to the left of a clump of trees and lines of old workings and waste hillocks mark the course of PERSEVERENCE RAKE, sometimes called White Rake from the abundance of cerussite. The remains of Perseverence Mine include two shafts near the crest of the hill, one within the remains of a coe. There are the rectangular stone-edged trough of a buddle, a second coe and a settling pond. The workings below are a complicated warren of galleries adjacent to the rake. In the 1820s Perseverence Mine was owned by a partnership of three Brassington miners and produced 219 loads of ore in five years, sold for £658. CARSINGTON PASTURES CAVE lies in a hollow some 200 yards to the south and has yielded evidence of Neolithic occupation.

The footpath then crosses the ENE-trending YOUNG FLAXPIECE RAKE with ruined coes near fenced off shafts. The ancient Portway track between Derby and Lancashire climbed on to the plateau about here. The path then turns steeply down the slope into the western end of Carsington village. Good views over Carsington Reservoir made be had hereabouts. The Reservoir covers the site of a substantial Roman settlement, which included lead smelting and may have been the site of Lutudarum, a name stamped on several Roman pigs of lead.

In descending the slope the path passes mines with picturesque old names, such as Old Horse, Appletree Swang, Sing-a-Bed, etc. At the second of two old quarries the workings of TOWNHEAD MINE (248 536) lie beneath the track. This mine was working in 1811. New Townhead Mine lay beneath the hillside above the first houses. Continue eastwards into the Carsington village where a welcome break may be had at the MINERS ARMS.

To continue the itinerary, take the narrow path up between the houses by the point where the lane meets the bend in the road. On reaching the gate at the top of the gardens turn right climbing uphill to the top of the wood. Left of the path are five hillocks on YOKECLIFFE (Oakcliff) Rake. On the right of the path by the wall is NURSERY END MINE (253 536) which was producing calamine (zinc carbonate, used in brass-making) as well as lead ore in 1815. On the left here, in a line down the hillside are four shafts of the Cow and Calf Mines.

On reaching the corner of the wood turn left along the wall side. Following the wall one reaches the KINGS CHAIR (253 539), a dolomite crag hollowed out in the form of a throne, probably as an 18th century imitation antiquity or folly.

The rough ground on the Pasture west of the Kings Chair includes the remains of CHILDRENS FORTUNE MINE (251 537). This has a line of shafts running down the hillside to Carsington with a coe at the top and a washing area below. The mine was producing lead ore in the late 18th century: 454 loads of ore were sold in 1797 and a further 1316 loads between 1797 and 1802. Further west is INNOCENT MINE (250 538). William Duesbury, the founder of the Crown Derby porcelain works, invested in this mine about 1770 owing to the alleged discovery of "china clay" there. A hard, white clay, halloysite, occurs in football-sized lumps known to the quarrymen call "snowballs" in some of the silica sand pits, but it is not in economically useful quantities and is no substitute for real china clay.

The route continues northwards towards the road and 400 metres before reaching it and some 400 metres west are the remains of BRECK HOLLOW MINE (246 543). There are two coes within a boundary wall, one with a shaft in it. When debris was removed the second coe was found to have a well-preserved fireplace and chimney. The fireplace had a square recess beside it, containing tools. Other corners were recessed possibly to conceal ore from the Barmaster! The floor is of polished limestone slabs. The Breck Mines (and there were at least ten) were sunk near the intersection of several veins with northwest and northeast trends. The early history is unknown but a little lead ore was still being produced in 1880. Some baryte was raised around 1940.

Just before reaching the road are the remains of CONDWAY MINE (248 545). This was worked in the 1940s for baryte. Earlier, in 1877, it had yielded only $7^1/_2$ dishes of lead ore (about 400 lbs). A little was raised later but the Barmaster served notice to work the mine properly in 1906. Presumably it was not so worked and it was later incorporated into the activities of the Golconda Mine.

Cross the road and climb on to the High Peak Trail along the former track of the Cromford and High Peak Railway. Down in the hollow to the right is the modern Hopton Mill building (260 548) erected about 1961 to extract magnesium metal from dolomite, though this soon proved an unsuccessful operation. Later the building was converted into a fluorspar flotation plant for Guilini Ltd., subsequently taken over by Dresser Minerals plc. All of these operations proved uneconomic. Waste tailings were pumped up to Manystones Quarry for disposal and the quarry is now nearly full.

Walking west along the High Peak Trail, the buildings away to the right are at GOLCONDA MINE (249 551). The buildings are now used as a baryte mill. There is a good coe preserved within a modern electricity sub-station. Golconda Mine was one of the most extensive mines in Derbyshire and takes its name from the fabulously rich mines in India. It was worked for lead at least from the 18th century and finally closed as a baryte mine in 1953. After then water was pumped up for use in the mill up to the 1960s. Golconda Mine's shaft reached a depth of 420 ft (126 m) and there are some 3 miles (5 km) of galleries on old mine plans. The workings encountered several large natural caverns developed along the dolomite/limestone contact. On a recent exploration the signature of I.Rawlinson 1777 was found smoked on to a wall, but the nearby signatures of Henry VIII and of King Tut, B.C.19 were not thought to be genuine! Occasional visits to this by mine by winch down the shaft are arranged by the Wirksworth Mines Exploration Group.

Continuing westwards along the High Peak Trail, Harborough Rocks form an escarpment on the right. Far to the left the chimney-like ruins of Breck Hollow Mine can be seen on the Pasture.

A few minutes walk reaches the brick works of Hoben Quarries Ltd. where silica bricks for furnace linings and other refractory purposes have been manufactured for over a century. A footpath crosses the Trail here and it is worth taking the right hand path past the old farm up on to the top of HARBOROUGH ROCKS for the view, and to visit the cave in the escarpment face. The cave has yielded Romano-British relics. There was a Romano-British site on top of the Rocks, one of which has been carved into a throne. The view also takes in the sand-pits around the works. Some have been filled with waste from the Hopton fluorspar mill but others are still being worked.

The ancient Portway road went over Harborough Rocks past the settlement there.

Descend to the Trail and go straight across on a path to join the road. Turn right along the road passing the works entrance on the right and the track to the sand pits on the left. The sands and associated clays are members of the Brassington Formation, a unique series of sediments of Miocene-Pliocene age which have yielded fossil plant remains including Sequoia wood. Once forming a sheet across the southern part of the limestone plateau the Brassington Formation is now preserved only in solution collapse structures, sometimes called Pocket Deposits. The high-silica sands are used in refractory brick manufacture. Patches of coarse chert gravel underlie the sand in the Bees Nest Pit and represent the insoluble residue from weathering of the limestone. The sands are overlain in places with boulder clay from an early episode of glaciation. Two adjacent pits have been worked in recent years – Bees Nest Pit, close to the site of a lead mine of that name, and Green Clay Pit.

The area of the Bees Nest pit was crossed by the ancient Portway trackway leading from Derby via the Roman settlement covered by Carsington Reservoir on towards Lancashire. Another ancient track, The Street, branched from the Portway near Bees Nest Pit and headed north towards Longcliffe and Bakewell. The Street was still in use in the 10th century when it was known as Kingstreet. Longcliffe still has a field named Street Knowl. Examination of detailed maps shows walls and field boundaries marking the routes of these ancient trackways.

About 200 metres past the works, take the public footpath on the left across badly disturbed ground along Harborough Rake and west of Green Clay Pit. Continue to the old road and turn right down the slope back into Brassington to complete the walk.

# 16 THE CRICH AREA

The wooden former head frame at Jingler Mine

BY P. LUNN, A. G. DIXON & R. HARTWELL

Maps: 1:25000 SK 35; 1:10000 SK 35 NW & SW

Walking distance about 4 miles (6 km)

Geographically the Crich area is a miniature of the Peak District. It is an upfolded mass of limestone 1.5 km long and 0.5 km wide, forming an anticlinal inlier surrounded by the shales and sandstones of the Millstone Grit and Coal Measures. The limestone is crossed by numerous mineral veins, particularly around the northern end.

The natural resources of the Crich area have been exploited for centuries. Roman relics have been found, but unfortunately no detail was recorded. Lead works were operational at the time of the Domesday Book in 1086. Later records are scanty but an early sough was being driven by 1658. An estimated 200 tons of lead ore were raised in 1782. A protracted dispute between the miners at Old End Mine and Glory Mine went as far as Chancery Court in 1831. Mining was important in 1833 when it was listed as the main occupation of the inhabitants. By 1868, operations at the three principal mines, Glory Mine, Old End and Pearson's Venture, were drawing to a close. Since then there has only been intermittent activity at Pearson's Venture, Wakebridge, Old End and Glory Mines, some aimed at producing fluorspar. Extensive quarrying has removed half the hill top firstly for lime-burning and later for roadstone and aggregate.

The summit of Crich Hill is a well-known landmark and viewpoint. It is crowned by the Sherwood Foresters' Memorial Tower. Part of the quarry area is occupied by the National Tramway Museum and the trams stop at a reconstructed lead mine.

The mineral veins are mostly at the northern end of the hill which they cross in NW-SE or NE-SW directions. Some are so close that they may be regarded as double veins with a rider of limestone between them. The old miners had evocative names for these veins – Silver Eye, Caulky, Leather Ears, Wanton Legs, Pig Trough, Shacky, Merry Bird, Kicker and many more.

Commencing outside the entrance to the TRAMWAY MUSEUM (345 548), take the Holloway Road towards Matlock. Soon after the CLIFF INN, the wooded area on the right (east) covers extensive landslips. Several mines were buried hy these, including Pearson's Venture and Rodney Mines, which were engulfed in 1882 as a result of massive slides of quarry waste. At that time the quarry was worked by the Clay Cross Company which had given warning of possible landslips two years earlier. Another slide buried the road and several cottages.

After about 1.5 km, approaching Wakebridge, JINGLER MINE lay in the wood on the left (west) (340 544). Its wooden head frame was erected in the 1920s but removed in 1979. The mine reached 75 m depth and was then worked mainly for fluorspar. Haulage was by an unusual arrangment of a winding drum with a cylinder on each side, one powered by steam from a coal-fired boiler and the other by compressed air. The mine buildings were mostly corrugated iron on wooden frames. There were also coes for the miners to change. Little can be seen today except a concrete slab over the shaft amidst the undergrowth.

Previously Jingler (or Gingler) Mine had been worked for lead ore and went below present water-level. Up to about 1850 it was known as Rolley Mine. Lee's Shaft lay across the road behind the houses. Drainage was by RIDGEWAY SOUGH (also known as Wakebridge or Whatstandwell Level). The sough branched under the adjacent lay-by and the branches went northeast to Wakebridge Mines and southeast to Cliff Side and Pearson's Venture Mines. The water from Cliff Side Mine was said to be lukewarm. An underground pumping engine was fuelled by coal taken up the sough by boat from its tail on the bank of the River Derwent, near Whatstandwell

Bridge (331 549). The entrance is now bricked up with water issuing from an iron pipe.

Ridgeway Sough was begun in 1803. Farey noted it as Wakebridge Sough in 1811. It was then over half a mile long and was being driven in shale and then limestone towards Cliff Side Mines. By 1829 there was a branch through Rolley Shaft to Wakebridge Mine. By the 1850s it was known as Ridgeway Sough, as noted in the Geological Survey Memoir. In 1880 Stokes said it was a mile (1.5 km) long. Although only $4^1/_2$ ft (1.3 m) high it was unusual in that it was used as a boat level with at least 15 inches (38 cm) of water maintained by simple lock gates.

Continuing along the road, turn right up the trackway to Cliff Farm (not to be confused with another Cliff Farm near Plaistow). Immediately on the right, a hillock in a garden marks the site of Bacchus Founder shaft (340 555) which led by a series of ladderways to BACCHUS PIPE. Connecting with Wakebridge Mine nearby, over 1.5 km of workings were still open when explored in the 1970s.

The ruins of WAKEBRIDGE MINE (339 557) are a little further along the track on the left. The ruins are more complete than many mines in the area. There is an engine house with adjacent shafts, either walled or fenced round, a water storage pond largely filled with rushes, and a workshop now used for farm storage. In 1967 another large shaft was uncovered between the walled shaft and the brook: it was 3 x 3.6 m across. The shafts served for haulage, pumping and climbing.

Mining has been carried out at Wakebridge since at least the early 19th century. The engine house appears to have erected on the site of an earlier house with a thatched roof. A circular "engine race" on a plan of 1829 indicates that winding was by horse gin. A steam engine was installed in 1857. Built by Thornewill & Wareham of Burton-on-Trent, it had a cylinder diameter of 60 inches (1.5 m) with a stroke of 8 ft (2.44 m) indoors and $7^1/_2$ ft (2.29 m) outdoors. The engine is said to have been moved to Millclose Mine at Darley Dale in 1889 though as Wakebridge was still working it may have been a little later. At Millclose it was nicknamed Alice and was still working in the 1920s. At Wakebridge it was used both for pumping water up to the level of Ridgeway Sough, 128 m below the surface, from a final depth of 198 m, and for winding ore to the surface. In the mid-19th century up to 42 miners were employed at 2s 6d ($12^1/_2$p) per day. The agent, James Else, received £55 per annum. The mine was large enough to employ a carpenter and a blacksmith. A breakdown in 1863 stopped operations and caused great distress to the miners. The lower levels were flooded and tools etc submerged. The mine first worked a pipe vein extending north, but by the 1880s the miners were working a vein 750 m NNE of the shafts. Haulage was by small wagons on a narrow rail track, pushed along by boys or youths. Illumination was by tallow candles. The lower levels had been abandoned as the cost of pumping was too high.

Mining at Wakebridge continued well into the 20th century, mainly for fluorspar and baryte. Between 1921 and 1931 between 5 and 18 men were employed (5 – 9 underground). During the last period of working from 1945 to the early 1950s, only 5 men were employed and ore was raised from Wakebridge No 2 shaft alongside the brook beyond Cliff Farm.

Continuing up the track from Wakebridge to Cliff Farm, the remains of several dams lie along the brook on the left. These supplied washing water for the ore and it was also piped to Jingler Mine in the 1920s. A concrete slab covers Wakebridge No 2 shaft just beyond the farm. Fluorspar was obtained from levels at 50 and 75 m depth. In 1952 the miners reached a point where the WNW Great Rake met the limestone-shale boundary. Hazel-hurst Vein was also worked near here. The shaft was equipped with an electric hoist and a diesel compressor. About 23 m south was another shaft which had a chimney and a tunnel linking it to No 2 shaft, apparently for ventilation.

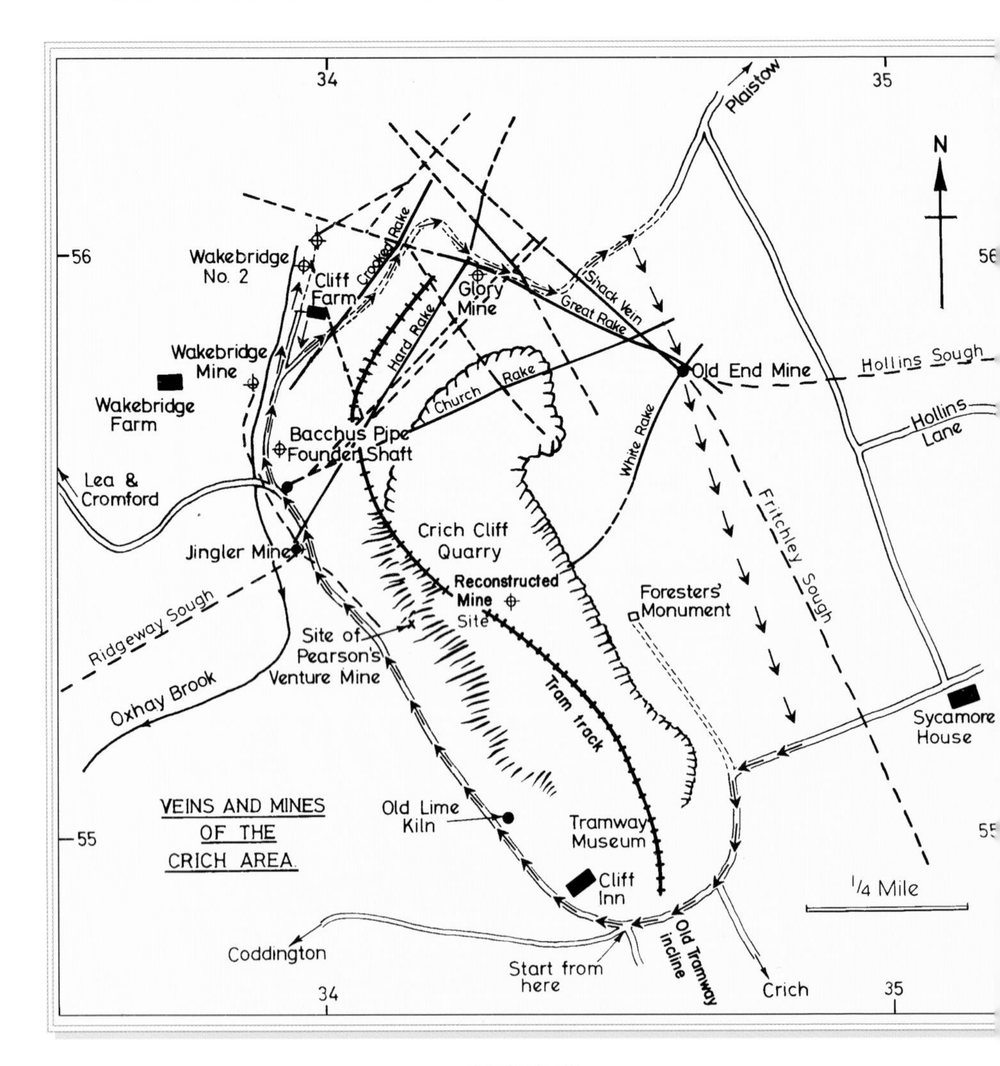

A crushing circle under reconstruction at Crich Tramway Museum

*N.B. The Wakebridge engine house and shafts are on private land. Permission to visit should be sought from Cliff Farm, Wakebridge.*

From Wakebridge No 2 shaft, return to the farm and take the footpath up the hillside. A terrace close by marks the site of a former fluorspar processing plant which has been removed. Continuing uphill the path passes beside the site of a 1967 mining venture known as Smith's Adit. It was driven into the Glory Vein and worked intermittently until 1977.

Soon afterwards, the path crosses the tram track near its terminus. Owing to quarry expansion the path has been re-routed away from GLORY MINE (343 559). The iron head frame has been removed and re-erected on the mining display further down the tram track. Glory Mine was last worked in the 1950s. It had been worked intermittently for at least 150 years, firstly for lead and later fluorspar. By the mid 19th century it had reached 146 m and had up to eight wagon ways operating. The mine is said to have been very rich and was one of the deepest in the area at 247 m depth. The shaft penetrated toadstone at 55 m and went through 18 m of it to work the vein in the limestone below.

As with many mines in Derbyshire, Glory Mine also had its disputes. The Barmaster, Luke Alsop, recorded in May 7th 1890 that a riot occurred between two factions of dissatisfied miners over the working of Glory Mine and they damaged much property. The miners were each fined 3s 4d (17p). Six months earlier he had imposed a fine of £3.9s.0d (£3.45p) on a miner after finding him guilty of nearly cutting through the winding rope, thereby endangering life.

Continuing on the footpath across the upper end of the quarry, the path reaches a stile to the lane to Cliff Farm, Plaistow. Below the quarry, in a field adjacent to the lane is the site of OLD END MINE on the Great Rake (346 558). Until 1981 the ruined engine house dominated the area, but all is removed and landscaped now. Only a concrete-capped shaft remains. Last worked in the 1940s Old End Mine reached a depth of 278 m and was one of the deepest shafts in

**Cornish Engine House at Wakebridge Mine near Crich**

Derbyshire, and it was the deepest sunk entirely in limestone. The mine was drained by the CRICH SOUGH (Fritchley Level) which entered the shaft at 128 m depth. It drained SSE to a brook at Fritchley, some 3 km away. The outfall arch bears the date 1753. It was driven to unwater "The Hollins Sough Lead Mines in the Parish and Manor of Crich". Some old mining maps show two soughs, Hollins and Fritchley.

An undated plan, probably from the 1840s, shows the engine house and a whimsey for winding, an ore house, a blacksmith's shop, a reckoning house and a store shed, all indicating a substantial mining operation. However, output had dropped to nil by 1864 and the plant was offered for sale. Three years later the Barmaster noted that a company had decided to erect machinery for draining the lower levels again. They had been abandoned owing to litigation over disputes among the shareholders. Work proceeded and in 1873 a vast cavern was discovered. However, in 1879 the owners started to withdraw their pumping gear and to abandon the mine owing to rising costs and the refusal of the Wakebridge Mine owners to pay their share of the costs. Less than a month later the lower levels of Glory Mine, some 300 m away, were flooded. The lower levels of Wakebridge Mine were abandoned six months later. It demonstrated the interconnection between all these mines so that when Old End stopped pumping all were flooded. Together with declining prices and rising costs the end of the lead mining industry was in sight.

In 1908 Drabble Brothers of Matlock took possession of the Title to Old End and Glory Mines, as well as all veins, meers, rights and privileges. Mining revived for a few years but declined in the 1940s. At that time the shaft was open to 91 m but the workings were in poor condition. The shaft has since been filled in and covered. Some fluorspar was obtained from open-cuts on Church Rake and the eastern end of Old End Rake nearby, whilst a little was raised from a shaft 50 m WNW of Old End Mine.

The route to the Old End mine site is along the lane until a public footpath is reached on the right (south), near Cliff Farm. After crossing the first field, the capped shaft is to the right of the path. Beyond, through a squeeze stile, the grassy area to the right is where the engine house and other buildings once stood. The footpath continues across the fields below the Monument on the hill top to reach Plaistow Green Road. Turn right and follow the road back to the Tramway Museum entrance.

As an alternative to the last section of the route, return along the farm lane and take the path skirting the quarry up to the Monument. From the triangulation point nearby there is a fine panoramic view of the countryside and a good idea of the Crich anticline can be gained. To the east are the scarps of the Millstone Grit while to the west is the top of the quarry face with the Tramway Museum below. The River Derwent lies in the low ground to the west, flowing across down-folded Millstone Grit. The lane south from the Monument lane leads back to the starting point.

Within the premises of the Tramway Museum is the MINING DISPLAY already mentioned, where members of the Peak District Mines Historical Society have constructed a typical lead mine site with the re-erected Glory Mine head frame at the centre. Items salvaged from various sites include a buddle, climbing shaft top, drawing shaft with stows and kibble, an adit, a miner's coe, crushing circle and a bole hearth. Also to be seen are a jaw crusher, a roll crusher, a jig, logwasher, meerstones and a water pump. A small museum has mineral specimens, old mining tools, mine plans, fossils etc. Demonstrations of modern mineral separation using a Wilfley Table are given at intervals. Access is provided by tram – alight at the Wakebridge stop.

**The Crich Sough tail of 1753 at Fritchley**

# 17 STONEDGE CUPOLA, ASHOVER

*The Stonedge Cupola chimney and pond*

BY L. WILLIES

Walking Distance – about 0.25 mile (0.5 km.).

OS 1:25 000 Outdoor Leisure Map No. 24: The Peak District: White Peak Area.

The chimney of Stonedge Cupola, near Spitewinter is a prominent landmark (334 670). It is to be found near the junction of the two main roads which brought ore from the mining areas. Lead Lane (B6015) runs from Darley Dale and Rowsley towards Chesterfield and served the mines near Wensley, Winster, Elton and Youlgreave. The other is nowadays the main Matlock to Chesterfield road (A632)and served Wirksworth, Bonsal, Matlock and the Ashover mines. Joining the two roads at the hamlet of Spitewinter is Belland Lane (a reference to lead poisoning). *Approach the site from the footpath leading southwest from the corner on Belland Lane. Parking is very limited indeed.* If you handle stones etc. on the site, be sure to wash your hands before eating!

The site is on the high gritstone moors (334 670)about three miles from Chesterfield, formerly a significant market for lead and home of a number of lead merchanting families. It is likely such a barren spot was chosen to help the dispersal of poisonous lead fumes but, as well as its convenience for ore supplies, it is not far from coal, which came from Walton Colliery just down the road, and is very close to a refractory clay necessary for the furnaces. The Pot Clay

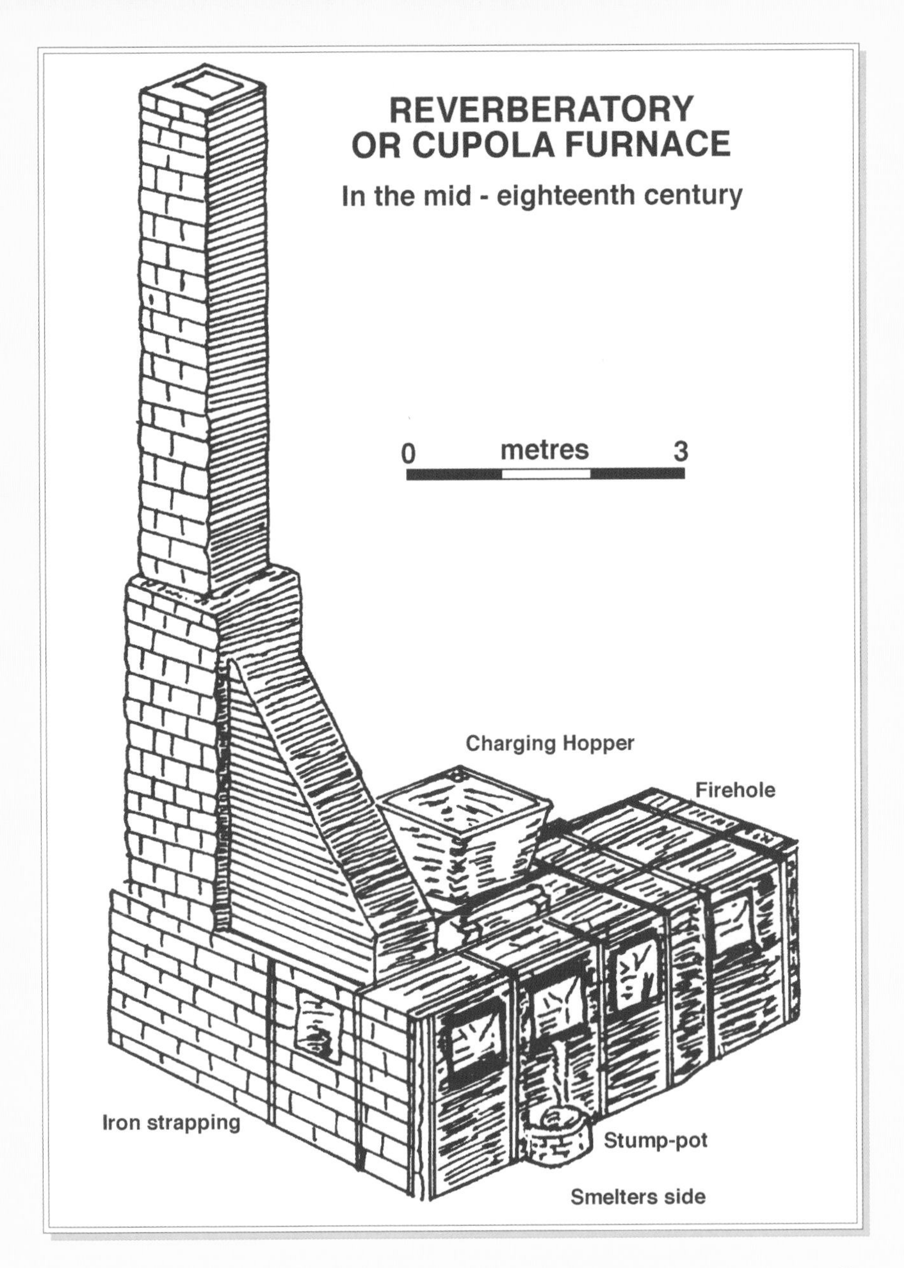


outcrop is found just a few hundred yards away.

Today the 55 ft (17 m) high, square, gritstone chimney is the most obvious feature, but much of the site has the robbed trenches of a former, complex, flue system which led from the furnaces to the chimney. Originally these were arched tunnels covered in earth or ash – small sections can still be found – and others still exist below the surface near the chimney. Nearby can also be found the remains of condensing chambers. Together with the flues, these were used to condense lead fumes, which could then be re-smelted. These were mainly developed after 1851 with the adoption of the Spanish slag hearth, but the use of a short flue was also recorded in 1811.

The cupola is a type of reverberatory furnace which was able to use coal as fuel. It used a high chimney to provide sufficient draught, did not need power for bellows, though an associated slag hearth did, for which the surviving dam and wheel-pit was constructed. The first cupola furnace to be used in Derbyshire was introduced by the Quaker London Lead Company about two miles from here about 1735, but Stonedge was not built until about 1770. The facilities were described about 1811 when there were four furnaces but only one in work. Then recently rebuilt, it then had a barn-like building just south of the chimney and it is just possible the remains of the flue still to be seen there belonged to this period of use. The slag hearth originally on site was a small water-powered blast furnace and was placed adjacent to the wheel pit below the dam. The later Spanish slag hearth was taller with a blast powered by a small steam engine. It produced very high temperatures to release almost the last vestiges of lead from slag, but was very "dirty" as a result – as much as a third of the lead went up the flue. This led to the poisoning of cattle – thus the name of the Lane and of Belland Piece, the land next to it – and the development of the flues. This was the second site in the country to have this type of furnace which was sited in the hollow north of the chimney where the remains of a loading ramp and a heat-reddened shaft-stump are visible.

The original owners were Thornhill and Twigge and then Twigge and Winchester. These went bankrupt about 1789. The site was taken over by Barker and Wilkinson who produced some 500 tons of lead a year until about 1807, then by Sykes, Milnes and Co.(a Hull lead merchant and a local gentleman lead merchant from Stubbing Edge, Ashover, respectively). It was being operated by William and Charles Milnes about 1830. About 1848-49 it was briefly operated by Charles Pasco who "came from Cornwall", and who may have been one of the Magpie Miners a few years earlier. From 1850 to 1860 the site was taken over by James Mitchel, lately returned from Spain, for slag smelting. Today the site is still owned by a distant descendent of the Milnes family.

During the summer the site has a rich metal-tolerant flora, including Leadwort (*Minuartia verna)* which grows in otherwise nearly bare areas and has tiny, white star-like flowers.The soil has up to about 3% lead content in such places.

Adjacent to the site is the former Pig of Lead inn and the weigh-house with its arched opening. The latter has been extended to form a house.

The cupola is a Scheduled Ancient Monument and, with the oldest industrial chimney in Britain (c.1770), is listed in the *Guinness Book of Records*. Please be aware the site is very fragile and avoid clambering over walls etc. The chimney was restored in 1979 by PDMHS with the agreement of the then owner, the late Mrs Marriott of Spitewinter. Financial help was given by the Grocers Company via the Ancient Monuments Society, Derbyshire County Council and the then Department of the Environment.

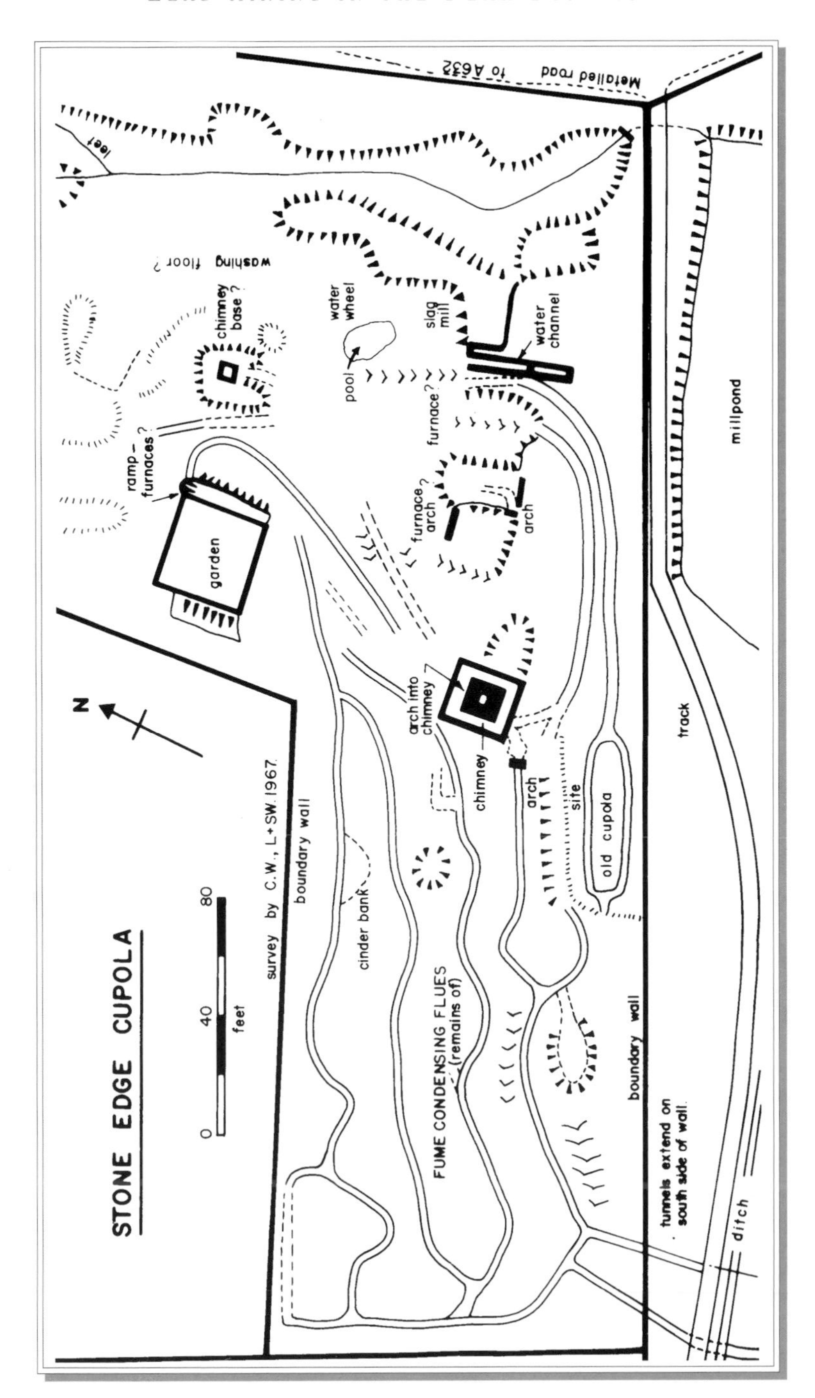
STONE EDGE CUPOLA
0
40
80
feet
survey by C.W., L+SW. 1967.
N
Metalled road to A632
leat
washing floor ?
chimney base ?
water wheel
pool
slag mill
water channel
furnace ?
ramp-furnaces ?
furnace arch ?
arch
garden
millpond
arch into chimney
chimney
arch
site
old cupola
track
boundary wall
cinder bank
FUME CONDENSING FLUES (remains of)
boundary wall
tunnels extend on south side of wall.
ditch

# 18 THE ECTON COPPER MINES

Walled entrance to Clayton Adit

By L. Porter

1:25000 White Peak Outdoor Leisure Map.

Walking distance 3.5 miles.

**Situated in the Manifold Valley in North Staffordshire, close to Warslow, is Ecton Hill (098.585). Here are the remains of a vast copper mine which was exceedingly rich. It may have been the richest mine in the Peak District if its 18th Century income was considered at today's values. It became well known in the mining industry throughout the country. Of non-ferrous metalliferous mines, it ranks in richness and reputation amongst the top mines in England, alongside Devon Great Consols at Tavistock, Parys Mountain in Anglesey, Dolcoath in Cornwall and a few more.**

Its huge workings are chiefly below river level and are now flooded, although it took seven years to fill with water. Its ores were owned by the Duke of Devonshire and the Burgoyne family. There were two principal deposits and the Duke was fortunate enough to be able to exploit the ore on his own ground and to find the one which existed on the Burgoyne royalty.

Stone hammers and an antler pick suggest that the mine was worked in prehistoric times, probably the Bronze

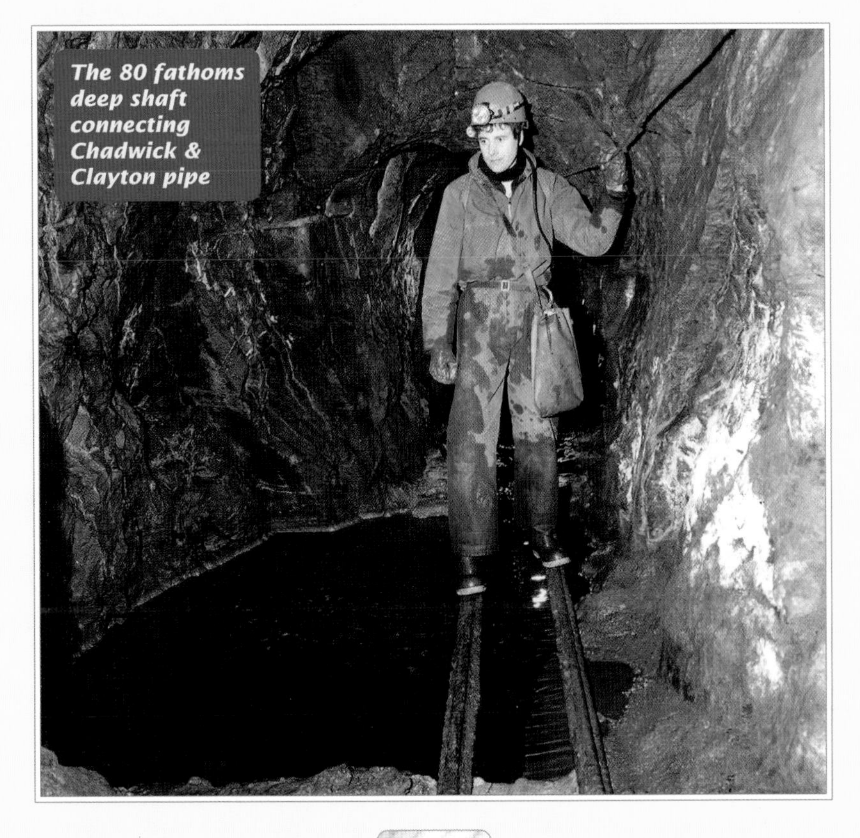
The 80 fathoms deep shaft connecting Chadwick & Clayton pipe

Age. In the 17th Century it was worked illegally, without the necessary licence from the Mines Royal. The ore was smelted too without the required licence, bringing "uncontrolled" and possibly cheaper metal onto the national market. Gunpowder was used here at a very early date, at least in 1672 and possibly earlier.

A century later, the Duke was able to take advantage of rich ores to challenge the monopolistic control over ore and metal prices established by Thomas Williams who was working, by open cast, the huge deposit at Parys Mountain. At one point, Ecton was the richest and deepest mine in Europe. The 18th Century also saw the introduction of an early underground canal for haulage, 200 ft below the river. There were other technological innovations as the mine became deeper and the Duke established one of the earliest vertically integrated mining concerns.

The early 19th Century saw declining revenues in the Ecton Mine. A further pipe deposit of huge size was found and worked by the Duke in the adjacent Clayton Mine. After 1820, the mines were worked by a succession of companies but to no avail. It was the last North Staffordshire non-ferrous metal mine to close in the 1880s, the end of an industry stretching back over 500 years.

The ores were initially found in veins, but two of these developed into huge vertical "pipes" or deposits. Today it is impossible to determine why this happened. It is known that in the Ecton Mine the ore was found in eight deposits arranged vertically, creating eight huge caverns once the ore was extracted.

It is also known that the ore was at its richest in "saddles". These could be anticlinal or synclinal formations. The ore was found in beds or "wings" each side of the axis and often there was a vertical deposit or "joint" down the axis. It is possible that the pipes are a series of "joints" linking one saddle to another with a particular weakness at one point which was exploited by the mineral-laden fluids from which the ores (chalcopyrite, chalcocite and bornite) emanated. This weakness could have been created where an east-west saddle was crossed by a north-south saddle (known locally as a double saddle). One of these is known to exist at the cavern at the 34 fathoms level. Clearly with two saddles crossing in this manner, the geology must be very complicated and no detailed geological examination was reported during the life of the mine.

In addition to the copper ore, quantities of lead ore were found and some zinc blende. In the 18th Century, the value of the zinc went unappreciated, until the visit of Viscount Torrington. The latter found great quantities of the ore abandoned by the miners. Zinc blende became of greater commercial value in the 1830's with the discovery of a more efficient method of smelting it. Thereafter it became a feature of the ore figures, especially in the period 1839-1845 when Melville Attwood sent 1146 tons to the smelters at Whiston, Ripley and Cheadle and again in the 1870/1890 period. There was also quite a lot of galena and in the 19th Century there were times when the complex was yielding more lead ore than copper.

Ecton copper mines ceased work in May 1889 and gave notice to terminate the leases on January lst 1891. Since that date, many features have disappeared for a variety of reasons.

The majority of the tips have been removed, firstly for use as ballast during the construction of the Manifold Light Railway, when the stone was purchased for three farthings per ton, and since by the Staffordshire County Council.The main buildings at Ecton were adopted for use as a creamery and cheese factory and other buildings used as a supply of building stone. In fact, only five buildings used by the miners remain intact and three of these are now dwellinghouses.

The site of the creamery and smelters is a mass of ruins, filter beds and tips. The filter beds were used to allow whey from the creamery to settle before being pumped over the road to Birches Level for disposal. All the buildings which existed here have been demolished and it is difficult to appreciate the pre 20th Century layout.

## ITINERARY

To examine the hill completely can take nearly a full day. However the views from Ecton Hill more than compensate for the effort involved. Many of the shafts on the hillside are deep, some descending several hundred feet. All should be considered to be dangerous, whether deep or not.

Commence at Stamps Bridge, SWAINSLEY (092 578) (1). The field between the river and road, looking downstream, is the site of the Stamps Yard. The Stamps date from 1818 when the vast quantities of waste ores regarded as worthless during the mines' heydey were reworked for the minerals which they contained. They were still in use until 1866.

The Stamps were connected to Ecton by a tramway and water channel (to supply a small water-wheel) which are shown on Staley's plan of 1820. The tramway roughly followed the line of the road, but the watercourse, which commenced approximately opposite Clayton adit entrance, took a wider sweep of the spur of the hill and followed the line of the road from Ecton Lea. It returned to the river some 200 feet downstream from Stamps Bridge. There was one long building here but no trace can now be seen.

Proceeding northwards (2) around the road towards Ecton the large field in front of ECTON LEA was formerly a "gentleman's bowling green," but again there are no traces. Ecton Lea was operated as a Temperance Hotel for a while at the beginning of the twentieth century. As Ecton comes into view, the quarry on the right was worked by Manifold Quarries Co. and closed in the 1950s. From the road at this point one can appreciate how much the landscape has been scarred by mining activities despite the many trees which cover the waste tips.

By the entrance to BIRCH'S LEVEL (originally known as Slag Level) existed the foundations of the lead slag mill which was fed with water from the Fish Pond launder. These also fed the dressing floors. Standing by CLAYTON ADIT entrance and looking towards the dressing floor, one could, until recently, see the stone channel which enclosed the launder, high in the gravel quarry. The water served a waterwheel at the slag mill but no traces remain.

Whilst looking above the adit entrance, the ramp from road level up towards the dressing floor is clearly visible. It was carried over the gravel pit by a wooden trestled bridge and carried a double tramway track up to the far side of the quarry, where it can still be traced.

Ecton Mine's former extensive tips are being hidden by trees. The Dale Mine tips can be seen to the left

There were originally two dressing floors, one for each royalty. The Burgoyne ores were dressed in front of Birch's Level and the Devonshire ores were dressed adjacent to The Ecton Deep Level Adit entrance. The latter moved up to the same horizon as Salt's Level following the completion of that adit in 1804. Following that time, ore was drawn up to this level and trammed out onto the hillside. The floor here used water from the gritstone launder, brought from the Fishpond, and this floor was used solely after companies started to work both royalties together.

The old road originally passed in front of ECTON DEEP ADIT entrance and this too can be seen. By taking this old track, to the left of the road, on the right the foundations of the South Smelthouse can be seen (3). This was a single storey 18th Century stone and tile building and the south-east corner was below road level at the eaves. In the 1880s it was used as a smith's forge, carpenter's shop and miner's changing room.

The large concreted slab about 2 feet above the present road level and a little further north is the site of the Clockhouse smelter (4), so called because it had a large stonefaced clock on its north side, some three ft (1m) in diameter. This building was two-storey and built of stone and tile, with gable ends, standing flush with the dirt-track classed as the road. Between the two smelters existed the sawpit, of timber construction and with a wooden plank roof. This was situated across the site of the present cabin and cannot be traced. On the other side of the road existed two buildings, one of which received the ore from the dressing-floor. Both were opposite the present cabin and the site was later used by the railway constructors for their site office. This was a wooden building and was converted to a chapel by Sir Thomas Wardle of Swainsley Hall after the railway opened in 1904. The Clockhouse smelter became the main building of the creamery.

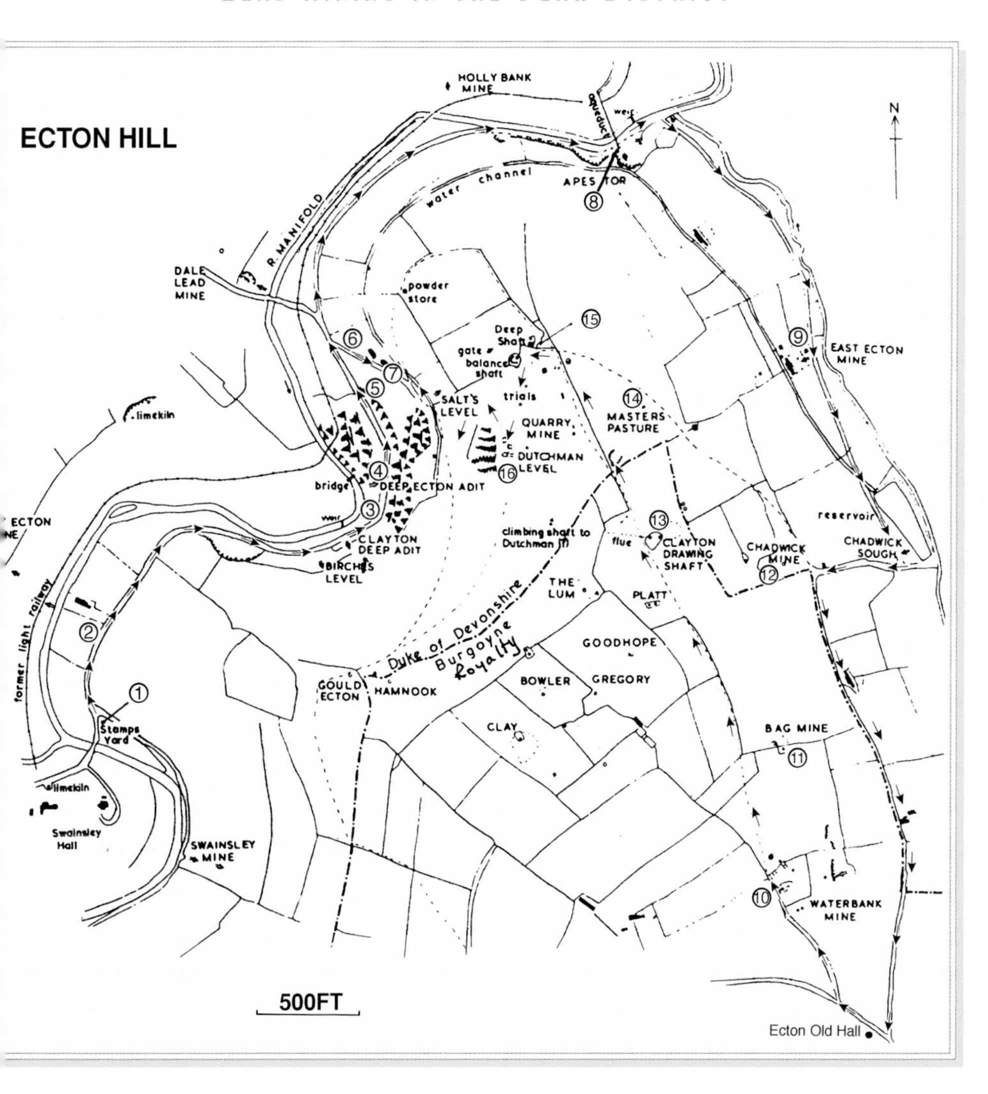


A little to the north of the smelters and on the river side of the road was a small dwellinghouse. An overhead cable passed near this cottage, bringing waste material to be tipped by the river. The waste rock was held behind two high retaining walls to prevent it from falling into the road. The tips then stood to a height of some 20-30 ft (6-10m) right up to the road but much of it was removed in the construction of the railway.

Further north still and opposite the southern end of the Manager's Cottage could be seen four foundation stones which were all that remained of the school built by the Duke. The track onto adjacent land, sometimes used by caravans, is approximately across the site of the school. It was used until the National School opened in Warslow. The latter opened under the aegis of the National Society for promoting Anglican Education. At one point the mine school had a register of over 60 children.

The Manager's Cottage (5) is a fine stone and tile structure and was the home of Samuel Bonsall, mine captain for 33 years until his death in 1870. At the rear of the house is a road up to the castle folly, the latter being built in 1933. The road is known as Manchester Road and originally went along the western edge of Ecton to Wetton Mill via Broad Ecton Farm and The Sugar Loaf, near Dale Farm. Manchester Road probably has its origins in the days of the mid-19th century when Ecton was financed by the Manchester-based firm of Mather & Platt Ltd., which was run by Colin Mather who also held the mines on lease. The first building above this road was the sales and auction room (6), whilst the next cottage was the office (7). Just above the latter a bridle path turns northwards into a copse, past the small powder house of 1884, and up to the Ecton Engine House.

The path now leaves Ecton and follows the road around the north part of the hill to APES TOR. The road gives a good view of the DALE LEAD MINE, above the road is the launder from the Fish Pond. It is still in working order and is controlled by a valve where it crosses the bridle path. The water runs in a gritstone trough, some six inches wide. Above Apes Tor Quarry, a short and little known trial can be seen. The quarry has unfortunately obliterated a number of features. Although Apes Tor shaft cannot be seen from here, one can trace the channel on the other side of the valley which brought water to provide the motive force of a 30 ft x 6 ft (9 x 2m) waterwheel which drove the pumps in the Ecton Mine and replaced the hydraulic pumping engine in 1823. The water crossed the valley on a 40 ft (12m) high wooden aqueduct which blew down in the mid 1850s, but site investigation still reveals traces of it.

At Apes Tor shaft (8), there existed a horse-whim for haulage. The flat space and curved stone face of the cliff where the stone was cut away to accommodate the whim is visible to the south of the shaft collar. The adit level is not visible from the road but the remains of a launder could be seen a few yards distant from, and running parallel to the road and away from the shaft. It passed under the road and was fed by a weir across the river a few yards higher upstream, providing water for the hydraulic pumping engine situated in the Ecton Mine at adit level. Both this initial supply and the supply to the waterwheel were diverted into the Apes Tor Adit Level. The small "shaft" to the north of the engine shaft is a brick-lined limekiln.

The next point of interest is EAST ECTON, where the engine shaft (9), 9 ft (2.7m) in diameter, is still visible, but is mostly filled with domestic waste, covering the pumping pipes which are intact but no longer visible. The engine house, carpenter's and smith's shops have also gone. Two retaining walls remain of a bridge (presumably wooden planks) which was used to deposit waste material on the far side of the road. An adit exists here but access is severely limited because of coloured flowstone formations on the floor. It had been sealed for many years before being relocated and entered by Lindsey Porter in 1972.

Further up the road is the Fish Pond, originally a reservoir for the slagmill and dressing floors. It is still a collecting ground for Chadwick mine water and the sough tail can still be seen. At the bend in the road here, the ruins of four cottages (Called Fispond Cottages) are a reminder of a period when Ecton had a population far greater than at present. At the end of the road stands the Manor House, dated 1825, at Wetton-in-the-Hollow which, despite its present charm, has had its share of industrialisation in the past. At one time, the building was used as a public house (the "Pepper Inn") on the ground floor and as a button factory on the top floor. Peppercorns were given away with each pint of ale and it is held locally that the pub was one of the last bastions of cock fighting in the area.

Walking up the road from Ecton Old Hall, now in ruins and not used as a dwelling since at least around 1870, there was a shaft, subsequently filled in, a few yards to the west of the green lane to WATERBANK MINE and by the road side. At Waterbank (10), there are six shafts of which the two on the south side are separate and date from 1887. The main shaft was surrounded by the engine house, rebuilt in 1884. Judging by the foundations, it was a four-roomed stone and tile structure of which only part of the back wall remains. The rooms housed a steam engine, boiler, compressor and winding headgear. Adjacent to the building is a large stone-lined depression which was the reservoir. Cinders abound, indicating the use of coal, whilst ground calcite indicates the position of Marsden's patent crusher mentioned in the 1868 prospectus.

To the east of the reservoir, the sawpit can be found among the tips. It is stone lined, about 3 ft (1m) wide, 10 ft (3.3m) long and 6 ft (2m) deep. The other buildings can be distinguished easily and it is not difficult to reconstruct the scene as it must have looked just over 100 years ago, with the engine house dominating the area. The other buildings were situated to the north and on a level about 10 ft (3.3m) lower from the engine house. An undated, unmarked plan of a ball mill (crusher) appears to be of Waterbank, situated just to the north of the engine shaft on the lower level, where the retaining wall has collapsed.

Before leaving for Bag Mine, note the ruinous state of the smithy and carpenter's shop just to the east of the stile. The open climbing shaft situated by the stile was formerly covered by this single storey stone and tile building. The building in the north-west corner of the compound was also single storey and had two rooms, possibly for storage of ore.

From Waterbank, a good view of the series of mines known collectively as "Bonsall's Trials" can be seen. They include Clay, Bowler, Gregory, Goodhope and Platt mines. The term is misleading, however, for Bonsall only reworked Clay, Bowler and Goodhope. The history of the other mines mentioned is obscure. It is probable that Platt is named after Mather & Platt Ltd. It dates from 1870-71 when Colin Mather worked Ecton. All of these shafts are off the footpath.

The name of Capt. Bonsall lives on and he is regarded locally as a notable 19th Century figurehead. He was the Ecton Mine Captain for 33 years and was responsible for discovering several ore deposits, of which East Ecton and Goodhope deserve mention. He is buried at Wetton and the stone bears the effigy of a hand holding a pick. It was erected "by 178 subscribers as a token of their esteem and respect for his integrity." The stone is close to the south wall of the churchyard. An interesting article appeared in the Leek Times of September 17th 1870: "The Ecton Mining Co. (stricty the Ecton, Clayton and Waterbank Mining Co. Ltd.) has been driving for lead and on the 6th inst., the vein was reached. News was instantly conveyed to Captain Bonsall who had been in such a precarious state of health for the previous two months, and such was its effect on him, that he suffered a relapse and died the following evening".

Just north of Waterbank is BAG MINE (11), which is off the footpath but visible from it. Only one open shaft exists here, but the engine shaft can be seen on the north side of the boundary wall. The coe has disappeared completely and was shown on the 1818 plan as being situated to the west of the engine shaft.

CHADWICK MINE (12), also off the path, is a little further north from Bag Mine and is similar as far as surface features are concerned. Here the coe was situated on the north side of the engine shaft and was a small stone structure of which the foundations remain. There are four shafts here, but only three are visible, viz: the engine shaft, some 200 ft (60m) deep, and two climbing shafts on the sough. The easterly climbing shaft opened up in 1965 just after the other collapsed.

On a higher contour above Chadwick, and close to the path, is the CLAYTON PIPE-WORKING (13). During the 19th century it was used as a 'smoke chimney' and on the northern side of the enclosure, a former flue to the chimney can be seen running in a north-westerly direction up the hill.

**Left: The Ecton Deep Adit portal**

**Opposite page: The 160 fathoms deep internal shaft in Clayton Mine**

This is the site of the 1672 dispute and the original gunpowder work. Near the entrance to the flue exists a covered shaft which was Clayton drawing shaft (later used as a climbing shaft). The large opening appeared when the top of the working collapsed. Old plans show a gin or horse-whim and that a building existed on the south side of the drawing shaft. The site of the building (and whim?) is probably the grassy platform which exists just to the south of the shaft. At the base of the tip two small shafts are visible. There used to be a chimney on top of the old pipe working to help draw up the smoke from the engine in the adit, 420 ft (126m) below.

Proceeding northwards along the path there are remains of an old lime kiln on the left. As the stile is reached, the shafts on MASTERS PASTURE VEIN can be seen in Dukes Pasture to the north-east (14). The boundary wall housing the stile is the dividing line of the two Ecton royalties (see plan). Looking northwards towards the Ecton engine house, a number of workings on a north-south vein can be discerned. The views of the surrrounding countryside from here are memorable.

The ECTON ENGINE HOUSE (15) has been modified since it was built in 1788 to house a Boulton & Watt beam engine. It is a two storey stone and tile structure, but the roof was lowered some 70 years ago. Only about 10 ft (3.3m) of the chimney remains, it is square and firebrick lined. Internally, the building is divided lengthways by a wall. The boiler was situated on the right and connected with the engine situated on the far side of the dividing wall. The engine was a typical early Boulton and Watt winding engine with a large spiral counterbalancing drum outside the building; an unusual feature was a secondary beam to work the house water pumps.

No machinery remains intact. The engine shaft may be seen, boarded over, in the enclosure behind the building. No attempt should be made to go near this: the shaft is about 800 ft (240m) deep. A horse-whim existed also and was certainly used after the removal of the engine in 1855, if not prior to then as well. The site can be clearly seen to the north of the building. To the south of the building a hollow is the former reservoir. Water was pumped up the shaft for the boiler. Cinders from the engine hearth still remain on the south side.

When viewed from this side, to the left of the building is a stone wall. The heavy weight of the shaft rope was counterbalanced by a weight in an adjacent shaft. However the land falls away and the shaft was therefore built up to be on the same horizon as the drawing, or engine, shaft.

Several hammer stones have also been found in this locality. These and an other pick would seem to indicated workings in the Bronze Age.

From the engine house, a grass lane leads down to DUTCHMAN MINE (16). The adit is now used as a domestic water supply. In the upper workings of the Dutchman Mine, to the south of the engine house, an antler pick has been recovered recently, having first been recorded as being in the mine some 50 years ago. The building on the north side of the adit was a two roomed structure and used as the smithy and carpenter's shop. In the smithy, the base of the hearth may be seen as well as remains of the chimney. The walls are generally only two-three feet high, but site investigation reveals that it was a single storey stone and tile structure. Tile seems to have been used on a widespread scale at Ecton, in preference to flagstone or slate.

To the south of the adit was the engine house. Two walls are partially intact and contain a large number of holes containing lengths of wood to strengthen the walls. It was a single storey stone and tile building with a limestone block floor. The stone engine base is still intact.

Just to the north of this building, there is a platform on a lower level which may have been the site of the boiler. The engine house measured approx. 12 ft (4m) square and 10-12 ft (3.3-4m) high. A further small building existed opposite the smithy, but its function is not known. On the top of the tip is a fenced enclosure which may have been a buddle, but it is difficult to distinguish any details which may prove this.

From Dutchman, the path going directly towards SALT'S LEVEL brings one to the launder from the Fish Pond, which can be seen as a pronounced ditch running along the hillside. Near here, a locked gate leads to the dressing floor. Formerly a tramway brought ore out along the level from the engine shaft to the dressing floor (all the buildings have been demolished), but with the help of a photograph taken about 1885, one can reconstruct the scene without much difficulty. The present retaining wall on the north side of the compound was an open-fronted, single storey building which housed three jiggers and a small hand crusher. The back wall contained three holes, approximately 6 ft (2m) high and 2.5 ft (0.8m) wide. The wall itself is some 50-60 ft (15-20m) long. It was through these holes that water from the launder was fed to supply the jiggers.

Adjacent to this building, but at right angles to it, was the engine house. This was a two storey, span-roofed building. The ground floor housed the engine, and the stone engine bed is still intact. Accumulations of mine waste hide any other features. The first floor was where the ore from Clayton was received. Traces of the supports of the ramp can be seen and the track traced to the quarry edge. The incline was built in 1885.

Abutting the engine house was a single storey open-fronted building with a corrugated iron roof. This building extended to the edge of the tips where an ore-chute carried ore down to the road side. The stumps of wood here are probably the remains of the top of the chute. The building was dismantled and re-erected at West Side Mill, where it existed until recently. It was open-fronted, the front supported by three cast iron pumping pipes which still remain.

In front of this building were the two buddling pools and the bases are intact although regrettably, the Peak Park Planning Board have planted trees in the pools as part of their reforestation scheme. The buddles and jiggers were Cornish and purchased together with the crusher for £155 in 1885. They were convex round buddles, about 18 ft (6m) in diameter by 12 inches (30cm) deep. A vertical shaft existed above a central inverted cone which carried two wooden arms which in turn carried brushes to smooth the surface of the ore during separation. The crushed ore was fed onto the cone suspended in water brought in wooden launders from the Fish Pond water channel, along the length of the engine house and finally down on to the dressing floor. The water and waste sediment left the wooden bottom of the buddles along wooden channels and was deposited on the hillside. The latter channels remain amid large masses of grey slurry.

From the top of the tips, rectangular blocks of slag can be seen in the tips and during the excavation of waste material, a mould of a key in a slag block was uncovered. It is now preserved in Buxton Museum.

In conclusion, it will be obvious that the long and varied history of the mines has had a pronounced effect upon the local environment. The history of the mine has recently been published and details of this and other articles are given below.

# LEAD MINING GLOSSARY

The terms listed below are the most commonly used of about a thousand words peculiar to the Derbyshire lead mining industry, or which have special meanings therein. The definitions given are the usual ones but many had different shades of meaning in different parts of the mining field. A full list with explanations and historical context is given in "Glossary of Derbyshire Lead Mining Terms" compiled by J.H Rieuwerts and published by the Peak District Mines Historical Society (1998).

ADIT – a horizontal tunnel into a hillside, often called a level, and sometimes functioning as a sough.

ADVENTURERS – investors or shareholders in a mine or sough.

AGENT – the representative of the mine owner or the adventurers; usually concerned with the day-to-day management of the mine.

BARMASTER – the representative of the Crown, or the Crown lessee, responsible for the administration of mining law and courts, measuring ore and measuring out meers along the length of a vein. Deputy Barmasters were often appointed when the amount of mining required it.

BARMOTE (or BARMOOT) – the lead miners' court of law, originally held twice a year in each liberty, but now only once a year. The jury was once 24 in number but now 12, charged with judicial duties continuously from one court to the next. The jury is called "The Body of the Mine". The biannual (annual) courts were sometimes called Great Barmotes, whilst lesser disputes could be settled by ad hoc Small Barmotes.

BARYTE (formerly barytes) – the mineral barium sulphate ($BaSO_4$); commonly called cawk, caulk, calk or heavy spar.

BASSETT – the outcrop of a vein or stratum.

BELLAND – finely powdered lead ore, usually as in mine waste.. Poisonous if ingested by animals or humans. Animals grazing on meadows contaminated with belland are said to be "bellanded". A belland yard is a walled enclosure to prevent stock trying to graze on the mine waste.

BING – large pieces or ore drawn from the mine and requiring little further processing.

BLACK JACK – the mineral zinc sulphide (ZnS), properly known as Sphalerite.

BLENDE – another name for zinc sulphide (see Black Jack).

BLUE JOHN – a purple-to-blue and white banded variety of fluorspar, found only in Treak Cliff, Castleton.

BOLE – a primitive type of smelting hearth, usually sited on hilltops, hence the frequent place name Bole Hill.

BOUSE – lead ore as raised from the mine before dressing.

BUCKER – a broad, flat-headed hammer used mainly by women to break up the ore to separate it from the gangue minerals.

BUDDLE – a wooden or stone trough or series of troughs used to wash light minerals away from the lead ore particles trapped by baffles. To buddle is the act of using a buddle.

CALCITE – the mineral calcium carbonate ($CaCO_3$); sometimes worked as calc-spar for decorative purposes.

CALK, CAULK, CAWK – baryte (see above); the chief source of barium chemicals in industry; also widely used as baryte mud in oil-well drilling.

CALAMINE – the mineral zinc carbonate ($ZnCO_3$), strictly smithsonite. A weathering product of Blende; widely used in cosmetics and medicine; alloyed with copper to manufacture brass.

CAT DIRT – decomposed toadstone; weathered basalt lava.

CHANNEL – weathered toadstone.

CHEEKS – the walls or sides of a vein.

CHERT – a hard siliceous rock, like flint, found as nodules and layers in the limestone. Often black but weathers white. Sometimes replaces crinoidal limestone and is then known as screwstone.

CLIMBING SHAFT – a narrow shaft specifically for access into the mine. Usually fitted with stemples to act as rungs in a ladder.

COE – a small building or shed, usually of stone, over or near a mine, in which the miners kept their tools and a change of clothing. The climbing shaft was sometimes under a trapdoor in the floor of the coe.

COMPOSITION – money paid to sough drivers in reward of profits from lead ore rendered accessible.

COPE – a duty originally paid by the miners, later by the smelter, to the Lord to allow them to sell their ore to whoever they wish. Usually a fixed price per load.

COPPER – traces of copper minerals occur throughout the ore-field but were only in economic quantities at Ecton, Staffordshire, where the chief ore mineral was chalcopyrite ($CuFeS_2$) though several other minerals were worked.

CORFE or CORVE – a crude wooden sledge used to convey ore etc. underground, sometimes along a wooden plankway.

CROSS-CUT – a passage driven through solid rock from one vein to another.

CUPOLA – a reverberatory furnace for smelting ore.

DEADS – waste rocks from mine workings usually stacked in abandoned stopes, sometimes on timber platforms which are now unstable.

DIAL – a miners' compass used in surveying underground.

DIP – the inclination of strata.

DISH – a measure for lead ore, either oblong or circular. It varied between liberties but was usually about 14 or 15 Winchester pints capacity. Nine dishes make one load; about $3^3/_4$ to 4 loads make one ton. One dish is about 65 lbs. A standard dish made in 1513 is kept in the Moot Hall at Wirksworth.

DOLOMITE – either the mineral or the rock mostly composed of the double carbonate of calcium and magnesium ($(CaMgCO_3)_2$). Outcrops are chiefly around Brassington and Elton. Sometimes used as a source of refractory brick material or as a source of magnesium metal.

DUNSTONE – an old name usually applied to dolomite, but in some areas it refers to toadstone or to iron ore.

EGG AND EYE – the notch and slot made in opposite walls of a vein to hold a stemple or wooden beam.

ENGINE – any winding or pumping machinery whether worked by hand, horse, steam or water-power.

ENGINE SHAFT – a larger shaft equipped with winding or pumping machinery instead of a stowes.

FANGS – wood or metal pipes used to convey fresh air to the workings.

FATHOM – a measure of six feet, commonly used to express depths of mines or shafts.

FAULT – a geological term denoting the fracture and displacement of strata.

FIRING or FIRE-SETTING – the practice before the days of explosives of lighting a fire against the face of the vein to open cracks and thus to ease the extraction of rock. Fire-setting could only be done after 4 p.m. and before 8 a.m.

FISSURE – a crack or joint in the rocks, either open or filled with loose stones.

FLAT – a body of ore generally lying more or less horizontal with equal length and width, often parallel to the local stratification. By elongation flats graded into pipes.

FLUORSPAR – the mineral fluorite ($CaF_2$); a common constituent of the Derbyshire mineral veins. Widely used as a flux for fluidizing slag in furnaces, as a source of fluorine in chemical industry, in ceramics and special glasses. Clear, white, yellow, pink and blue varieties occur as well as the banded Blue John at Castleton.

FOREFIELD – the active working face in the mine, usually the furthest point from the shaft.

FOTHER or FODDER – a measure of lead metal used by the merchants, varying from liberty to liberty and between markets and ports. Ranges from 1680 to 2520 lbs usually nearer the latter.

FOUNDER – the first miner to work a mine, or the first meers allocated by the Barmaster, or the first shaft sunk on a vein.

FREEING – the act of delivering to the Barmaster a dish of ore to establish ownership of a new vein or mine.

GALENA – the mineral lead sulphide (PbS); the chief ore of lead.

GANG or GANGUE – the minerals found with the lead ore, generally regarded as waste, but the fluorspar and baryte may be more valuable nowadays and many hillocks have been re-processed for them.

GATE – a way or passage in a mine, an access route.

GIN – a winding engine; often driven by horses, also known as a whim.

GIN CIRCLE – the circular track around which the horse(s) walked to work the gin.

GINGING – the dressed stonework around the shaft holding the loose ground near the surface.

GRAVEL ORE – loose lumps of ore, found in shacks or self-opens.

GROVE or GROOVE – a mine; sometimes applied to a length of vein being worked as a single mine; occasionally restricted to open workings at the surface.

HADE – the slope of a vein from the vertical.

HEADING – alternative name for a gate, cross-cut or adit.

HEMATITE – the common oxide ore of iron ($Fe_2O_3$) found in a few veins around Hartington.

HILLOCKS – old waste heaps.

HILLOCKING – re-working waste for unrecovered minerals.

ICLES – stalactites, as in caves (also called Watricle or Water-icicles).

JAGGER – one who carried lead ore from the mine to the smelter on mules or horses.

JIG – a box-like device used to separate lead ore from gangue minerals by shaking them up and down on a sieve in water.

JURY or GRAND JURY – the jury of the Barmote Court, once 24 but now 12 in number, drawn from amongst working miners.

KIBBLE or KEBBLE – a large bucket used to raise ore up a shaft.

LEVEL – a horizontal tunnel, adit, sough or gate. A level may also be a surveying instrument.

LIBERTY – the district in which the miner searches for lead ore. Derbyshire has possibly 50 liberties with slightly varying laws and customs. Some are Crown liberties (via the Duchy of Lancaster), other Crown liberties are leased to the Dukes of Devonshire and Rutland. Several smaller liberties are privately owned.

LOAD – a measure of lead ore, being 9 dishes, about $3^3/_4$ loads to the ton.

LORD – the owner of the mineral liberty (sometimes as a lessee or farmer from the Crown). The Lord received the Lot and Cope and freeing dishes.

LORD'S MEER – a length of vein laid out by the Barmaster for the Lord, who receives all the ore mined from it, or who makes special arrangements with the miners.

LOT – the share of ore due to the Lord, usually every 13th dish, though he might take anything from a 10th to a 25th according to the Liberty or according to the difficulty of extracting the ore.

MARBLE – in the geological sense it is a limestone which has been recrystallized by later application of heat. Commercially the term describes any limestone which takes a good polish.

MEER – a measure of the length of a vein, varying in different Liberties from 27, 28, 29, or 32 yards. Two founder meers are allocated to the finder of a new vein. The Lords's Meer followed and then taker meers were added as required.

MINE ROYAL – a mine containing gold or silver to a value greater than the base metals. Occasaional claims were made of these in Derbyshire but none have been substantiated by modern investigation.

NICKING – failure to work a mine may result in another miner claiming it by asking the Barmaster to "nick" the stowes, i.e. to cut a piece of wood out. Three nickings allow the mine to be handed over to the claimant, unless work has been obstructed by water or lack of ventilation.

OFFAL – waste, gangue and rock, sometimes including unrecoverable lead ore.

OLD MAN or T'OWD MAN – places worked by former miners, or the former miners themselves.

OPEN – sometimes Self-Open – a naturally open cavern or fissure.

ORE – the valuable mineral from which metal may be extracted. In Derbyshire this refers to lead ore.

PIG or PIG O'LEAD – a block or ingot of lead metal cast at the smelter's works. Commonly 8 pigs make one fodder.

PIPE or PIPE VEIN – a body of ore and other minerals lying more or less horizontally but longer than wide. Many pipes are infillings or linings of pre-existing caverns. Pipes may branch out of rakes. The copper ore pipes mined at Ecton, Staffs. were different – irregularly vertical ore bodies at the intersections of veins.

QUARTER CORD – ground allowed to the miner either side of his vein to deposit his waste and build his coe. Usually a quarter of a meer in width.

RAG AND CHAIN – primitive pumps which raised water by wads of rags wedged in a chain wound through hollowed out tree-trunks.

RAKE – the main type of mineral vein – a body of ore and gangue disposed more or less vertically and running across country for a mile or more. The boundary between a rake and the smaller scrin is not clearly definable.

RANGE OR RANDOM – the expected direction and extent of a vein beyond current workings.

RIDER – a mass of rock dividing a vein. Also called a horse.

RISE – an underground shaft driven upwards above a working.

SCRIN – a short vertical mineral vein, of no great width not normally more than a few hundred metres long. Often branching out of a rake, sometimes in groups or "swarms".

SELF-OPEN – a large natural cavern.

SHACK – a natural opening in the ground, either at the surface or underground; often filled with loose rocks. Sometimes known as a shake or shake-hole.

SHALE-GATE – a tunnel driven through shale.

SINKERS – men who make shafts.

SLAG – the waste material produced in smelting ore. Sometimes re-processed to recover more metal at a later date.

SLICKENSIDES – the grooved surface produced by the movement of strata along faults. Sometimes with shiny surfaces on galena, and sometimes in a state of stress and liable to explode on being disturbed by mining. Explosive slickensides is sometimes known as cracking-whole.

SMELTING – the process whereby metal is extracted from ore.

SMITHAM – finely ground ore produced during crushing.

SOLE – the floor of a mine or sough; the lowest level worked.

SOUGH – an adit or level specifically driven to drain a mine or mines.

SOUGHERS – men who excavate soughs.

SOUGH MASTERS – investors who finance the driving of soughs.

SPAR – a collective term for minerals accompanying the lead ore; includes fluorspar, baryte (heavy spar), and calcite (calcspar).

STEMPLE – a piece of wood wedged across a vein or stope intended to act as a rung in a ladder; sometimes part of a platform for disposal of deads or for roof support. Dressed stone stemples occur in a few mines.

STEWARD – the presiding officer at the Barmote Court; the Lord's executive officer.

STOPE – the cavity left after working out a vein.

STOWES, STOCE, STOES – the wooden windlass over a shaft for raising ore. Though a single item, stowes were usually referred to as a pair. Stowes had to be made to a definite pattern without nails. The existence of a stowes on a mine was proof of ownership.

STRIKE – the course or direction of the strata or of a vein.

SUMP – an internal shaft, not connected to the surface, may be called a winze or a turn. A sump may also be a hollow in the bottom of a mine where water collects before pumping out.

SWALLOW or SWALLET – a natural opening which takes water away. May also refer to a hole on the surface where a stream goes underground.

TAILINGS – the finely ground waste from mineral processing.

TOADSTONE – a collective term for volcanic basalt of several types; it may be massive, columnar, vesicles (with gas bubbles); it may be altered to a green clay or it may be a volcanic fragmental rock known as tuff.

TUFA – a soft calcareous deposit sometimes precipitated around springs, as at Matlock Bath. Also known as Travertine.

TURN – an underground shaft, also called a sump or winze. Several turns in a climbing shaft may be alongside a single engine shaft.

TURNTREE – an alternative name for a stowes.

THE TWENTY-FOUR – the Grand Jury of the Barmote Court, the "Body of the Mine"; later reduced to twelve.

UMBER – an impure, brown earthy form of wad, a manganese ore sometimes used as a pigment.

VEIN – a body of minerals enclosed by rock.

VEIN-STUFF – the minerals in a vein.

WAD – impure manganese ore, usually a mixure of iron and manganese oxides. Black in colour and sometimes worked as a pigment.

WATER-GATE – a drainage level or sough.

WATER-ICICLES or WATRICLES – stalactites.

WAYBOARD – a clay bed between limestone beds, usually not more than a few inches thick; often a volcanic dust layer and greenish in colour.

WHEAT ORE or WHITE ORE – lead carbonate (cerussite $PbCO_3$). Occasionally worked as a lead ore, once used in paint manufacture.

WHIM – a winding engine, worked by horses or steam.

WHIMSEY – a steam-driven winding engine.

WINZE – an underground shaft connecting one level with another.

WOUGHS – the limestone walls or cheeks of a vein.

# FURTHER READING

## (A) GENERAL WORKS

AGRICOLA, G. 1556. De Re Metallica. English translation by H.L. Hoover (1912), Reptd by Dover Press, New York (1950).

CARRUTHERS, R.G. & STRAHAN, A., 1923. Lead and zinc ores of Durham, Yorkshire and Derbyshire with notes on the Isle of Man. Geological Survey Special Report on Mineral Resources. vol.26, Derbyshire pp.41-88.

DUNHAM, K.C. 1952. Fluorspar. Geological Survey Special Report on Mineral Resources, vol. 4, 4th edition, 143pp.

FAREY, J. 1811. A General View of the Agriculture and Minerals of Derbyshire. Vol. 1, 532pp. Reptd by PDMHS, 1989.

FORD, T.D. 1969. The stratiform Ore deposits of Derbyshire. pp.73-96 "Sedimentary Ores, ancient and modern – revised", Proc. 15th Inter-University Geological Congress, Leicester edited by C.H.James.

FORD, T.D. 1976. The Ores of the South Pennines and Mendip Hills – a comparative study. in K.H.Wolf's "Handbook of Strat-bound and Stratiform Ore Deposits", vol. 5, pp.161-195. Elsevier, Amsterdam.

FORD, T.D. (editor) 1977. Limestones and Caves of the Peak District. Geo-Books, Norwich 469pp.

FORD, T.D. 2000. Derbyshire Blue John. Ashbourne Editions, Ashbourne. 112pp.

FORD, T.D. & INESON, P.R. 1971. The Fluorspar Mining Potential of the Derbyshire Orefield. Transactions of the Institution of Mining & Metallurgy, Vol. B80, pp.186-210.

FORD, T.D., SARJEANT, W.A.S. & SMITH, M.E. 1993. Minerals of the Peak District. Bull PDMHS, vol. 12, no.1, pp.16-55.

GLOVER, S. 1829. History and Gazetteer of the County of Derby. H.Mozley, Derby. 450pp + 107pp appendix.

HARDY, W. 1747. The Miners Guide or Compleat Miner. Sheffield. 240pp.

HARRIS, H. 1971. Industrial Archaeology of the Peak District. David & Charles, Newton Abbot. 256pp.

HOOSON, W. 1747. The Miners' Dictionary. Wrexham.

HOPKINSON, G.G. 1958. Five Generations of Derbyshire Lead Mining and Smelting. Derbyshire Archaeological Journal, vol 78, pp.9-24.

KIERNAN, D. 1989. The Derbyshire Lead Industry in the Sixteenth Century. Derbyshire Record Society, Chesterfield, 338pp.

KIRKHAM, N. 1968. Derbyshire Lead Mining Through the Centuries. Bradford Barton, Truro. 132pp.

MANLOVE,E. 1653. The Liberties and Customs of the Lead Mines within the Wapentake of Wirksworth in the County of Derby" In verse – included in the PDMHS (1996) reprint edition of Stokes, 1880-82.

NIXON, F. 1969. The Industrial Archaeology of Derbyshire. David & Charles, Newton Abbot. 307pp.

PARKER, H.M. & WILLIES, L.M. 1979. Peakland Lead Mines and Miners. Moorland, Ashbourne. 64pp.

PERCY, J. 1870. The Metallurgy of Lead. Murray, London.

RAISTRICK, A. & JENNINGS, B. 1965. A History of Lead Mining in the Pennines. Longmans, London. 347pp.

RIEUWERTS, J.H. 1978. The Inquisition or Quo Warranto of 1288. Bull PDMHS, vol.7, pp.41-49 & 96-98.

RIEUWERTS, J.H. 1980. Derbyshire's Early Soughs. Bull PDMHS, vol.7, pp.241-314.

RIEUWERTS, J.H. 1987. History and Gazetteer of the Lead Mine Soughs of Derbyshire. Rieuwerts, Sheffield. 143pp.

RIEUWERTS, J.H. 1998. Glossary of Derbyshire Lead Mining Terms. PDMHS, Matlock. 192pp.

ROBEY, J.A. & PORTER, L.M. 1972. The Copper and Lead Mines of Ecton Hill, Staffordshire. Moorland, Ashbourne. 92pp.

SMITH, E.G., RHYS, G.H. & EDEN R.A. 1967. Geology of the Country around Chesterfield, Matlock and Mansfield. Memoir of the Geological Survey, London. 430pp.

STEVENSON, I.P. & GAUNT, G.D. 1971. Geology of the Country around Chapel-en-le-Frith (and Castleton). Memoir of the Institute of Geological Sciences, London.

STOKES, A.H. 1880-1882. Lead and Lead Mining in Derbyshire. Trans. Chesterfield & Derbys. Inst. Civ. Mech. Eng. (Reptd 1996 as PDMHS Special Publication No.2. 89pp).

VARVILL, W.W. 1959. The Future of Lead-Zinc and Fluorspar Mining in Derbyshire. pp.175-232 in "Symposium on the Future of Non-Ferrous Mining in Great Britain". Institution of Mining & Metallurgy, London.

VARVILL, W.W. 1962. Secondary Enrichment by Natural Flotation. Mine & Quarry Engineering, vol. 27, pp. 64-73, 112-118, 156-161, 208-214.

WILLIES, L.M. 1971. The Introduction of the Cupola to Derbyshire. Bull PDMHS, vol.4, pp.384-394.

WILLIES, L.M.1979. Technical Development in Derbyshire Lead Mining. Bull PDMHS, vol.7, pp.117-151.

WILLIES, L.M., RIEUWERTS, J.H. & FLINDALL, R. 1977. Wind, Water and Steam Engines of Derbyshire Lead Mines: a List. Bull PDMHS, vol.6, pp.303-320.

## (B) REFERENCES FOR THE ITINERARIES

**1. Castleton**

FORD, T.D.1955. Blue John Fluorspar. Proceedings of the Yorkshire Geological Society, vol.30, pp.35-60.

FORD, T.D. 1990. Speedwell Cavern, Castleton – guide book. Harrison, Castleton. 32pp.

FORD, T.D. 1992. Treak Cliff Cavern and the Story of Blue John Stone. Harrison Taylor, Castleton. 24pp.

FORD, T.D. 1996. The Castleton Area. Geologists Association Guide no. 56. London, 94pp.

FORD, T.D. 2000. Derbyshire Blue John. Ashbourne Editions, Ashbourne. 112pp.

RIEUWERTS, J.H. & FORD, T.D. 1976. Odin Mine, Castleton. Bull PDMHS, vol.6, no.4, pp. 1-54.

RIEUWERTS, J.H. & FORD, T.D. 1985. The mining history of the Speedwell Mine or Oakden Level, Castleton. Bull PDMHS, vol.9, no.3, pp. 129-170.

**2. Peak Forest.**

HEATHCOTE, C. Surface remains at New Venture Mine, Bradwell Moor. Mining History, vol.13, no.3, pp.53-56, no.4, pp.51-54 & no.6, pp.23-24.

**3. Eyam**

BRAMLEY, J.V. 1991. Fluorspar Mining in Derbyshire. Bull PDMHS, vol.11, no.3, pp.153-8.

KIRKHAM, N. 1964-6. Eyam Edge Mines and Soughs. Bull PDMHS, vol.2, pp.241-254, 315-335; vol. 3, pp. 43-57 & 103-118.

KIRKHAM, N. 1966. Longstone Edge Mines and Soughs. Part 1 Cave Science (BSA series), vol.5, no.39, pp.354-368; part 2 vol.6, no.40, pp.440-469.

WILLIES, L.M.1974. The Lords Cupola, Stoney Middleton. Bull PDMHS, vol.5, pp.288-301.

**4. Magpie Mine and Sheldon**

ROBEY, J.A. 1966. Fieldgrove Mine. Bull PDMHS, vol.3, pp.93-101.

WILLIES, L.M. 1974. The re-opening of the Magpie Sough. Bull PDMHS, vol.5, pp.324-331.

WILLIES, L.M., ROCHE, V.S., WORLEY, N.E. & FORD, T.D. 1998.
The History of Magpie Mine, Sheldon, Derbyshire. PDMHS, Special Publication No.3, 5th edition – in press.

**5. Ashford Black Marble Mines**

BOWERING, G. & FLINDALL, R. 1998. Hard Times: a history of the Derbyshire Chert Industry. Mining History, vol. 13, no.5, pp.1-31.

FORD, T.D. 1968. The Black Marble of Ashford-in-the-Water. Liverpool & Manchester Geological Journal, vol.2, pp.44-59.

FORD, T.D. 1964. The Black Marble Mines of Ashford-in-the-Water. Bull PDMHS, vol.2, no.4, pp. 179-188.

TOMLINSON, J.M. 1996. Derbyshire Black Marble. PDMHS Special Publication no.4, (with appendices by T.D.Ford), 96pp.

**6. Lathkill Dale**

RIEUWERTS, J.H. 2000. Lathkill Dale: its Mines and Miners.
Landmark Publishing, Ashbourne. 100pp.

**7. Monyash**

KITCHEN, G. & PENNEY, D. 1973. New Pumps for Old. Bull PDMHS, vol.5, pp.129-136.

ROBEY, J.A. 1961-3. The Mines Northwest of Monyash. Bull PDMHS, vol. 1, no.5, pp.30-36; vol. 1, no.6, pp.29-32; vol.2, no.1, pp.51-56. Supplementary notes in vol.5, pp.149-155.

ROBEY, J.A. 1965. The Drainage of the Area between the Rivers Wye and Lathkill. Proceedings of the British Speleological Association, no.3, pp. 1-10.

**8. Alport**

KIRKHAM, N. 1961. The draining of the Alport Mines. Transactions of the Newcomen Society, vol.33, pp. 67-91.

KIRKHAM, N. 1964-65. The Ventilation of Hillcarr Sough. Transactions of the Newcomen Society, vol. 37, pp. 133-138.

RIEUWERTS, J.H. 1981. The Drainage of the Alport Mining Field. Bull PDMHS, vol.8, no.1, pp.1-28.

**9. Winster**

HEALD, D. 1978. The exploration of Wills Founder Mine, Winster. Bull PDMHS, vol. 7, no.2, pp.51-66.

RILEY, L. & WILLIES, L.M. 1979. The recovery of the pumps from Wills Founder Shaft, Winster. Bull PDMHS, vol. 7, no.4, pp. 199-205.

**10. Wensley, Darley and Mill Close.**

OAKMAN, C.D. 1980. Derbyshire sough hydrology and the artificial drainage of the Stanton syncline, near Matlock. Transactions of the Cave Research Group of G.B. vol. 6, no.4, pp.169-194.

TRAILL, J.G. 1939. The geology and development of Mill Close Mine. Economic Geology, vol.34, pp.38-47.

WARRINER, D. et al. 2000. Old Mill Close Mine. Mining History, vol. 14, (in press).

WILLIES, L.M., GREGORY, K. & PARKER, H.M. 1989. Millclose, the mine that drowned. Scarthin Books, Cromford; and PDMHS, Matlock.

**11. Matlock.**

FLINDALL, R. & HAYES, A. 1972. Wapping Mine and Cumberland Cavern, Matlock Bath. Bull PDMHS, vol.5, pp. 114-127.

FLINDALL, R. & HAYES, A. 1973. The Mines near Upperwood – the Tear Breeches – Hopping – Fluorspar – Speedwell Complex. Bull PDMHS, vol.5, pp.182-199.

FLINDALL, R. & HAYES, A. 1976. The Caverns and Mines of Matlock Bath: 1 The Nestus Mines; Rutland and Masson Caverns. Moorland, Ashbourne. 72pp.

HURT, L. 1970. A Survey of Ball Eye Mines, Bonsall. Bull PDMHS, vol.4, pp.289-305.

KIRKHAM, N. 1963. The Draining of the Wirksworth Lead Mines. Derbyshire Archaeological Society, Local History Section 19pp.

WARRINER, D., WILLIES, L.M. & FLINDALL, R. 1981. Ringing Rake and Masson Soughs and the Mines on the East Side of Masson Hill, Matlock. Bull PDMHS, vol. 8, no.2, pp.109-150.

**12. Cromford & Bole Hill**

RIEUWERTS, J.H. 1998. Early gunpowder work in Longe or Cromford Sough, 1662-3 and 1676-1680. Mining History, vol. 13, no. 6., pp.1-5.

**13. Goodluck Mine**

AMNER, R. & NAYLOR, P. 1973. Goodluck Mine, Via Gellia. Bull PDMHS, vol.5, no.4, pp.217-249.

FLINDALL, R. & HAYES, A. 1972. A survey of Goodluck Mine and adjacent levels in the Via Gellia. Bull PDMHS, vol.5, no.2, pp.61-80.

**14. Wirksworth**

KIRKHAM, N. 1953. The tumultuous course of Dovegang. Derbyshire Archaeological Journal, vol.73, pp.1-35.

KIRKHAM, N. 1963. The draining of the Wirksworth lead mines. Derbyshire Archaeological Society, Local History Section, 19pp.

OAKMAN, C.D. 1980. The artifical drainage of the Wirksworth-Cromford area, Bull PDMHS, vol.7, no.5, pp.231-240.

**15. Carsington Pastures**

FORD, T.D. & KING, R.J. 1965. Layered epigenetic galena-baryte deposits in the Golconda Mine, Brassington. Economic Geology, vol.60, pp.1686-1701.

FORD, T.D. & KING, R.J. 1966. The Golconda Caverns. Transactions of the Cave Research Group of G.B. vol.7, no.2, pp.91-114.

SLACK, R. 1985. Brassington mining 1792-1826. Bull PDMHS, vol.9, no.3, pp. 186-194.

SLACK, R. 1991. Lands and lead miners: a history of Brassington in Derbyshire. Slack, Chesterfield. 197pp.

SLACK, R. 1991. Pauper's Venture – Children's Fortune; the lead mines and miners of Brassington. Scarthin Books, Cromford. 52pp.

**16. Crich**

GREGORY, N. 1966. Notes and Impressions of Jingler Mine, Wakebridge. Bull PDMHS, vol.3, pp. 58-62.

KIRKHAM, N. 1969. Lead Mining at Crich. Proceedings of the Manchester Association of Engineers. 133th session, No.5, 17pp.

**17. Stone Edge Cupola**

WILLIAMS, C.J. & WILLIES, L.M. 1968. Stone Edge Cupola. Bull PDMHS, vol.3, pp. 315-322.

WILLIES, L.M. 1969. Cupola Lead-smelting Sites in Derbyshire 1737-1900. Bull PDMHS, vol. 4, no1, pp. 97-115.

**18. Ecton**

BARNATT, J., RIEUWERTS, J.H. & THOMAS, G.H. 1997. Early use of gunpowder in the Peak District: Stone Quarry Mine and Dutchman's Level, Ecton. Mining History, vol.13, no.4, pp.24-43.

BARNATT, J. & THOMAS, G.H. 1998. Prehistoric Mining at Ecton, Staffordshire. Mining History, vol.13, no.5, pp. 72-78.

CRITCHLEY, M. 1979. A geological outline of the Ecton copper mines, Staffordshire. Bull PDMHS, vol.7, no.4, pp. 177-191.

PORTER, L & ROBEY, J, 2000
The Copper & Lead Mines around the Manifold Valley, Staffordshire
Landmark Publishing, Ashbourne.

PORTER, L 1970 Ecton Hill – Part II – Underground, Bull. PDMHS, Vol4, No3, pp195-216.

PORTER, L 2000 The Ecton Mine, Staffordshire, 1883-1891, to be published in Mining History.

# INDEX

Published in association with **Peak District Mines Historical Society Ltd**
c/o Peak District Mining Museum, Matlock Bath, Derbyshire DE4 3NR

by **Landmark Publishing Ltd,**
Waterloo House, 12 Compton, Ashbourne, Derbyshire DE6 1DA England
Tel: (01335) 347349 Fax: (01335) 347303 e-mail: landmark@clara.net

4th fully revised and expanded edition
ISBN 1 901 522 15 6

**© 2000 Peak District Mines Historical Society Ltd**

The right of the authors of this work has been asserted by them in accordance
with the Copyright, Design and Patents Act, 1993.

All rights reserved. No part of this publication may be reproduced, stored in a retrieval
system or transmitted in any form or by any means, electronic, mechanical, photocopying,
recording or otherwise without the prior permission of Landmark Publishing Ltd.

British Library Cataloguing in Publication Data:
a catalogue record for this book is available from the British Library.

**Print:** Gutenberg Press Ltd, Malta

**Designed by:** James Allsopp

## ACKNOWLEDGEMENTS

The editors and also the several authors who have made contributions towards the production of this book are indebted to so many individuals, librarians and other archivists, that it is an almost impossible task to include everyone.

We would particularly like to express our thanks and appreciation to the following:

His Grace the Duke of Devonshire for access to the lead mining archives held at Chatsworth House. Mr. Peter Day and Mr. Tom Askey, the archivists at Chatsworth have been ever helpful and patient during the course of many years. The Barmaster's Collection is owned by the Duchy of Lancaster, but it is also held at Chatsworth House and for access to this collection thanks are due not only to His Grace and Mr. Day and Mr. Askey, but also to the Barmaster, Mr. William Erskine.

Mr. Roy Smith, archivist to the Duchy collections held at Lancaster Place, London has allowed one of us, Dr. J.H.Rieuwerts to examine lead mining manuscripts held in that office.

The major part of the Duchy archive is housed in the Public Record Office, Kew and staff there are thanked for assistance during extensive research, which is still ongoing.

His Grace, the late Duke of Rutland permitted both Dr. Lynn Willies and Dr. J.H.Rieuwerts, limited access to the lead mining collection formerly housed at Belvoir Castle. We are both extremely grateful for the favours granted to us.

Mr. Joseph Wisdom, Librarian of St. Paul's Cathedral and Mr. Stephen Freeth, Keeper of the Manuscripts at the Guildhall Library, London, both gave much assistance whilst the Marples Papers housed there were being examined. Thanks are due to them and also to the other very friendly members of their staff.

The archivists and librarians at the British Museum, London; Derby Public Library; Derbyshire County Library; Derbyshire Record Office; Northumbrian Record Office, Newcastle; the John Rylands Library, Manchester; Sheffield Archives (formerly Local History Department, Sheffield City Libraries) have all been most helpful and provided necessary guidance.

Many people have allowed access to lead mining documents in their private possession and we sincerely thank Mr. Michael Cockerton, Steward of the Derbyshire Barmote Courts; Mr. John Harrison, Speedwell Mine, Castleton; Mr. Douglas Nash; Mr. and Mrs. Wright, of Eyam Hall and their archivist, Miss. Caroline Fookes.

Photographs have been provided by Mr. James Allsopp, Mr. Paul Deakin; the Derbyshire Pennine Club, Laporte Industries, Mr. Harry Parker, Mr. Barry J. Samuels. We wish to thank all of them for their kind assistance.

Finally a sincere debt of gratitude is due to the numerous individuals who, although not providing a chapter within this publication, have nevertheless contributed a very significant amount of data, often derived from their personal explorations of Derbyshire's old lead mines. Many of them are members of the Peak District Mines Historical Society.